AN
INTRODUCTION
TO
Human
Anatomy

FOURTH

EDITION

329
Illustrations

15
In Color

CLYDE MARSHALL, M.D.
Formerly Assistant Professor of Anatomy,
Yale University School of Medicine

Revised By

EDGAR L. LAZIER, Ph.D.
Professor of Zoology,
University of California at Los Angeles

W. B. SAUNDERS COMPANY

Philadelphia   1955   London

PREFACE TO THE FOURTH EDITION

IN PREPARING the fourth edition of Dr. Marshall's book there has again been no intent to alter the original plan or purpose. The major changes are the following:

The discussion of the tissues has been rearranged in conformity with the principle that some understanding of the materials of which an organ system is built is a necessary preliminary to study of that system.

Some of the introductory paragraphs, setting forth briefly the function accomplished by the organ system to be studied, have been rewritten.

The most extensive revision has been made in the treatment of the neurosensory system. The organs of common sensation have been put in the same chapter with the nervous system. A brief discussion of the neuron and the supporting elements in nerve tissue is followed by an account of the main structural features of the nervous system which, it is hoped, will prepare the student to find his way about in it. Then a few functional systems, or pathways, are described in terms of their constituent neurons. After the student has gone this far it should be relatively easy for the instructor to present any additional systems he may wish his students to know. To include in this chapter any considerable number of pathways would make it too long.

The chapter on endocrine glands has been revised, especially the statements regarding function. These latter are probably too brief to arouse much enthusiasm on the part of endocrinologists, but if they serve for identification, however imperfect, for the student, or as a point of departure for the lecturer, they are, perhaps, worth while.

It is hoped that the figure numbers placed at the top of each page, on the inside edge, will make reference to the illustrations more convenient for the student and encourage him to make constant use of them.

I am greatly indebted to Dr. Edwin B. Steen for systematically

iii

examining the third edition and calling my attention to errors. He also made many excellent suggestions. These have all been most helpful. I am also indebted to Dr. Clara Szego Roberts and Dr. Sidney Roberts for illuminating conversation regarding the present state of endocrinology, though, of course, only the writer can be held responsible for inadequacies or errors of statement in the paragraphs in this book. Anyway, anything regarding endocrinology that has been in print for more than twenty-four hours should be viewed with suspicion by instructor and student alike. Dr. Charlotte W. Dawley made a number of useful suggestions for which I am grateful. Dr. O. H. Perry Pepper will recognize in the footnotes material from his *Medical Etymology,* a book I have found myself browsing in when I should have been doing other things. Several new illustrations were made by Mrs. Betty Bomeisler, who was most cooperative and helpful. Thanks are also due the many publishers who have consented to continued use of illustrations as well as to the use of new ones. Finally, I am grateful to the publishers of this book for forbearance and encouragement, as well as for both giving and accepting suggestions.

Edgar L. Lazier

University of California at Los Angeles

PREFACE TO THE FIRST EDITION

During some years' experience in teaching a course in elementary anatomy, the need became apparent for a simple textbook, written from the standpoint of an anatomist, and containing, in addition to the facts of anatomy in the narrow sense, brief accounts of the functional activities of the different organs, and of related problems of practical interest. This text is an attempt to supply that need. It was begun some years ago in the form of mimeographed sheets which were used by the students, and it underwent several revisions during the course of time. From the final revision this book was made.

The order of presentation adopted here differs from the currently accepted one, in that instead of starting with cells and tissues and proceeding to larger divisions, the student is introduced immediately to gross anatomy and only later comes to the finer structures. The current method has the advantage of logical sequence; the method adopted here has, in my hands at least, been found pedagogically more satisfactory. The student, on coming into the anatomical laboratory for the first time, has his natural curiosity satisfied immediately by the handling of the bones of the skeleton; only later is he asked to settle down to the more detailed study of microscopic structure. For those who prefer the current logical method, Chapter 3,* on Tissues, may be taken up immediately after Chapter 1.

The subject of developmental anatomy is included in the text. Since many instructors question its value in an elementary course, it is put in a separate chapter at the end of the book, which may be used or omitted as desired. If it is used it may be taken up, at the discretion of the instructor, in the position in which it is now found; it may be inserted earlier in the course, as for example, after the study of cells and tissues; or the general developmental features may be studied early, while the embryology of each indi-

---

* The material on tissues has been redistributed in the present edition.

vidual system is considered along with the corresponding chapter in the general text.

Completeness and clarity of illustration are essential in an elementary book, and great pains have been taken to achieve them here. The figures have been selected from a great many sources, and thanks are due to the many publishers who kindly consented to their use.

Certain sections of the book are differentiated from the others by the use of finer type. Some of these deal with function, describing the chief physiological activities of the organ under discussion; others contain features grouped under the heading "Practical Considerations." In the latter are included many observations of practical and general interest which are intended as answers to questions arising in the minds of intelligent students. The aim has been not to teach anatomy solely for its own sake, but also to show its relations to the other sciences, and to point out some of its everyday applications.

The terminology employed is the B N A. The old terminology, however, is also given, separated by parentheses and indicated by the abbreviation O.T.

Many of the terms of anatomy are difficult for the beginner to understand. To aid in comprehending them, their derivation and meaning are given in footnotes. Where a proper name forms part of the anatomical term, a short biographical note is also included.

In the preparation of this book I am particularly indebted to my colleagues, Dr. Edgar Allen, Dr. H. S. Burr, Dr. H. B. Ferris, Dr. Ralph G. Meader, and to my wife, Dr. Frances B. Marshall, who each read the entire manuscript and made many valuable suggestions; to Dr. G. M. Smith, and Dr. L. S. Stone who read many chapters; to Dr. R. T. Hill who read the section on endocrines and suggested certain portions; to Miss Dorothy Spang who prepared many revisions of the manuscript; to Mrs. Katherine Burford who prepared parts of it; and to Mr. Bertram G. Bruestle who drew certain of the figures. And finally, I wish to express my appreciation to the publishers, and to several individual members of their staff, who cooperated in many ways in the preparation of the book for publication.

CLYDE MARSHALL

Yale University
New Haven, Connecticut

CONTENTS

Chapter 4

Chapter 5

Chapter 6

EPITHELIUM, EPITHELIAL MEMBRANES AND SKIN ....

Chapter 7

THE DIGESTIVE SYSTEM ....

Chapter 14

THE ORGANS OF SPECIAL SENSE 342

Chapter 15

THE DUCTLESS GLANDS 359

Chapter 16

DEVELOPMENTAL ANATOMY 368

Formation of the Limbs, 379. The Bones and
Joints, 379. The Digestive System, 382. The
Lungs and Pleural Cavities, 384. The Urinary
System, 386. The Reproductive System, 386.
The Circulatory System, 388. The Nervous
System, 393. The Development of External
Form in Relation to Age, 395

CHAPTER 1

INTRODUCTION

Definitions. The term *Anatomy* in its broadest sense is defined as the science of the structure of animals or plants. In a more limited meaning it refers to the structure of animal bodies only, and it is frequently still more restricted to include only the structure of the human form. The word itself comes from the Greek meaning "to cut up," and in its original sense it meant the knowledge of body structure gained by dissection. This indeed was the only technique of study available to the older anatomists. The invention of the microscope, however, around the beginning of the seventeenth century, opened up new fields of study, and since then the finer details of structure have been gradually revealed. The term "Anatomy" was broadened to include these newer fields; the older science was then designated as *Gross Anatomy*, the newer as *Microscopic Anatomy*. Microscopic Anatomy may now be subdivided into two branches, *Histology*, the study of tissues, and *Cytology*, the study of cells.

Certain special fields of study in anatomy have been given descriptive names. *Developmental Anatomy* deals with the growth and development of an individual organism through its entire life. *Embryology* is a part of this larger study and treats of the growth of the organism from conception until the time of birth. The developmental history of an individual is often referred to as *Ontogeny;* its ancestral or evolutionary history through the lower animal forms is called *Phylogeny*.

Method. Anatomy may be further described as regional or systematic, according to the method by which it is studied. In *regional anatomy* the body is subdivided into a number of gross divisions or regions, and the entire contents of one of these is studied before passing on to the next. The parts usually designated as gross regions are as follows:

1. The head and neck
2. The thorax or chest
3. The abdomen
4. The upper extremity
5. The lower extremity.

In *systematic anatomy* the body is divided for convenience of description into a number of functional systems which are studied as units irrespective of their position in the gross regions. The functional systems are the following:

1. The skeleton, which includes the bones and their related structures
2. The joints, or the articulatory system. To consider the joints as distinct from the skeleton is of no advantage in a book as brief as this, and the two will be described together
3. The skin, or integument
4. The muscular system
5. The digestive system
6. The respiratory system
7. The urinary, or excretory, system
8. The reproductive system, differing in the two sexes
9. The circulatory system
10. The nervous system
11. The organs of sense
12. The endocrine system, which consists of the ductless glands.

The regional method is the one usually adopted in medical schools, where there is adequate time for a complete dissection of the body. Without a dissection the systematic method is followed more easily and will, therefore, be adopted here.

Some Spatial Relations. Before passing on to the description of the body systems, it is necessary to become familiar with certain terms used to describe the relations of one part of the body to another. For the purpose of these definitions the human subject is always regarded as standing upright, arms down, with the palms of the hands directed forward. Four common terms are the following:

Superior: equivalent to upper or higher
Inferior: equivalent to under or lower
Anterior: toward the front
Posterior: toward the back.

In some instances, particularly when comparing organs in the human body with those of an animal on all fours, these terms may give rise to some confusion. For instance, the superior surface of the liver of man would correspond to the anterior surface of the liver of the dog. The following terms avoid the difficulty by referring to the long axis of the body irrespective of its position in space.

Cranial: toward the head end of the animal
Caudal: toward the tail end of the animal
Ventral: toward the animal's belly
Dorsal: toward the animal's back.

The following four terms should cause no difficulty:

Medial: toward the median plane (see below)

Lateral: away from the midline
Proximal: closer to the trunk (used chiefly for the limbs)
Distal: farther away from the trunk (used chiefly for the limbs).

Adverbs are formed from these adjectives by substituting for the ending *-al* the ending *-ad* or *-ally,* e.g., ventrad, ventrally. The former ending indicates to or toward.

Planes of Reference.   In addition to the foregoing terms, three planes of reference are commonly used.

The *median plane* divides the body into right and left halves. Figure 29, for example, is made in this plane. The median plane or any plane parallel to it is often referred to as a *sagittal plane.*

A *frontal* or *coronal plane* is one that divides the body into anterior and posterior portions (see Fig. 99). (It would divide the body of a dog or cat into dorsal and ventral halves.)

A *horizontal* or *transverse plane* is one that divides the body into superior and inferior portions (see Fig. 112). It is often referred to as a "cross section" or "transverse section."

CHAPTER 2

THE TISSUES OF THE SKELETON

THE HUMAN BODY, like that of all animals, is made up of a variety of structural materials called *tissues*. As an engineer must know the properties (strength, hardness, and so forth) of the steel, wood, concrete and other materials out of which he constructs machines or buildings, so must the student of gross anatomy have some understanding of the tissues of which the body is built: bone, muscle, gristle and others less familiar.

Since it is most convenient to begin the study of anatomy with the skeleton, we shall first examine the tissues that compose it. The bone of the upper arm will serve. This bone is called the *humerus*. When the surrounding tissues have been removed and the bone has been dried, its surface is fairly smooth. It seems neither crystalline nor granular in texture. It can be broken, but it is quite strong and not particularly brittle (though brittleness increases with the age of the individual). It is dense and compact. This hard bone[1] forms only the outer part of the humerus, however. If the bone is sawed in two lengthwise, it is found to be hollow throughout most of its length, the inner portion of the ends consisting of spongy bone, that is, filled with thin sheets and bars of bone (Fig. 11). This restriction of compact bone to the outer shell makes the bone lighter than it would be if it were solid, but does not materially decrease its strength. The cavity in the bone and the spaces within the spongy bone are, in the living condition, filled with other important tissues which have nothing to do with the skeleton as such.

The humerus is roughly a long cylinder. It extends throughout the length of the upper arm from the shoulder to the elbow, providing stiffness and strength. Its surface provides attachment for muscles, tendons and ligaments, and many of the irregularities of the surface are associated with these. Of special interest are the ends of the bone, because each joins another bone and the nature of these articulations affects the function of the arm by permitting

---

[1] Note the two uses of the word *bone:* (1) as the term for any structure or organ composed primarily of bone, e.g., the humerus; (2) as the name of a tissue.

4

or limiting movement at the shoulder and the elbow. At the shoulder the proximal end of the humerus attaches to the corner of a triangular bone, the *scapula* (Fig. 20), lying in the shoulder and back. This joint permits a wide range of movement, how wide the student can easily determine by experimenting with his own arm,[2] and it also permits some rotation of the arm on its own long axis. The elbow, on the other hand, permits only the limited movement characteristic of a hinge, with the added ability to rotate or, more exactly, to twist the forearm so that the wrist can be turned through almost 180 degrees.

The shoulder joint is relatively simple in its construction. The upper end of the humerus consists of a hemisphere called the *head of the humerus,* which is turned at an angle to the long axis of the bone (Fig. 35). The surface of this hemisphere, in the dried bone, is quite smooth. This head fits into a shallow depression on one corner of the scapula, the *glenoid fossa* (Fig. 36). The surface of this depression is also smooth. If one now examines a bone preserved in fluid or, better, a fresh bone from a beef, sheep or pig, he will find each of these smooth surfaces covered by a thin layer of gristle, or *cartilage.* This cartilage is jelly-like and translucent, but quite firm and tough. It is securely attached to the bone beneath, and its outer surface is smooth. When the arm is moved, this smooth cartilage on the head of the humerus slides over the smooth cartilage lining the depression on the scapula. A little fluid resembling the white of egg keeps the two surfaces moist and lubricated.

The two bones are held together by tough, white, fibrous bands called *ligaments.*[3] These attach to each bone around the edges of the smooth, cartilage-covered articular surfaces, forming a closed capsule around the joint. The surrounding muscles give added strength. The type of joint just described is known as a *synovial joint.*[4] It is described in more detail on page 23.

We have now identified the three tissues, bone, cartilage and fibrous tissue, that compose the skeleton, and we can proceed to a more detailed study of each.

---

[2] Through much of the study of anatomy the student's own body is important laboratory material. He cannot dissect it with any comfort, but he can study its configuration and locate and examine both the surface features and those structures that lie not too far beneath the surface. His body has the great virtue of being alive and under his control, so that he can study the functional consequences of many structural peculiarities.

[3] Ligament: L. *ligamentum,* a bandage. (In these footnotes "L." indicates Latin origin; "G.", Greek.)

[4] Synovial; G. *syn,* with, plus L. *ovum,* egg, probably referring to the appearance of the synovial fluid. Purists frown on combining Greek and Latin roots in one word, but this one goes back to the sixteenth century.

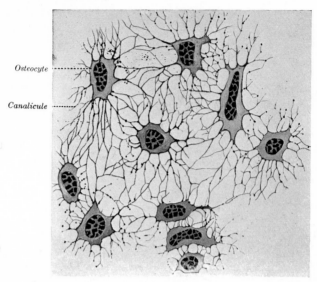

Osteocyte

Canalicule

Figure 1.   Thin, transparent bone of a mouse. × 710. (From Maximow and Bloom.)

BONE

Study of the microscopic structure of bone reveals that it is composed of *living cells* imbedded in a non-living, hard, *intercellular material* (Fig. 1). This intercellular material consists of both organic and inorganic matter. The former consists principally of exceedingly fine fibers composed of a substance related to protein. These fibers, which will be described in detail, comprise 30 to 40 per cent of the intercellular substance. The remaining 60 to 70 per cent consists of complex inorganic minerals made up chiefly of calcium, phosphate and carbonate. The fibers are imbedded in these minerals.

The spaces in which the cells lie are called *lacunae*.[5] The lacunae are connected with one another by numerous small branching canals called *canaliculi*. In compact bone there is, in addition, a system of larger canals mostly running lengthwise of the bone, that contain very small blood vessels (Fig. 2). They are the *haversian*[6] *canals*. The lacunae are usually arranged in concentric layers around them.

---

[5] *Lacuna*, L., ditch, pit, lake, anything hollow; diminutive of *lacus*, lake.

[6] Named after Clopton Havers, an English physician of the seventeenth century. Many anatomic structures have been named after the person who discovered or first described them. In recent years such names have been replaced in gross anatomy by descriptive terms. In microscopic anatomy and comparative anatomy many of them persist.

Figure 2   **The Tissues of the Skeleton   7**

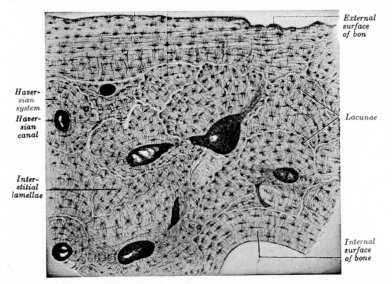

Figure 2.   Cross section of a human bone. × 140. (After Schaffer.)

The living cells, the *osteocytes*,[7] are irregular in shape. Each completely fills its lacuna and sends fine threads of living protoplasm some distance along the adjoining canaliculi. The canaliculi permit substances to pass from one cell to another and to and from the blood vessels in the haversian canals. In this way the living cells are nourished.

THE CELL. "Life" and "living" are words difficult to define, but without entering upon a prolonged discussion we may say that the living part of the body is that part which is active, that is, which takes in food and oxygen, oxidizes the food, gives off waste products and heat, and does work or manufactures materials needed by the body. This is in contrast with such things as the fibers and minerals described before. They are necessary to the body, but passive, like the frame of an automobile.

The living portion of bone and of all other tissues is always organized into discrete units called *cells*. These appear as microscopic bits of more or less transparent jelly. This jelly is called *protoplasm*.[8] Protoplasm should not be thought of as a substance, however, unless in the sense that a factory building is full of a "substance" called machinery, for the bit of jelly that comprises a cell is an unbelievably complex "factory" which is constantly carrying on a number of physical and chemical activities and, in addition, adapting itself to changing conditions and modifying its activities to meet its own needs and those of the whole body.

The cell is made up chiefly of proteins, fats and related compounds, most of them organized into large, complex molecules, with a great deal of water, partly

---

[7] Osteocyte, from G. *osteon*, bone, and *kytos*, hollow vessel. *Kytos* is used in biological terms to denote a living cell which is, of course, not hollow.

[8] Protoplasm: G., first form.

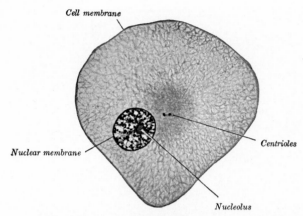

Figure 3. Interstitial cell from the ovary of a rabbit. Iron-hematoxylin stain. × 1300. (Maximow and Bloom.)

free and partly combined with other substances, some carbohydrate, and small quantities of calcium, magnesium and other inorganic ions. Details of the structure of the cell are, for the most part, too small to be seen with the ordinary microscope, and much of our knowledge of them has been secured by indirect means. How much will be learned with the aid of the electron microscope remains to be seen. Recently the phase microscope has revealed additional details of living protoplasm.

Some details of the cell structure can be made out with the aid of the compound microscope, however. The living protoplasm is homogeneous optically, and in order to see very much it is necessary to kill the cell in such a way as to produce a minimum of change in its structure and then to stain it. It is impossible to kill a cell or even to interfere seriously with its activities, however, without profoundly changing it structure, and this fact must always be kept in mind by the histologist or cytologist. Certain structures in the cell stain differently from others, and this makes it possible to see features otherwise invisible.

A cell fixed and stained for microscopic examination is shown in Figure 3. The most conspicuous feature is the *nucleus,*[9] a more or less spherical structure surrounded by a definite membrane and containing granules of a darkly staining substance called *chromatin.*[10] Surrounding the whole cell is the *cell membrane.* This is not to be confused with a "cell wall," which sometimes, most commonly in plants, encloses the cell. The cell wall is an inert structure manufactured by the cell it surrounds. The cell membrane, on the other hand, is living; it is a part of the protoplasm. It constantly controls what may enter and leave the cell.

The material composing the nucleus is often referred to as *nucleoplasm,* the material outside the nucleus as *cytoplasm,* and the two together as *protoplasm.*

Cells vary widely in size, shape and appearance as well as in the part they play in the total activity of the body. Every cell carries on certain fundamental processes such as taking in food and oxygen and combining them to release energy. Every cell responds in some way to sudden changes in its environment (stimuli), and the effect of stimulation at one point is transmitted to other parts of the cell. Every cell keeps itself in repair. In addition to these activities, each cell has special duties to perform which will be mentioned in connection with the different tissues.

---

[9] Nucleus: L., the kernel of a nut, diminutive of *nux,* nut.
[10] Chromatin, from G. *chroma,* color.

Figure 4   **The Tissues of the Skeleton** 9

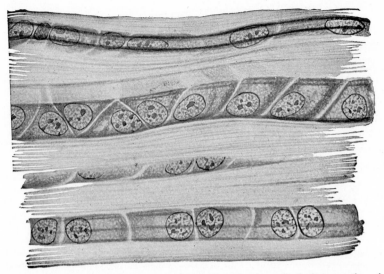

Figure 4. Fibrous tissue, from a tendon. The rows of tendon cells lie between the collagenous bundles. $\times$ 520. (Maximow and Bloom.)

New cells arise only by the division of an existing cell. New living matter is produced only by the incorporation of non-living matter into an already existing cell. When a cell has reached a certain size, it may divide into two. Cell division is an elaborate process which insures that the two daughter cells shall be complete and like the mother cell, at least as regards the nucleus, which carries the factors controlling heredity. The nucleus divides first by a complicated procedure known as *mitosis*. Then the cytoplasm divides. The two daughter cells may grow to full size and in turn divide to produce four cells. It is in this way that the millions of cells of the body arise from the single cell that was the egg.

The general activities of the osteocytes are carried on at a low rate. Their special activities are the production and maintenance of the intercellular material. How this is accomplished is not understood. Besides its functions of support and protection, bone serves as a reservoir of calcium for the body. Small quantities of this move constantly from the bone into the blood stream or from the blood stream into the bone as circumstances make necessary. The osteocytes must of certainty take an active part in this process.

CONNECTIVE TISSUE PROPER

Ligaments and Tendons. *Ligaments* are white, fibrous cords or bands that fasten bones together. *Tendons*[11] are similar cords or bands that attach muscles to bones or other structures. Ligaments and tendons are strong and flexible. Microscopic examination shows

[11] Tendon: L. *tendo*, from *tendere*, to stretch. Tendons do not stretch appreciably, however.

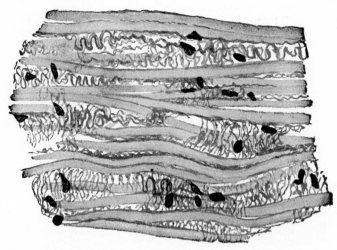

Figure 5. Longitudinal section of a part of the ligamentum nuchae of an ox. The thick, elastic fibers form most of the tissue. Between them are fibroblasts (only the darkly stained nuclei show) and wavy collagenous fibers. × 330. (Maximow and Bloom.)

the fibers of which they are composed to be bundles of very fine fibrils. Most of the fibers are from 1 to 12 microns in thickness (a micron is 0.001 mm.). The fibrils are 0.3 to 0.5 micron thick. They are protein in nature, long chains of polypeptides. When boiled, they yield glue, and for this reason the fibers are called *collagenous*[12] *fibers.* The fibrils seem to be held together in bundles by some kind of cementing substance. Collagenous fibers are not elastic to any extent.

The fibers comprising the organic part of the intercellular substance of bone seem to be identical with these collagenous fibers. Instead of lying in a hard matrix of mineral, however, the fibers of ligaments and tendons lie in a fluid or semifluid ground substance. The fibers of ligaments and tendons are continuous with fibers in the bone, and it is in this way that the firm attachment is accomplished.

The cells of ligaments and tendons are called *fibroblasts*[13] (Fig. 4). They lie between the fibers in rows. Their special function is doubtless the production, in some manner not yet understood, of the fibers.

The tissue that has just been described is a form of *connective tissue proper.* Connective tissue proper, as contrasted with bone and cartilage, is characterized by a semifluid ground substance so that it is always flexible.

---

[12] Collagenous: G. *kolla,* glue.
[13] Fibroblast: G., fiber-bud.

Figure 6   *The Tissues of the Skeleton* 11

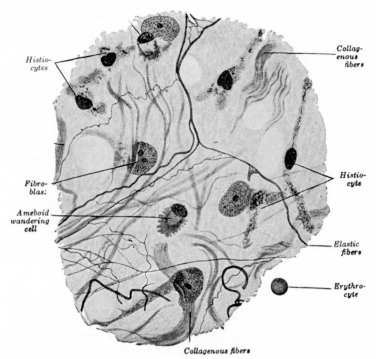

Figure 6. Areolar or loose connective tissue, showing the important types of cells and fibers. Erythrocyte for size comparison. Iron-hematoxylin stain. × 650. (Maximow and Bloom.

Elastic Tissue. Some ligaments, instead of being white, are yellow and are elastic like rubber. These properties are due to the fact that they are made up largely of an entirely different type of fiber known as *elastic fibers*. These, unlike collagenous fibers, seem not to be made up of fibrils, but to be homogeneous. They are composed of a substance called *elastin,* protein in nature, but doubtless of a molecular structure different from that of the collagenous fibrils. Elastic fibers are of various sizes. They branch and unite freely, forming a structure like a stretched fish net. Between the large elastic fibers are small quantities of collagenous fibers (Fig. 5).

Elastic fibers will be found in other structures besides elastic ligaments. In the walls of some blood vessels there are fenestrated sheets of elastin.

Loose Connective Tissue. In this tissue, sometimes called *areolar tissue,* the fibers, both collagenous and elastic, are but loosely packed together, with large amounts of ground substance between them (Fig. 6). The fibers run in all directions, forming a loose feltwork. The fibroblasts are of irregular shape with large oval nuclei. In addition to the fibroblasts, several other types of cells are present, but since their special functions are not concerned with the connective tissue as such, they will not be discussed here. The loose texture of this tissue permits the student to get a clearer idea of the elements of connective tissue than he can from the denser types, and Figure 6 should be studied with care. Note that though the elastic fibers and collagenous fibers branch frequently, the fibrils that compose the collagenous fibers seem never to branch.

Loose connective tissue fills spaces throughout the body that are not otherwise occupied, such as clefts and angles between organs. It forms a loose layer beneath the skin, attaching the skin firmly to underlying structures while allowing some movement. It is this glistening white tissue that is cut when an animal is skinned.

Fibrous Membranes.   Connective tissue is in some places organized into membranes. These may be thick or thin, substantial or tenuous. The fibers may run in all directions, or, if the membrane must withstand a pull—that is, serve as a tendon or ligament—they will be parallel. Membrane-like tendons are called *aponeuroses*.[14] Muscles and many other organs are surrounded by a membranous sheath. Indeed, the active tissues of most organs, including muscles, require the support of fibrous tissue.

Bone is covered by a layer of dense connective tissue proper called the *periosteum*.[15] Its fibers are continuous with fibers in the bone, so that it is firmly adherent in most places. When a bone is fractured, the fibroblasts of the periosteum regain some of their embryonic characteristics and take an active part in forming new bone.

Cartilage has a similar covering, the *perichondrium*.[16] The articular surfaces in synovial joints are naked cartilage, however, without any perichondrium.

Adipose Tissue.   In many regions of the body the fibroblasts may accumulate fat as small droplets in the cytoplasm. As the quantity increases, the droplets coalesce into one large drop which occupies most of the space in the enlarged cell. The nucleus is crowded to one side, and the cytoplasm forms hardly more than a membrane around the fat. Loose connective tissue in which large quantities of fat have thus accumulated is called *adipose*[17] *tissue* (Fig. 7), and the fibroblasts are called *fat cells*. The process of

---

[14] Aponeurosis: G., from a neuron. The term "neuron" originally meant anything white and fibrous, e.g., nerves, tendons and ligaments. An aponeurosis is essentially a flattened-out tendon.

[15] Periosteum: G. *peri*, around, plus *osteon*, bone.

[16] Perichondrium: G. *chondros*, cartilage.

[17] Adipose: L. *adeps*, fat.

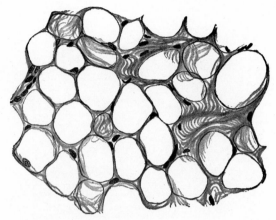

Figure 7. Adipose or fatty tissue. The fat has been dissolved in preparing the section. About × 200. (Maximow and Bloom.)

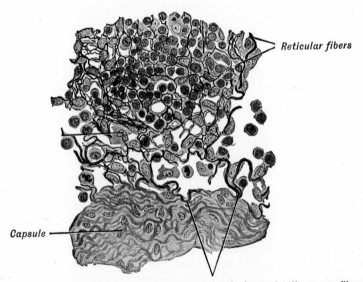

Reticular fibers

Capsule

Connection of reticular and collagenous fibers

Figure 8. Reticular fibers in a lymph node. × 500. (Maximow and Bloom.)

accumulation is reversible, and the cell may give up its store. Adipose tissue, therefore, serves as a reservoir of fat.

Reticular Tissue. In certain parts of the body the connective tissue fibers are very fine and branch to form a network around the cells they support (Fig. 8). These are called *reticular fibers*.[18]

---

[18] Reticular, like a net, L. *rete*, a net.

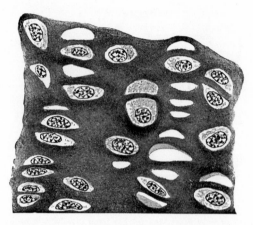

Figure 9. Hyaline cartilage. Some of the cells have fallen out of their cavities. × 750. (Maximow and Bloom.)

In some respects they resemble collagenous fibers. There is reason to believe that reticular fibers are the precursors of collagenous fibers and that in certain situations they have remained in the immature condition. Where reticular tissue is contiguous to connective tissue proper, the reticular fibers are continuous with collagenous fibers (Fig. 8).

CARTILAGE

Cartilage is a firm, slightly elastic, translucent tissue. It is somewhat like a stiff jelly. The intercellular substance appears to be homogeneous, but investigation shows it to consist of a feltwork of collagenous fibers, similar to that of bone, imbedded in a jelly-like ground substance. The fibers are not ordinarily visible because they have the same refractive index as the ground substance.

The cells, *chondrocytes*,[19] are more or less spherical, but may be flattened in some situations, as, for example, beneath articular surfaces. They lie singly or two or more together in spaces corresponding to the lacunae in bone. There are no canaliculi or haversian canals, however, and substance passing to or from the chondrocytes must diffuse through the intercellular substance.

Clear, more or less transparent cartilage is known as *hyaline cartilage*[20] (Fig. 9). It occurs on the articular surfaces in synovial joints and is the substance of the costal cartilages. The intervertebral disks are of *fibrocartilage*, a tissue intermediate between con-

---

[19] Chondrocyte, from G. *chondros,* cartilage.
[20] Hyaline: G. *hyalos,* glass.

nective tissue proper and cartilage, and distinctly fibrous in appearance.

Supporting the external ear and in certain other parts of the body is a third type, *elastic cartilage*. It contains large numbers of elastic fibers and, as would be expected, is yellowish in color.

The surfaces of cartilage not adjacent to bone are usually but not always covered with a fibrous membrane, the *perichondrium*. (See under *Fibrous Membranes*, p. 12.)

THE CONNECTIVE TISSUES IN GENERAL

We have studied three types of connective tissue: connective tissue proper, bone and cartilage. They are alike in that each consists of a mass of fibers with cells scattered through it. They differ in the nature of the ground substance or matrix in which the cells and fibers lie: semifluid, hard or jelly-like.

It is a striking fact that no natural ends to the fibers can be found. It appears, therefore, that the entire connective tissue system of the body—bone, cartilage and connective tissue proper—is a single, continuous, ubiquitous system of fibers, varying from point to point in its properties and functions, but structurally indivisible. *It is important to bear this conception of the connective tissues in mind throughout the study of anatomy.*

CHAPTER 3

THE BONES AND JOINTS

THE BONES with their associated cartilages and ligaments form the essential framework of the body, called the skeleton.[1] This framework has several functions. It provides support for the softer structures; it gives attachment to the muscles which make locomotion possible; it forms protective enclosures for many internal organs, such as the brain, heart and lungs; and it contains centers for the manufacture of some of the blood cells.

The skeleton is divided for purposes of study into two parts. (1) The *axial skeleton* (Fig. 10) forms the framework for the trunk and head, and consists of the bones of the vertebral column, thorax[2] and skull. (2) The *appendicular skeleton* forms the framework for the limbs, and consists of the bones of the upper and lower extremities, including those of the pelvic and shoulder girdles.[3]

The bones are fastened together in various ways. The connection between two or more adjacent bones is called a *joint* or *articulation*. The movements which the several joints permit, limit or prevent are, of course, important elements of the mechanics of movement of the body and its parts.

If a bone which has been sawed longitudinally (Fig. 11) is examined, it can readily be seen how it provides strength without unnecessary weight. The outer portion consists of a hard shell of *compact bone*. The inner portion of the ends is composed of a spongelike network of *cancellous* or *spongy bone*. The meshes of the network appear at first sight to be arranged in no apparent order, but careful investigation has shown that the pattern follows

---

[1] The term "skeleton" is derived from the Greek and originally meant a dried body or mummy.

[2] Thorax: G., chest.

[3] The bones are often classified according to their shape into four groups: long bones, short bones, flat bones and irregular bones. For example, the bones of the upper arm and thigh, the humerus and femur, are long bones; the bones of the wrist and ankle are short bones; the scapulae and parietal bones are flat bones; the vertebrae and many of the bones of the skull are irregular.

Figure 10   **The Bones and Joints   17**

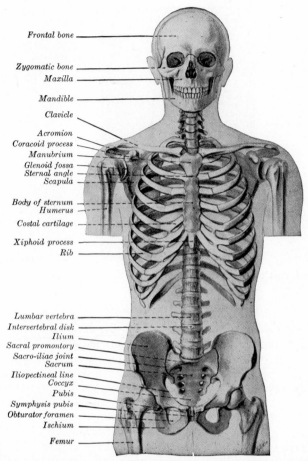

Frontal bone

Zygomatic bone
Maxilla

Mandible

Clavicle

Acromion
Coracoid process
Manubrium
Glenoid fossa
Sternal angle
Scapula

Body of sternum
Humerus

Costal cartilage

Xiphoid process
Rib

Lumbar vertebra
Intervertebral disk
Ilium
Sacral promontory
Sacro-iliac joint
Sacrum
Iliopectineal line
Coccyx
Pubis
Symphysis pubis
Obturator foramen
Ischium

Femur

Figure 10. Skeleton of the head and trunk, anterior view. (Reduced from Warren: Handbook of Anatomy. Harvard University Press.)

the lines of stress and strain to which the bone is exposed. The
center of the shaft is hollowed out into a cavity called the *medullary* or *marrow cavity*.[4] In life both the medullary cavity and the
meshes of the spongy bone are filled with a soft tissue called *bone
marrow*.

In the case of the flat bones of the cranial vault (Fig. 29) the
compact bone forms outer and inner layers called external and
internal tables. The thin layer of spongy bone in between the two
is called the *diploë*.[5]

---

[4] Medulla: L., marrow, innermost part.

[5] Diploë: G., a fold or doubling. Originally used for the tables of bone, and
later applied to the substance between the tables.

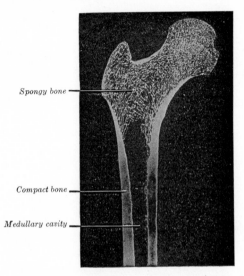

Spongy bone

Compact bone

Medullary cavity

Figure 11.   Longitudinal section through part of the femur. (Koch.)

THE VERTEBRAL COLUMN

The vertebral column or backbone (Figs. 21, 10, 20) is a long, flexible rod that supports the trunk and neck, enabling them to be held upright, but permitting the bending and twisting necessary to the activities of the body. The column consists of alternate segments of bone and cartilage, the former longer than the latter. The bony segments are called *vertebrae*,[6] and the cartilaginous segments, *intervertebral disks*. In dried skeletons the intervertebral disks are missing or, if the skeleton is mounted, have been replaced by pieces of felt or other material.

In very primitive vertebrate animals, such as lampreys, there is, instead of a vertebral column, a strong, unsegmented, elastic rod, the *notochord*,[7] consisting mostly of a tissue peculiar to this structure. The notochord lies just ventral to the spinal cord, a part of the nervous system. A notochord appears early in the development of all vertebrates, but in higher forms, including man, it is replaced in the course of development by the vertebral column. As this replacement is taking place, there appears on each bony segment an arch of bone that surrounds and protects the delicate and vital spinal cord. Each vertebra comes, therefore, to consist of a cylindrical segment of the rod, plus an arch (Figs. 12, 13, 16).

The Vertebrae.   The first twenty-four *vertebrae* are subdivided

---

[6] Vertebrae, pleural of vertebra: L., from *vertere,* to turn, change.

[7] Notochord: G. *noton,* the back.

Figure 12   **The Bones and Joints**   19

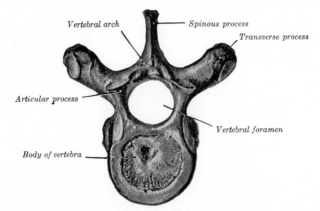

Figure 12. Thoracic vertebra, superior view. (Reduced from Warren: Handbook of Anatomy. Harvard University Press.)

into three groups, named according to the position in which they are found. There are seven in the neck called *cervical*[8] *vertebrae,* twelve in the back called *thoracic*[9] *vertebrae,* and five in the loin called *lumbar*[10] *vertebrae.* They all have a similar general structure, but there are certain characteristic differences in each of the three regions. We shall select a thoracic vertebra for study and then compare the others with it.

Each *thoracic vertebra* (Fig. 12) consists of a short, cylindrical portion, the *body,* to the posterior aspect of which is attached a bony arch, the *vertebral arch.* Enclosed by the vertebral arch is the *vertebral foramen.*[11] The bodies of the vertebrae are solid and carry the weight of the parts above. In the spinal column as a whole they become progressively larger from above downward. The arch has on its external surface three processes,[12] one pointing backward, called the *spinous process,* the other two extending laterally, called the *transverse processes.* The spinous processes mark the midline of the back, and their rounded tips can be readily felt beneath the skin. The transverse processes give partial attachment to the ribs. Four small elevations (*articular processes*) which interlock with similar elevations on the vertebrae above and below can also be found. The *vertebral canal* formed by the series of vertebral foramina encloses the spinal cord.

The *lumbar vertebrae* (Fig. 13) are larger than the thoracic

---

[8] Cervical, derivative of cervix, L., neck.
[9] Thoracic, derivative of thorax, G., a cuirass.
[10] Lumbar: L. *lumbus,* loin.
[11] Foramen, a small opening or perforation. From L. *forare,* to bore, pierce.
[12] Process: L. *processus,* projection.

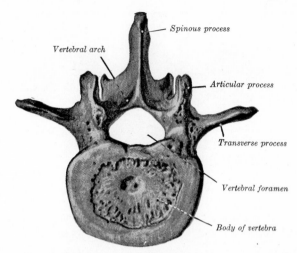

Figure 13.   Lumbar vertebra, superior view. (Reduced from Warren: Handbook of Anatomy. Harvard University Press.)

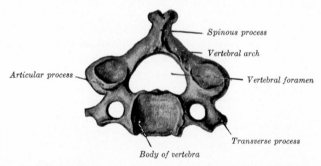

Figure 14.   Cervical vertebra, superior view. (Reduced from Warren: Handbook of Anatomy. Harvard University Press.)

vertebrae, and their transverse processes do not give attachment to ribs.

The *cervical vertebrae* (Fig. 14) are easily distinguished from the others by their transverse processes. These are unusually wide and contain a canal for the transmission of an artery (the vertebral artery). The seventh cervical vertebra is further distinguished by its prominent spinous process, and it has been called the *vertebra prominens*. The first and second cervical vertebrae are markedly different from the others and are especially modified so as to permit movements of the head. The second cervical vertebra, called the *epistropheus*,[13] or *axis*[14] (Fig. 15), possesses a body that

---

[13] Epistropheus, from two Greek words, meaning upon, to turn.
[14] Axis: L., axle.

Figure 15   **The Bones and Joints**   21

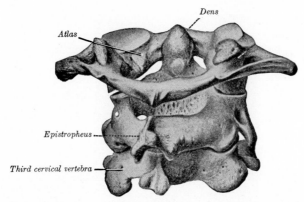

Figure 15. First three cervical vertebrae, posterior view. (Sobotta and McMurrich.)

is much reduced in size, and has projecting upward from it a prominent projection known as the *dens*[15] (O.T., odontoid[16] process). The dens passes through a special canal in the first cervical vertebra and forms the axis of rotation for the skull and first vertebra, which turn together.

In the first cervical vertebra or *atlas*[17] (Fig. 15) the body is still further reduced and the whole bone little more than a large ring. Its cavity is divided by a transverse ligament (Fig. 18) into two compartments, a larger posterior one for the spinal cord, corresponding to the vertebral foramina of other vertebrae, and a smaller anterior one for the dens of the epistropheus. On the upper surface of the bone are two smooth oval areas for articulation with the under surface of the skull.

The Intervertebral Joints. We described the vertebral column as consisting of alternate segments of bone and cartilage. Another way to look at the matter is to consider the pads of cartilage as constituting the articulations between the bodies of the successive vertebrae. This is the conventional way of describing them. Each disk of cartilage is firmly attached to the adjacent bone. (Recall that the fibers in connective tissue pass without interruption from one type of tissue to another). In this manner the bodies of the successive vertebrae are held together by the cartilage, but there is still permitted some degree of movement. The disks are of fibrocartilage (p. 14) and not only permit more movement than would the firmer types of cartilage, but also absorb shocks that might otherwise damage the column.

The cartilage alone, however, is not sufficient to hold the verte-

---

[15] *Dens,* L., a tooth.
[16] Odontoid: G., toothlike.
[17] Atlas, from Atlas, the Greek divinity who held the world on his shoulders.

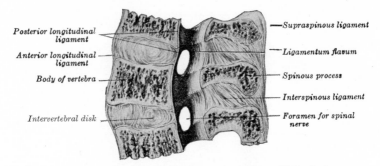

Figure 16. Sagittal section through part of the vertebral column. (Callander.)

brae together, and there are in addition numerous strong ligaments. These are white fibrous bands or cords that pass from one bone to another. Only the more important ligaments of the vertebral column will be described. The *anterior longitudinal ligament* (Figs. 16, 42) is a broad band that runs up and down the front of the column over the anterior faces of the vertebral bodies. Its deeper fibers attach firmly to each bone. The *posterior longitudinal ligament* runs along the posterior faces of the vertebral bodies, on the anterior wall of the vertebral canal. It is similar to the anterior ligament, but narrower. The *supraspinous ligament* (Figs. 16, 43) runs over the tips of the spinous processes and attaches firmly to each. The *ligamenta flava*[18] consist of yellow elastic fibers (p. 11) and are, therefore, much more elastic than the white ligaments. Each extends from one vertebral arch to the next, thus forming, with the arches, a roof over the vertebral canal. Their great elasticity permits them to stretch when the vertebral column is bent forward, and still not form folds that might press on the spinal cord when the arches are brought close together by movement in the opposite direction.

During movements of the vertebral column the articular processes on the successive vertebral arches *slide* over one another. Examination will show that the adjacent surfaces, where the sliding takes place, are smooth. In life these surfaces are covered by a thin layer of hyaline cartilage. The surface of this cartilage has no perichondrium and is very smooth, forming a good "bearing." Friction is further reduced by the presence of a lubricating fluid somewhat resembling the white of egg. This fluid is produced by, and is held in the joint by, a membrane that lines a capsule of fibrous tissue which loosely joins the bones together around the edges of the cartilage-covered surfaces (Fig. 17).

---

[18] L. *flavus*, yellow.

Figure 17   **The Bones and Joints   23**

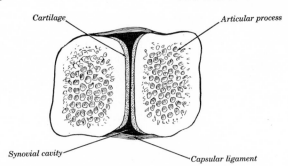

Figure 17. Diagram of section through two articular processes, showing the synovial joint between them. In life the two layers of cartilage would, of course, be in contact.

The movements possible at the intervertebral joints are forward bending or *flexion*, backward bending or *extension*, sideward bending or *abduction*, and *rotation*. The amount of movement possible at any one joint is relatively small, but when several participate, the total movement is considerable.

Types of Joints. We have found in the vertebral column three ways in which bones are joined together, and it will be well to name these and other types of articulation before we go further.

The joint between the bodies of adjacent vertebrae, where the bones are connected by a layer of cartilage, is a *cartilaginous joint*. In some situations the layer of cartilage will not be as thick as it is between the vertebrae and but little movement will be possible. A cartilaginous joint is always supplemented by ligaments around its periphery.

The ligamenta flava and the interspinous and supraspinous ligaments form a second type of joint, the *fibrous joint* between the vertebral arches. Where the fibers are long enough to permit movement as they do here, the joint is called a *syndesmosis*.[19] Where, on the contrary, the fibers are short and permit no movement, but bind the bones firmly together, the joint is called a *suture*. Sutures are found only in the skull.

The joint between articular processes of the vertebrae, where the bones can slide over one another, is called a *synovial*[20] *joint* (Fig. 17). This is the only type of joint that will permit extensive movement between two bones, such as is necessary, for example, in the elbow. The articular surfaces are always covered with cartilage which reduces friction and absorbs shocks. The bones are always held together by a ligamentous capsule (or *capsular liga-*

---

[19] G. *syn*, together, plus *desmos*, ligament.

[20] Probably from G. *syn*, together, and L. *ovum*, egg, referring to the synovial fluid in the joint.

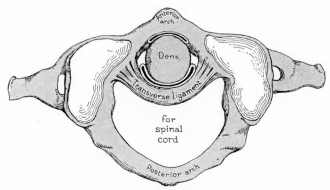

Figure 18. Articulation between odontoid process and atlas. (Redrawn from Gray's Anatomy.)

ment), reinforced by other ligaments and by muscles. Lining the capsular ligament is the *synovial membrane.* The space enclosed by the synovial membrane and the cartilaginous articular surfaces is the *synovial cavity* which contains the *synovial fluid.*

The Joints between the Skull, Atlas and Axis.   The articulations between the skull and the oval areas on the atlas (Figs. 15, 18) are synovial joints. These two concave areas (and the corresponding convex areas on the skull, Fig. 27, (*occipital condyle*) are discontinuous segments of one elliptical surface. This configuration permits the head to tip forward and backward and from side to side, or any combination of these movements, but allows little or no rotation around a longitudinal axis. A model of the joint can be made by holding a hen's egg in the cupped palm of the hand. The dorsal and ventral arches of the atlas are attached to the skull by ligaments forming a syndesmosis.

Rotation of the head takes place between the atlas and the epistropheus with the dens as the pivot. Synovial joints are found between the dens and the anterior arch of the atlas, between the dens and the transverse ligament of the atlas (Figs. 18, 19) and between the superior articular surfaces of the epistropheus and the inferior articular surfaces of the atlas (Fig. 15). Ligaments, of course, attach the atlas to the epistropheus, and one runs from the tip of the dens to the skull.

The Sacrum.   The *sacrum*[21] (Figs. 10, 20, 21) lies directly below the fifth lumbar vertebra. As seen from the front it is more or less

---

[21] Sacrum: L., sacred. Two explanations for this term have been given. One is that it was a part of the body especially used in sacrifices in ancient times. The other is that it came from the idea of Jewish rabbis, that the bone, which they called the *luz,* would resist decay and become the germ from which the body would be raised.

Figure 19 **The Bones and Joints 25**

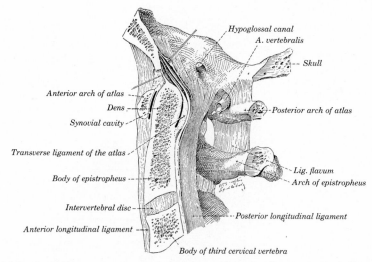

Figure 19. Median section through epistropheus atlas and adjacent structures. (Anson: Atlas of Human Anatomy.)

triangular; as seen from the side it is concave anteriorly. It rests with its base directed upward and its apex pointing downward. It represents the fusion of five sacral vertebrae and their shortened ribs, all of which are distinct bones in early embryonic life. In adults, in a good specimen, one can still make out the constituent parts. The four transverse lines across the anterior surface represent the lines of fusion of the bodies of the five vertebrae; the rough elevation down the midline of the posterior surface is the fusion of the spinous processes; the two rows of holes just lateral to the original bodies are the places of exit of the sacral nerves; the rough areas just lateral to these are the transverse processes; and the anterolateral parts that attach to the hip bones are the costal (rib) elements. In more primitive vertebrates, e.g., the alligator, the sacral vertebrae and ribs are distinct throughout life.

The Coccyx.   The coccyx[22] (Figs. 10, 20, 21) is the name given to the three, four or five rudimentary coccygeal vertebrae attached to the tip of the sacrum. They constitute a vestigial structure representing the bony remnants of the tail of lower animals.

The Vertebral Column as a Whole.   If we examine the vertebral column as a whole, we see that as observed from the front or back (Figs. 10, 20) it forms a straight line, but that as seen from the side (Fig. 21) it presents definite curvatures. The posterior aspect is concave in the cervical region, convex in the thoracic region,

---

[22] Coccyx: G., a cuckoo; so called because of its fancied resemblance to a cuckoo's beak.

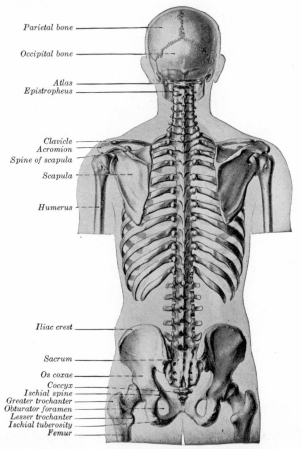

Parietal bone

Occipital bone

Atlas
Epistropheus

Clavicle
Acromion
Spine of scapula
Scapula

Humerus

Iliac crest

Sacrum

Os coxae
Coccyx
Ischial spine
Greater trochanter
Obturator foramen
Lesser trochanter
Ischial tuberosity
Femur

Figure 20.   Skeleton of the head and trunk, posterior view. (Reduced from Warren: Handbook of Anatomy. Harvard University Press.)

and concave again in the lumbar region. Continuing into the sacrum and coccyx, the line is again convex. In walking and jumping these curves give resilence and spring to the column as a whole, which is, therefore, enabled to absorb shocks more readily than would a perfectly straight series of vertebrae.

Note that the vertebrae increase in size from above downward to the sacrum. This is in accord with the increased weight each must bear.

Finally, the relation of the spinal cord and spinal nerves to the column as a whole should be noted. The spinal cord lies in the vertebral canal and is protected dorsally by the bony arches. The spinal nerves emerge from the vertebral canal through openings,

Figure 21   **The Bones and Joints   27**

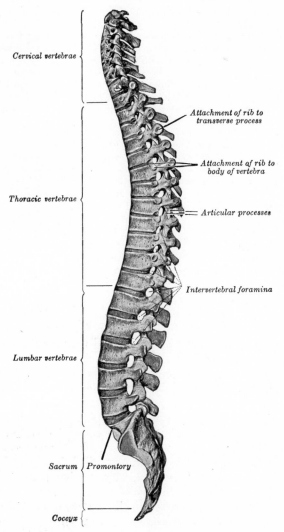

Cervical vertebrae

Attachment of rib to
transverse process

Attachment of rib to
body of vertebra

Thoracic vertebrae

Articular processes

Intervertebral foramina

Lumbar vertebrae

Sacrum } Promontory

Coccyx

Figure 21.   The vertebral column seen from the left side. (Sobotta and McMurrich.)

intervertebral foramina, immediately posterior to the bodies of the
vertebrae and between the bases of the successive arches (Fig. 21).

PRACTICAL CONSIDERATIONS.   The vertebral column not infrequently shows
abnormal curvatures. These are frequently due to poor posture, although they
are sometimes produced by disease of the vertebrae themselves. Correction of
these deformities is one of the tasks of the orthopedic surgeon, and prevention of
them is an important phase of preventive medicine.

Severe injuries to the vertebral column may result in fracture or dislocation or, as frequently happens, a combination of the two. A fracture running across the body of a vertebra must of necessity weaken it, and the weight of the parts above dislocates the upper portion forward. In addition to the immediate shock, the complication most to be dreaded is injury to the spinal cord, which, in some cases, may be totally cut through. Such damage to the cord will produce paralysis and loss of sensation below the level of injury; if the injury is high in the cervical region, respiration will no longer be possible and death will ensue.

Tuberculosis not infrequently attacks the bodies of the vertebra and practically eats them away. If untreated, the bones eventually become so weakened that they are crushed by the weight of the parts above and a "hunchback" is produced. This deformity, once prevalent, is now rarely seen, thanks to the better treatment of tuberculosis in children. This disease of the spine requires long periods of complete rest in bed, with the vertebral column made immobile by strapping the patient to a special kind of frame. Children being subjected to this form of treatment are a common sight in orthopedic wards.

THE BONES OF THE THORAX

The *thorax,* or chest is occupied principally by the heart and lungs. Its contents are protected by a bony cage consisting of the thoracic vertebrae and intervertebral disks, the ribs and their cartilages, and the sternum. This cage not only supports and protects the organs, but also serves as part of the mechanism for pumping air in and out of the lungs.

The Sternum. The sternum,[23] or breastbone (Fig. 10), lies in the midline of the thorax in front. It is shaped much like an old Roman sword, with a short handle, called the *manubrium,*[24] above, and a longer blade, called the *body* of the sternum, below. The two pieces meet at a slight angle called the *sternal angle.* It can be readily palpated beneath the skin and forms an important landmark. It lies over a number of important structures inside the thorax, and on the surface it marks the place of attachment of the second costal cartilage. It thus forms a convenient reference point in determining the number of any given rib. A small piece of cartilage at the lower end of the sternum is called the *xiphoid process.*[25]

The Ribs. The ribs (Figs. 10, 20), twelve pairs in number, form the bony portions of the walls of the thorax or chest. They are long, slender bones attached to the vertebrae behind and curving gently forward to the sternum in front. The attachment to the vertebra is by two points, one to the body and one to the transverse process. The end of a rib that articulates with the body of a vertebra is called its head. All the ribs but the first, tenth, eleventh and twelfth attach opposite an intervertebral joint, and each is fastened to its intervertebral cartilage by a ligament. On each side of this ligament is a small synovial joint so that the head

---

[23] Sternum: G., the chest. Galen limited its meaning to the breastbone.
[24] *Manubrium:* L., handle.
[25] Xiphoid: G., sword-shaped.

Figure 22   **The Bones and Joints   29**

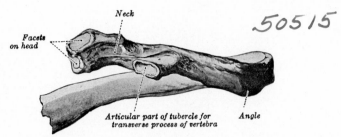

Figure 22. Fifth right rib as seen from behind. (Redrawn from Cunningham's Textbook of Anatomy, 7th edition.)

shows two articular facets, and there is a corresponding facet, or "demifacet," on each of the adjacent vertebrae (Figs. 21, 22, 23). The first, tenth, eleventh and twelfth ribs each articulate with only one vertebra. About an inch from the head of the rib is a small swelling, the tubercle, which, except on the last two or three ribs, bears a facet that articulates with the transverse process of the vertebral arch. This also is a synovial joint. *The double articulation of the rib with the vertebral column limits the movement of the rib to rotation around an axis passing through the head and tubercle.* This gives rigidity to the thoracic wall while allowing the movements necessary to breathing and to flexion of the trunk.

The curvature of the ribs is not entirely uniform and is sharpest at a posterior point called the *angle.* Nor is the curvature directly forward, but forward and downward so that a line drawn horizontally around the chest starting at the sixth rib in the nipple line[26] would pass through the eighth rib laterally and the tenth rib behind.

In front the attachments vary. Each rib ends some distance short of the sternum, but is continued by the *costal*[27] *cartilage,* a piece of hyaline cartilage (Fig. 10). The first pair of costal cartilages attach to the sternum by syndesmoses. The attachments of the next six usually contain small synovial cavities that tend to disappear in old age. The eighth, ninth and tenth costal cartilages do not reach the sternum, but each attaches to the preceding cartilage. The eleventh and twelfth end freely among the muscles of the body wall and are called "floating ribs." The thorax is smaller above than below, so that the upper ribs are shorter than the lower, with the exception of the two floating ribs, which are also short.

Note that the thorax is much narrower above than below and that the first pair of ribs, together with the first thoracic vertebra

---

[26] Nipple line: an imaginary vertical line passing through the nipple.

[27] Costal, from L. *costa,* rib.

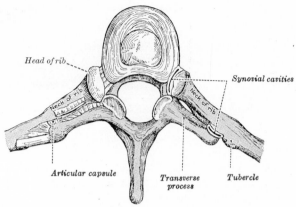

Figure 23. Costotransverse articulation, seen from above. Synovial cavities are shown on the right, ligaments on the left. (Redrawn from Gray's Anatomy.)

and the manubrium, enclose an aperture measuring only about 2 by 4 inches (Fig. 10). This bony aperture is sometimes called the *inlet* of the thorax.

The ribs and sternum play an important part in respiration. The ribs can be elevated by certain muscles that will be described later. As each rib turns about the axis through its head and tubercle, its anterior end moves upwards and forwards as well as a little laterally. This moves the costal cartilages and sternum upwards and forwards; the anteroposterior diameter and, to some extent, the transverse diameter of the thorax are increased, and air is drawn into the lungs. Other factors in breathing will be discussed later.

PRACTICAL CONSIDERATIONS.   Fracture of one or more ribs is a relatively common condition. Its site and nature depend upon the way in which the bones are broken. If, for example, the ribs are hit with a small instrument driven with considerable speed, they will usually break at the point struck, and the fragments will be driven inward. If, on the other hand, the blow is applied over a large area on the front or back of the chest, as occurs when the patient has been run over, the result will be different. Here the ends of the ribs will be driven together and the fracture will be not at the point struck, but on the curvature, much as a dried twig will break when its ends are approximated. The fragments will then be driven outward.

An accessory rib attached to the lowest cervical vertebra is not infrequent. It may press on structures in the neck, particularly the nerves, when it will then be the cause of pain radiating into the arm. If this occurs, the accessory rib must be removed.

THE SKULL

The skull is the skeleton of the head, face and jaws. The head contains the brain, the nerves that arise from it, the blood vessels

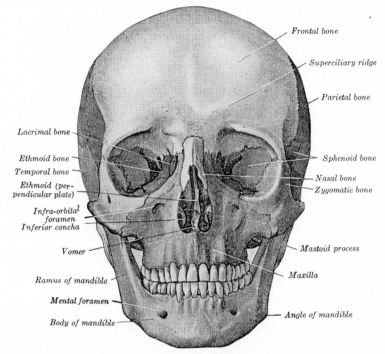

Figure 24. Anterior aspect of the skull. (Cunningham's Textbook of Anatomy.)

that nourish it, the pituitary body or hypophysis, the ears, the eyes, the organ of smell, certain respiratory (nasal) passages, the mouth and its glands, the tongue, and the jaws and their muscles. Except for the lower jaw and the ossicles of the ears, the bones of the skull are immovably united by sutures.[28] The number of distinct bones varies with age, since there is a tendency for the fibers of the sutures to become ossified and the joints obliterated.

Anterior Aspect

Observing the skull from in front, we see two deep pits which, in life, contain the eyeballs and related structures. These pits are the *orbits.* Only the upper part of the nose is seen, the lower part being supported by cartilages which are not present on the dried skull. Below the bony part of the nose is the *anterior bony aperture of the nose.* Within it may be seen the vertical *septum* that divides the nasal cavity into two parts. The anterior part of the septum, like the lower part of the nose, is of cartilage and is missing from the dried skull. Above the orbits is the *frontal region,* the anterior

---

[28] Suture: L. *sutura,* seam.

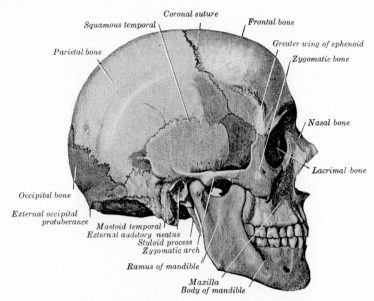

Figure 25.   Lateral aspect of the skull. (Cunningham's Textbook of Anatomy.)

wall of the brain case. Below the aperture of the nose is the upper jaw, or *maxillary region,* the lower edge, or *alveolar*[29] margin of which bears the upper teeth. The bone of the lower jaw is the *mandible.*[30]

Lateral Aspect

In examining the skull from the side, the mandible is seen to possess a posterior upwardly projecting part, the *ramus.* At the top of the ramus are two projections. The anterior one, the *coronoid process,* is for the attachment of muscles. The posterior one is the *condyloid process,* by means of which the mandible articulates with the rest of the skull (Fig. 26).

The condyloid process fits into a concavity on the skull, the *mandibular fossa.* The process and the fossa are not of corresponding shapes, however, and in life do not articulate directly with one another. Between the two is a piece of fibrocartilage, held in place by the capsular ligament of the joint, with a synovial cavity above the cartilage and one below it (Fig. 26). This makes the joint a double one, and the different shapes of the two pairs of articular

[29] Alveolar, from L diminutive of *alveus,* hollow. The name comes from the fact that this part carries the sockets for the teeth.

[30] Mandible: L. *mandibula,* from *mandere,* to chew.

Figure 26   **The Bones and Joints** 33

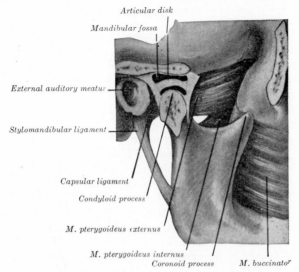

Articular disk

Mandibular fossa

External auditory meatus

Stylomandibular ligament

Capsular ligament

Condyloid process

M. pterygoideus externus

M. pterygoideus internus

Coronoid process   M. buccinator

Figure 26. Sagittal section of the articulation of the mandible, lateral view. (Anson and Maddock: Callander's Surgical Anatomy. 3rd edition.)

surfaces permit the complex movements of the jaw necessary for mastication, which could not be accomplished if this were a simple hinge joint.

Immediately posterior to the articular fossa is the opening of the external ear, the *external auditory meatus*.[31] Movements of the condyloid process can be felt if the tip of the little finger is placed against the anterior wall of the opening of the ear. From a point just above the articular fossa a bar extends forward and is continuous with the lower margin of the orbit. This is the *zygomatic*[32] *arch*. It can easily be palpated above the cheek.

The muscles that close the jaw have their lower attachments on the ramus and coronoid process of the mandible. The more superficial of these muscles attach above to the zygomatic arch. They can be felt below the arch when the jaw is clenched; the deeper muscles pass medial to the zygomatic arch and attach to the wall of the brain case above it where they also can be felt with the fingers. The space occupied by these deeper muscles is the *temporal fossa*. Its upper and posterior boundaries are indicated by a faint line starting near the superior-lateral edge of the orbit and swinging up and back and forward again to the posterior end of the zygomatic arch.

---

[31] *Meatus:* L., a passage.
[32] Zygomatic, from G. *zygoma*, a yoke.

Inferior Surface

The lower surface of the skull should be examined with the mandible removed. Within the horseshoe-shaped area bounded by the upper teeth is the *bony palate*. Above the posterior edge of the bony palate are the two *posterior bony apertures of the nose*, or the *choanae*. In life a membrane, the soft palate, extends back some distance from the bony palate so that the posterior nasal openings are farther back in the mouth.

At about the center of the lower surface of the skull is a large opening, the *foramen magnum*.[33] Through this the spinal cord, which is continuous with the brain, enters the brain case. The foramen magnum is, therefore, in line with the upper end of the vertebral canal within which the cord lies. On each side of the foramen magnum is an oval elevation, the *occipital*[34] *condyle*, which bears a smooth, convex articular surface. This rests against the corresponding oval area on the upper surface of the atlas to form the joint that was discussed earlier (Figs. 15, 18). The ligament from the tip of the dens of the epistropheus attaches to the anterior edge of the foramen magnum.

Some distance lateral to the occipital condyle and just below the external auditory meatus is the slender *styloid process*. (See also Fig. 25.) Median to the styloid process are two openings. The more posterior one is the *jugular foramen*, which transmits the internal jugular vein and certain nerves. The more anterior is the *carotid canal*, which transmits the internal carotid artery. Antero-median to the carotid canal is the *foramen lacerum*, an opening with jagged edges.

Just anterior to the foramen lacerum is the *foramen ovale*. Through it passes the mandibular nerve, which goes to the muscles that close the jaws, to the lower teeth, to the tongue and to various other structures (Fig. 263).

Extending posteriorly from the foramen magnum is a low ridge of bone ending in a rough, irregular area. This marks the attachment of the *ligamentum nuchae*,[35] which is the upper, expanded end of the supraspinous ligament from the spine of the seventh cervical vertebra to the skull. In man the ligamentum nuchae is a triangular sheet separating the muscles of the two sides of the neck. In an animal like the horse it is a heavy elastic cord that helps hold up the head.

The posterior and superior aspects of the skull show little but the rounded wall of the brain case.

---

[33] *Foramen magnum:* L., great opening.

[34] Occiptal, from occiput, L. *ob*, over against, plus *caput*, the head.

[35] Nuche, from L. *nucha*, nape of the neck.

Figure 27   **The Bones and Joints** 35

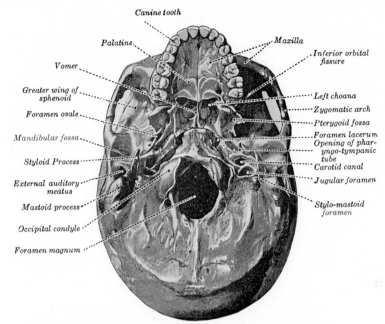

Canine tooth

Palatine

Vomer

Greater wing of
sphenoid

Foramen ovale

Mandibular fossa

Styloid Process

External auditory
meatus

Mastoid process

Occipital condyle

Foramen magnum

Maxilla

Inferior orbital
fissure

Left choana

Zygomatic arch

Pterygoid fossa

Foramen lacerum
Opening of phar-
yngo-tympanic
tube

Carotid canal

Jugular foramen

Stylo-mastoid
foramen

Figure 27. Lower surface of skull. (Cunningham's Textbook of Anatomy.)

Floor of the Cranial Cavity

Upon looking down into a skull from which the top has been removed, one immediately recognizes the foramen magnum. Lateral to it is the jugular foramen, and some distance anterior to this is the foramen lacerum, which, on the inside of the skull, is an oblique, slit-like aperture. Between these two foramina is a high ridge of bone. The carotid canal will be found to have turned forward so that it opens into the foramen lacerum. The internal carotid artery crosses the latter and lies in a groove on its antero-median border.

On the median-posterior side of the ridge of bone that lies between the jugular foramen and the foramen lacerum is the *internal auditory meatus* (Figs. 28, 29). This transmits two nerves, one of which is the auditory nerve, the nerve of hearing, which goes to the internal ear. The internal ear is the part of the ear that contains the sensory cells. It is within the compact bone beneath the ridge.

Some distance anterior to the foramen magnum is a distinct saddle-shaped structure, the *sella turcica*.[36] The seat of the saddle is the *hypophysial fossa,* in which lies the hypophysis or pituitary body. Just anterior to the pommel of the saddle (*tuberculum*

[36] *Sella turcica:* L., Turkish saddle.

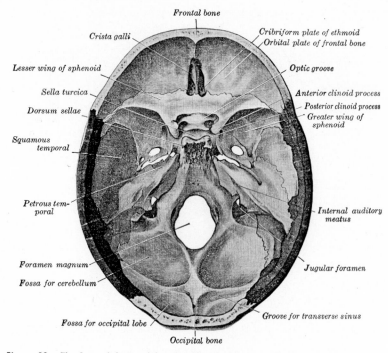

Figure 28. The floor of the cranial cavity. (Cunningham's Textbook of Anatomy.)

sellae) is a short transverse groove, the *optic groove*. Both tuberculum and groove may be indistinct in some skulls. At each end of the groove is the *optic foramen,* which transmits the optic nerve, or nerve of sight, to the orbit.

Anterior to the optic groove is a median ridge or process, the *crista galli.*[37] On each side of it is a depression at the bottom of which is a perforated plate, the *cribriform plate.*[38] Each olfactory nerve, or nerve of smell, is divided into a number of strands which pass through the holes in the cribriform plate to the nasal cavity.

Sagittal Section

Figure 29 shows the left half of a skull divided just to the left of the median plane. Below and anterior to the hypophysial fossa is the *sphenoidal sinus.*[39] Above and between the orbits are the paired *frontal sinuses.* These sinuses are air spaces in the bones, connected with the nasal cavity. In life they are lined with a membrane continuous with that lining the nasal cavity.

---

[37] *Crista:* L., crest; *gallus,* L., a cock.

[38] Cribriform: L., like a sieve.

[39] Sinus, an opening or hollow; L. *sinus,* a curve, bay.

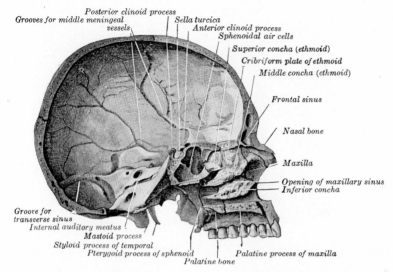

Figure 29. Medial aspect of the left half of the skull sagitally divided. (Cunningham's Textbook of Anatomy.)

On the lateral walls of the nasal cavity are three delicate, scroll-like bones, the *superior, middle* and *inferior nasal conchae.*[40] In life these are covered by a moist, vascular membrane which helps to warm and moisten the air as it is inhaled.

On the sides of the brain case are grooves for blood vessels.

PRACTICAL CONSIDERATIONS. The frontal sinuses are sometimes infected from a cold in the head. In milder cases there is swelling of the lining membrane with pain in the forehead, while in more severe cases the cavity may contain large quantities of pus. The pus, once formed, may not drain away, either because the opening into the nose is naturally too small, or because the swelling of the lining membrane has blocked it up. In either case the surgeon may introduce a probe and make the opening larger, or he may find it necessary to remove the anterior walls of the sinuses.

Figure 30 shows a part of the other half of the skull. This includes the nasal septum as well as the crista galli, structures that lie in the median plane.

The Bones of the Skull

We may now examine the individual bones that compose the skull. In the skull of a young child the sutures between the bones are, for the most part, quite distinct. With increasing age some of the sutures are obliterated and the boundaries between bones

---

[40] Concha, plural conchae, L., a marine shell.

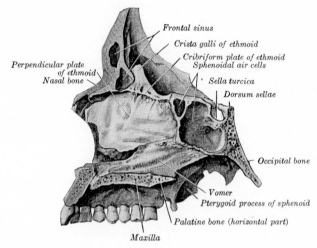

Frontal sinus

Crista galli of ethmoid

Cribriform plate of ethmoid
Sphenoidal air cells

Perpendicular plate
of ethmoid
Nasal bone

Sella turcica

Dorsum sellae

Occipital bone

Vomer
Pterygoid process of sphenoid

Palatine bone (horizontal part)

Maxilla

Figure 30.   Roof, floor and septum of nose. (Cunningham's Textbook of Anatomy.)

disappear. This occurs in fairly constant sequence and is of use in estimating the age of the person to whom a given skull belonged.

The Mandible.   This bone has been described previously (p. 32). In addition may be mentioned the *mandibular foramen* on the median side of the ramus. This admits a nerve, an artery and a vein to the roots of the lower teeth. Branches of the nerve and artery emerge through the *mental foramen* to supply the chin and lower lip (Fig. 24). At birth the bone is paired, but the two halves are united by the end of the second year. The plane of union is the *symphysis*.

PRACTICAL CONSIDERATIONS.   Because the nerve supply for all the teeth on each side of the mandible passes through the mandibular foramen, it becomes an important region in dentistry. Local anesthetics injected here paralyze the nerves and render the whole half of the jaw insensitive. There is no single point where all the teeth on one side of the maxilla can be so affected.

The Frontal Bone.   The frontal bone consists of a more or less vertical portion which forms the bony part of the forehead, and two thin orbital plates that project backward to form the roofs of the orbits. The *frontal sinuses* (Fig. 282) are in this bone. Like the mandible, the frontal is paired, but the suture between the two halves usually disappears by the sixth year. Sometimes the fusion of the two bones does not take place, however, and a frontal suture is present in a small percentage of adults.

The Parietal Bones.   The parietal[41] bones (Fig. 25), two in number, form the main portions of the sides of the cranial vault.

---

[41] Parietal: from L. *paries,* wall.

Figure 31   **The Bones and Joints   39**

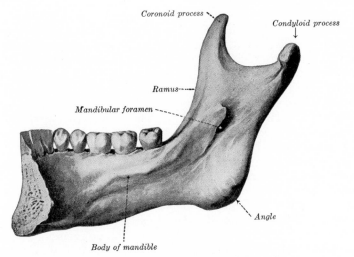

Figure 31. The mandible, right half, from within. (Spalteholz.)

They are almost square in outline. Their superior margins meet in the midline to form the *sagittal suture*,[42] while their anterior margins come in contact with the frontal bone to form the *coronal*[43] *suture*. The sagittal and coronal planes are named from these sutures.

The "soft spot" in a baby's head is at the intersection of the sagittal, coronal and frontal sutures where the rounded corners of the developing bones leave a considerable area of soft tissue (Fig. 310). This space closes at about one and one-half years.

The Occipital Bone. The occipital bone forms the posterior part of the vault and floor of the brain case. It surrounds the foramen magnum and meets the parietals above. It forms one side of each jugular foramen and of each foramen lacerum. In the midline it ends just behind the sella turcica, but the suture at this point has disappeared by the end of the twenty-fifth year. At birth the occipital consists of four bones, one on each side of the foramen magnum, one behind it, and one in front of it. The various lines and rough areas on the ventral surface of the bone are for the attachment of the muscles and ligaments of the neck.

The Temporal Bones. Each temporal[44] bone is developed from four parts that are not only distinct in the embryo and in the adults

---

[42] Sagittal: L. *sagitta*, arrow. It is applied to this suture because of its arrow-like appearance in the infant's skull. The adjective is also used to mean "straight" and to mean running in an antero-posterior direction.

[43] Coronal: L. *corona*, crown.

[44] Temporal bone: the bone in the region of the temple; L. *tempus*, time. Gray hairs appear first on the temples.

of lower vertebrates, but are diverse in origin and function. It will, therefore, be most practical to describe the parts separately, even though they are fused into a single bone in the adult. The *squamous*[45] *part* (Figs. 24, 27) contributes to the side of the brain case below the parietal. It bears the articular fossa for the condyle of the mandible and a zygomatic process which constitutes the posterior part of the zygomatic arch. The *mastoid*[46] *part* of the temporal is seen on the outside of the skull, posterior to the external auditory meatus and below the squamous and parietal bones. It projects down behind the external auditory meatus as a round protuberance, the *mastoid process*. This can be felt as a bony bump behind the ear. The *petrous*[47] *part* extends forward on the lower surface of the skull to the foramen lacerum, between the jugular foramen and the internal carotid canal, both of which it borders. On the inside of the skull it shows as the prominent ridge that bears the internal acoustic meatus. The petromastoid encloses the inner ear. (The structure of the ear, including the three ear bones, or ossicles, is described in detail in Chapter 14.) The *tympanic part* of the temporal bone forms the anterior, inferior and postero-inferior walls of the external auditory meatus and partially encloses the middle ear, or tympanic cavity. It extends medially to the foramen lacerum, forming the anterior margin of the carotid canal. From the ventral surface of the tympanic projects the *styloid process*, which is developed from one of the gill arches of the embryo and is secondarily attached to the skull.

The Zygomatic Bones.   Each zygomatic, or cheek, bone forms the anterior part of the zygomatic arch, part of the rim of the orbit and part of the floor and lateral wall of the orbit.

The Nasal Bones.   The pair of nasal bones form the upper part of the nose and a small part of the nasal septum.

The Maxillae.   The maxillae[48] (Figs. 24, 25) are the bones of the upper jaw. Each consists of a body and several processes. The body on its anterior and lateral aspects forms the part of the face below the eyes and above the teeth; on its medial aspect it forms part of the lateral wall of the nasal cavity; and its superior aspect assists in the formation of the floor of the orbit. The large, single cavity inside the bone (Figs. 32, 282) is called the *maxillary sinus* (O.T., antrum). It communicates with the nasal cavity through an orifice located some distance above its floor.

The processes of the maxilla are four in number. One (the

---

[45] Squamous, from L. *squama*, a scale. The name was applied to this part of the bone because of its thinness.

[46] Mastoid: G., like a breast, referring to the mastoid process.

[47] Petrous: L., stony. This part of the bone is particularly hard.

[48] Maxillae: plural of *maxilla*, L., the jawbone.

Figure 32   **The Bones and Joints**   41

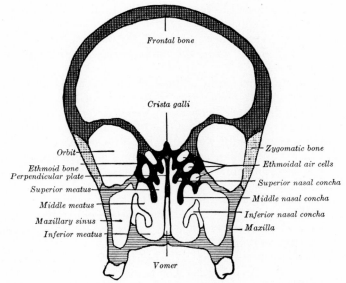

Figure 32. Frontal section through the skull, orbits, nasal fossae and paranasal sinuses to show the bones which enter into their formation. Variations in shading denote the individual bones. (Callander, after Corning.)

alveolar process) projects downward and carries the upper teeth. The second (the frontal process) forms part of the nose. The third gives attachment to the zygomatic bone. The fourth (the palatine process) projects medially and forms, in cooperation with the palatine bone, the hard palate, and thereby the roof of the mouth and the floor of the nose.

PRACTICAL CONSIDERATIONS. The maxillary sinus is of considerable importance, for, like all the other air spaces mentioned, it is readily infected from a cold in the head. In addition, it may be infected from an abscess around one of the upper teeth. It does not drain readily because its opening is so high above its floor, and in obstinate cases it may be necessary to remove the pus through an artificial opening made lower down.

The Palatine Bones. Each palatine bone (Figs. 27, 29) is shaped like a capital letter "L." The upright piece forms part of the lateral wall of the nasal cavity, while the horizontal piece forms part of the floor. It lies directly behind the maxilla.

The Lacrimal Bones. Each lacrimal[49] bone (Figs. 24, 25) is a small structure lying inside the orbit immediately behind the frontal process of the maxilla. It contains a groove, which with a similar groove in the maxilla forms a small canal called the lacrimal

---

[49] Lacrimal, from L. *lacrima*, a tear.

canal. The canal passes from the orbit to the nasal cavity and transmits the tear duct.

The Vomer. The vomer[50] (Figs. 27, 30, 32) is a flat bone shaped like a ploughshare. It forms the posterior and inferior parts of the nasal septum.

The Ethmoid Bone. The ethmoid[51] bone consists of the *crista galli,* the *cribriform plates,* the greater part of the *nasal septum,* which meets the vomer below, and the *superior* and *middle nasal conchae* (O.T., superior and middle turbinates). The ethmoid also contributes to the medial wall of each orbit just posterior to the lacrimal. Lateral to the conchae are numerous air cells, the *ethmoidal sinuses,* which communicate with the nasal cavity through small openings in the bone.

The Inferior Nasal Conchae. Each inferior nasal concha (O.T., inferior turbinate) (Figs. 29, 32) is a long, scroll-like bone attached to the lateral wall of the nasal cavity below the superior and middle conchae of the ethmoid.

The Sphenoid Bone. The sphenoid[52] is of complex shape, originating in the embryo from a number of separate bones. On the inside of the skull it extends, in the midline, from the occipital bone forward to the crista galli, and therefore includes the sella turcica, the optic groove and the optic foramina. This part is known as the *body* of the bone and contains the sphenoidal air cells. The *lesser wings* of the sphenoid extend laterally from the optic foramina, meeting the frontal bone anteriorly. They form part of the floor of the brain case and the posterior part of the roof of each orbit. Below and behind the lesser wings, the *greater wings* extend out to the parietals. The greater and lesser wings on each side are separated from one another by the *superior orbital fissure,* an oblique slit that opens into the orbit, and the greater wing forms the lateral wall of the orbit between the zygomatic bone and the superior orbital fissure. On the outside of the skull the greater wing lies between the squamous temporal behind and the zygomatic and maxilla in front. Part of the ventral border of the greater wing forms the edge of the *inferior orbital fissure,* an oblique slit in the floor of the orbit, which opens into the temporal fossa. Extending down from the bases of the greater wings are the *pterygoid processes.* Each consists of two plates of bone, the medial one forming the border of the posterior aperture of the nose and supporting the soft palate. The space between the two plates of each process is the *pterygoid fossa.* The greater wing forms the anterior border of the foramen lacerum.

[50] Vomer: L., ploughshare.
[51] Ethmoid: G., like a sieve.
[52] Sphenoid: G., like a wedge.

The Auditory Ossicles. There are three small bones, the auditory ossicles, in each ear. These are part of the mechanism for hearing and are described in connection with the ear on page 351.

The Nasal Cavity. The nasal cavity (Fig. 32) is a long, narrow, high channel, divided into two halves by the nasal septum. The sides converge slightly so that the roof is narrower than the floor. On each lateral wall are the nasal conchae. Most of the bones that participate in forming the nasal cavity are shown diagrammatically in Figure 32. To those shown should be added the nasals in front and the palatines and sphenoid behind.

The nose, below the nasal bones, is supported by cartilage (the nasal cartilages), of which there are several pieces on each side. The anterior part of the nasal septum is also composed of cartilage.

The several cavities that open into the nose, the frontal and maxillary sinuses and the ethmoidal and sphenoidal air cells, are called collectively the *paranasal*[53] or *accessory air sinuses*.

PRACTICAL CONSIDERATIONS. There are many kinds of fractures of the skull, and all are serious conditions. Their nature depends largely upon the way in which the injury was produced. Thus a small instrument brought smartly up against the skull will produce a local fracture with the fragments driven into the brain. If the blow is produced with a large flat instrument or its equivalent, as, for example, from a fall on the head, there may be no local indentation, but long radiating cracks may appear. These fractures frequently cross the base of the skull and may injure some of the blood vessels or nerves that pass through the various foramina. The chief danger of skull fracture in general is the associated damage to the brain.

The Joints of the Skull

The joints of the skull, with one exception, belong to the class of immovable joints or sutures. On the vault of the skull, for example, in the sagittal suture, the thin, irregular edge of one bone interlocks with the irregularities of the next. In other places, such as the zygomatico-maxillary articulation, a large rough area on one bone is applied to a similar rough area on another. The mandibular joint, which has already been described, is a compound synovial joint. The joints between the ear ossicles are also synovial joints.

The Hyoid Bone

The hyoid[54] bone (Fig. 33) is an isolated **U**-shaped bone, which lies in the front of the neck a short distance above the larynx. Its central portion is called the *body;* its two arms are known as the *greater horns.* Two small upward projections from the lateral aspects of the body are called the *lesser horns.* The greater horns extend back horizontally and are attached to the upper edge of the

---

53 Paranasal: by the side of the nose.
54 Hyoid: G., like the letter U.

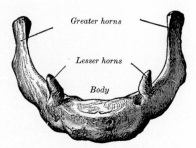

Figure 33. The hyoid bone from above. (Cunningham's Textbook of Anatomy.)

larynx, or voice box. From each lesser horn a ligament extends to the tip of the styloid process of the skull. The bone gives attachment to a group of muscles which move the tongue and serve an important function in swallowing.

THE BONES OF THE UPPER EXTREMITY

Before examining the bones of the upper extremity one should study his own hand, arm and shoulder. The four fingers each consist of three parts joined to one another by hinge-like joints, and each finger is joined to the palm by a hinge joint. When the fingers are extended, they can be separated from one another and brought close together again. When they are bent so that they touch the palm, however, they lie close together and cannot be separated. The thumb is more mobile. It consists of two segments joined by a hinge joint. The proximal segment is attached by a hinge joint to another segment that reaches to the wrist. This latter segment is considered part of the palm, but it can be moved independently of the rest of the palm, and it is this freedom that gives the thumb its mobility.

The palm is attached to the forearm by a different type of joint. At first sight it may appear that the wrist joint permits the hand to be rotated so that the palm may face either up or down if the hand is lying on a table, or forward or backward if the arm is at the side. However, by feeling the forearm while the hand is being rotated, it can be seen that this movement is accomplished, not by rotation at the wrist, but by twisting the forearm. If the forearm is not allowed to twist, it will be found that the wrist joint permits bending in any direction, from side to side or up and down or any combination of these, but permits no rotation at all. In this respect it is similar to the articulation between the atlas and the skull.

The elbow is a hinge joint. How it is possible to have a hinge joint and still allow the forearm to twist will be discovered when the bones and their joints are studied.

The upper arm is attached to the shoulder by a joint that permits a great range of movement. The arm can be held straight up, straight forward, down by the side, across the chest, or out to the side and a little back. The upper arm can also rotate. The degree of rotation can be discovered by feeling the elbow so as not to confuse rotation of the upper arm with twisting of the forearm. Rotation of the upper arm, together with twisting of the forearm, will permit the hand to be turned through about 270 degrees when the elbow is straight. When the elbow is bent, the two movements cannot, of course, be added, and twisting the forearm alone permits the hand to be turned through only about 180 degrees. With the elbow bent the amount of rotation permitted at the shoulder joint is easily determined. It proves to be about 90 degrees, which is what would be expected from the foregoing.

The shoulder itself can be moved to a limited degree forward and backward, up and down. The point of the shoulder, however, is always a fixed distance from the manubrium of the sternum, no matter how the shoulder is moved.

The English words "shoulder," "upper arm," "wrist," and so on, are adequate for the names of these parts, but their Latin (or Greek) equivalents should be memorized because they will be encountered in the names of muscles, blood vessels and nerves and in the form of anglicized adjectives. The Latin word for shoulder is *umerus.* This has, with some lack of logic, been used as the name of the bone of the upper arm (humerus). Derivations of the related Greek word, *omos,* will be encountered more often. The Latin names for the parts of the upper extremity are as follows: upper arm, *brachium;* forearm, *antebrachium;*[55] the whole hand, *manus;* the wrist (proximal part of the hand), *carpus;* the part of the hand between wrist and fingers and thumb, *metacarpus;* finger, *digitus;* thumb, *pollex.*

The bones of the shoulder, referred to as the *shoulder girdle,* consist of two bones on each side of the body, one bone to hold the point of the shoulder out from the manubrium of the sternum, the other, lying in the back, to provide articulation with the bone of the upper arm and also to afford attachment for numerous muscles.

The Clavicle. The clavicle[56] or collar bone (Figs. 34, 10) is a slender bone with a double curve and shaped like an italic letter *f.* Its inner end is round and is attached to the sternum. Its outer end is flattened and is fixed to the scapula.

---

[55] *Ante:* L., before; not to be confused with *anti,* G., against.

[56] Clavicle: L., a little key. It probably refers to an S-shaped door latch rather than to a key (Hyrtl, a German anatomist whose work on derivations of anatomic terms is a classic).

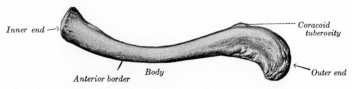

Inner end →

Coracoid
tuberosity

Outer end

Anterior border   Body

Figure 34.   The left clavicle seen from above. (Sobotta and McMurrich.)

The Scapula.   The scapula,[57] or shoulder blade (Figs. 35, 20), lies in the upper part of the back. Its body is flat and triangular. One edge, the *vertebral border,* is more or less parallel to the vertebral column. The *superior border* is almost horizontal, while the *axillary border* slopes steeply upward. (The axilla is the arm pit.) The *costal surface* looks toward the ribs. The dorsal surface is divided into two parts by the *spine,* which terminates laterally in a large flattened process, the *acromion*[58] *process.* The acromion process forms the tip of the shoulder and gives attachment to the clavicle. Since the clavicle, the acromion and the lateral portion of the spine of the scapula lie just beneath the skin, they can easily be palpated[59] on the student's own body. The lateral corner of the body of the scapula is modified to form a shallow articular surface, the *glenoid*[60] *fossa,* which in life receives the head of the humerus. Its cavity is made deeper by an encircling cartilage called the *glenoid labrum.*[61] The *coracoid*[62] *process* projects anteriorly from the upper border of the body near its lateral angle. Almost the whole surface of the bone gives attachment to muscles.

The Humerus.   The humerus (Figs. 35, 59), the bone of the upper arm, is a long bone consisting of a shaft and two modified extremities. On the upper or proximal end is the smooth, rounded *head,* which articulates with the scapula. It points medially from the shaft in order to reach the glenoid fossa. Below the head and on the anterior surface of the bone are two elevations, the *greater tuberosity* laterally and the *lesser tuberosity* medially. Between them is the *bicipital* or *intertubercular groove.* The bone has two necks, an *anatomical neck* situated just below the head, and a *surgical neck* below the tuberosities. The surgical neck receives its name because of its liability to fracture. The *shaft* is long and slender. Nearly halfway down, on the lateral surface, is a slightly elevated, roughened surface area, the *deltoid tuberosity.* The distal

[57] Scapula: L., the back; originally *os latum scapularum,* the broad bone of the back.
[58] Acromion: G., the outermost point of the shoulder.
[59] Palpate: L. *palpare,* to feel.
[60] Glenoid: G., like a socket.
[61] *Labrum:* L., lip.
[62] Coracoid: G., like a crow, from its resemblance to a crow's beak.

Figure 35   **The Bones and Joints   47**

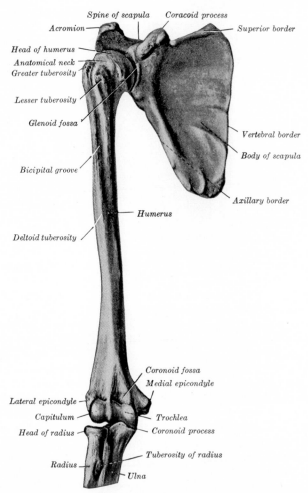

Figure 35. Humerus and scapula, anterior view. (Reduced from Warren: Handbook of Anatomy. Harvard University Press.)

end widens out and contains two smooth articular surfaces. One, the *capitulum*, is like part of a small sphere. The other, the *trochlea*, is shaped somewhat like a spool. Just above these areas on the anterior and posterior aspects of the bone are depressions or fossae into which portions of the upper end of the ulna fit in extreme flexion and extension. The two prominent projections from the medial and lateral margins of the distal end are called the *medial* and *lateral epicondyles*.[63]

---

[63] Epicondyle: G. *epi*, upon, plus *kondylos*, knuckle.

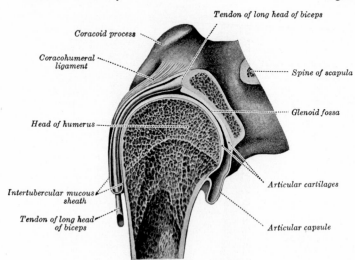

Tendon of long head of biceps

Coracoid process

Coracohumeral
ligament

Spine of scapula

Glenoid fossa

Head of humerus

Intertubercular mucous
sheath

Articular cartilages

Tendon of long head
of biceps

Articular capsule

Figure 36.   Section through the shoulder joint. (From Sobotta and McMurrich.)

The Joints of the Upper Arm and Girdle.   The shoulder joint, the
articulation of the humerus with the scapula, is a synovial joint of
the *ball and socket type.* The shallowness of the socket permits the
great range of movement characteristic of the arm. The articular
capsule is necessarily lax, and the head of the humerus is kept in
place largely by the surrounding muscles (Figs. 36, 62).

The clavicle is attached by a slightly movable joint to the
sternum, but the scapula is not attached to the axial or thoracic
skeleton by an articulation. It is held in place by the muscles which
lie over and under it. It can glide, therefore, a certain distance on
the back, being limited only by the tension of the muscles. This
method of attachment has an important bearing on the transmission of shocks and the location of fractures from a fall on the arm.
The scapula, being so loosely fixed, receives no injury, while the
clavicle receives the full force of the blow. Hence, under these
circumstances, it is the clavicle and not the scapula that breaks.

The different types of movement which can be produced at these
joints and the mechanism of the production of most of them are not
difficult to see. Thus the humerus can be pulled forward and backward, laterally and medially, by the muscles attached to it; similarly, the shoulder or acromion can be pulled in various directions.
A point of special interest is the mechanism for raising the arm to
the full extent above the head. This is accomplished partly by
raising the humerus at the shoulder joint, but also by a rotation of
the scapula about its middle, which elevates the glenoid fossa
and the humerus along with it.

PRACTICAL CONSIDERATIONS. Two features of special interest in the shoulder girdle and upper arm are fracture and dislocation. Fracture of the clavicle is common and of the scapula is rare for the reasons already given. Fracture of the humerus is frequent and may be produced either by a fall or by a blow on the arm. The break may occur anywhere along the bone, but especially common sites are the surgical neck and the junction of the middle and lower thirds of the shaft. The pieces on either side of the break tend to override because of the pull of the muscles attached to them. If they should be allowed to heal in this way, the arm would be permanently deformed and would be shortened and thickened. For this reason the fracture must be promptly "set" and the parts kept in correct position by splints. During the healing process new bone, called callus, is formed, and eventually the bone is as strong as, or even stronger than, it was before.

In dislocation of the shoulder joint, which incidentally is the most frequently dislocated joint in the body, the head of the humerus is forced out of the glenoid fossa and into some abnormal position. Its usual cause is a fall on the outstretched arm, when the head of the humerus is opposite the lowest and the weakest part of the joint. The pressure from the fall forces the head out of the glenoid fossa, tearing the capsule as it goes. It comes to rest usually on the front of the chest below the coracoid process. The problem of the surgeon is to return the bone to its original position by forcing it to retrace its course through the rent in the capsule.

The Ulna. The ulna[64] (Fig. 37) lies in the medial side of the forearm, i.e., on the little finger side. It has a long slender shaft and an enlarged upper end. The upper end contains two beak-like processes, one curving upward and forward and forming on its posterior aspect the tip of the elbow, the *olecranon*[65] (Fig. 59), the other pointing forward, the *coronoid process.* The *semilunar notch* intervening between the two has a smooth articular surface which encloses the trochlea of the humerus and forms the elbow joint. The distal end of the ulna is small and has on its medial side a small projection pointing downward, the *styloid process.* On the lateral surface of the ulna at both the upper and lower ends are small articular areas for the radius.

The Radius. The radius[66] (Fig. 37) is the lateral bone of the forearm. In contrast to the ulna, its lower end is large and its upper end is small. The upper end or *head* is flat on top and is rounded like a checker. It articulates with the side of the ulna and with the capitulum on the lower end of the humerus. On the shaft a short distance below the head is the *tuberosity,* a rough tubercle for the attachment of a muscle (the biceps brachii). The lower end has on its under surface a smooth concave area which articulates with the carpal or wrist bones. Laterally, the lower end projects downward to a point known as the *styloid process.*

The Bones of the Hand. The *carpal*[67] *bones* forming the wrist

---

[64] Ulna: G., the elbow, the forearm.
[65] Olecranon: G., the head of the elbow.
[66] Radius: named from its resemblance to a spoke of a wheel.
[67] Carpal, from G. *carpos,* the wrist.

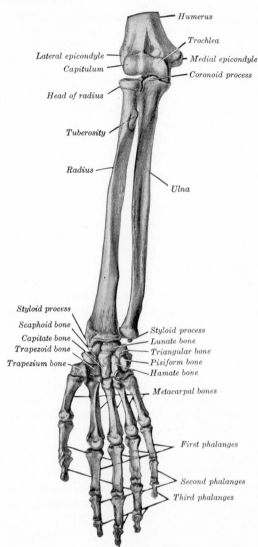

Figure 37. Bones of the right forearm and the hand, anterior view. (Reduced from Warren: Handbook of Anatomy. Harvard University Press.)

are eight in number (Fig. 37). Seven of them are arranged in two rows. The proximal row consists of:

Scaphoid[68] (or *navicular*) at the end of the radius

---

[68] Scaphoid: G., boat-shaped. The bone has a concave surface which gives it a slightly boat-shaped appearance. Navicular, L., also means "like a little boat."

Lunate[69]
Triangular, at the end of the ulna.
The distal row consists of:
> *Trapezium* (or *greater multangular*[70]), opposite the first meta-
> carpal, the one at the base of the thumb
> *Trapezoid* (or *lesser multangular*), opposite the second meta-
> carpal
> *Capitate,*[71] opposite the third metacarpal
> *Hamate,*[72] opposite the fourth and fifth metacarpals. The hamate
> has a hook at the distal end of its palmar surface.

The remaining carpal, the *pisiform,*[73] lies on the palmar surface
of the triangular, just proximal to the hook of the hamate. When
the wrist is flexed and relaxed, the pisiform can be grasped by the
thumb and finger of the other hand and moved slightly. The hook
of the hamate is too well covered by muscles to be palpable.

The carpals are closely fitted and bound together. They have
synovial cavities between them, however, and a little movement is
possible, especially along the line between the proximal and distal
rows.

There are five *metacarpal*[74] *bones* which form the bony structure
of the palm. They are not separately named, but are numbered
from one to five, beginning with the lateral or thumb side. The
bones are long and slender, and their rounded distal ends form the
knuckles. Proximally, they articulate with the carpal bones; distally,
with the phalanges.

The *phalanges,*[75] or bones of the fingers, are fourteen in all, three
for each finger, referred to as proximal, middle and distal, or first,
second and third phalanges, and two for the thumb. They are built
upon the same general plan as the metacarpals, but are shorter.
The distal phalanx is the shortest of all and has a rough distal end
which underlies the tip of the finger.

The Joints of the Lower Arm. The elbow is a hinge joint, permitting motion in one plane only (Fig. 38). The articulation is
mainly between the ulna and the trochlea, but the slightly concave
end of the radius moves against the capitulum. The articular capsule is reinforced by ligaments, the strongest being those from the
epicondyles of the humerus.

---

[69] Lunate: L., like the moon.
[70] Multangular: L., having many angles.
[71] Capitate: L., like a head.
[72] Hamate: L., hook-like.
[73] Pisiform: L., like a pea.
[74] Metacarpal, from G., beyond the wrist.
[75] Phalanges, from phalanx, a Greek battle formation, which the bones as a
whole resemble. The term originally referred not to a single bone, but to the
group.

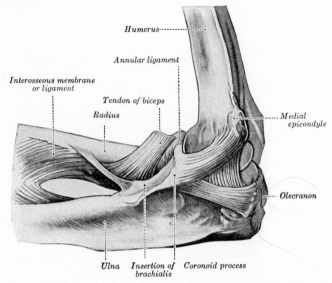

Humerus

Annular ligament

Interosseous membrane
or ligament

Tendon of biceps

Radius

Medial
epicondyle

Olecranon

Ulna   Insertion of   Coronoid process
brachialis

Figure 38. Medial aspect of the elbow joint. (Cunningham's Textbook of Anatomy.)

The wrist joint is between the large distal end of the radius and the proximal row of carpals. The articular surface on the end of the radius is extended medially by a shelf of cartilage (articular disk) which excludes the ulna from contact with the carpals (Fig. 39). The configuration of the articular surface of the radius and articular disk on one side and of the carpals on the other is such that the wrist can bend in any direction, forward and backward and from side to side, but it does not permit rotation of the hand around the long axis of the radius. As in the case of the atlanto-occipital joint, a working model can be made by holding a hen's egg in the cupped palm of the hand.

Neither the wrist nor the elbow will, then, permit *supination* or *pronation,* that is, turning of the palm up or down. These movements are accomplished by rotation of the radius. Its head is held in a shallow notch on the ulna by the annular ligament (Fig. 38). The synovial cavity of the elbow extends between the head of the radius and the ligament and ulna. When the radius rotates, its head turns within this ring and bears smoothly against the capitulum of the humerus regardless of the angle at which the elbow may be flexed. The articulation between the head of the radius and the ulna and annular ligament may be compared to the articulation of the dens with the atlas. The axis around which the radius rotates is a line from the center of the concave surface on the head of the radius to the pit on the distal end of the ulna where the articular disk is

Figure 39   **The Bones and Joints** 53

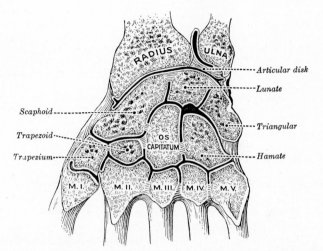

Figure 39. Section through the wrist to show the joint cavities and the interosseus liga-ments (diagrammatic). (Redrawn from Cunningham's Textbook of Anatomy.)

attached. The distal end of the radius travels around the ulna. The two bones are held together here chiefly by a ligament that goes from the median edge of the articular disk to the styloid process of the ulna. The end of the ulna bears against the articular disk and the side of the radius.

Throughout most of their length the radius and ulna are joined together by a fibrous *interosseus ligament* (Fig. 38).

If a blow is struck with the fist, or if weight is put on the hand, the force is transmitted from the carpals chiefly to the radius, from the radius in large part to the ulna through the interosseus membrane, and from the ulna to the humerus. To transmit this force, most of the fibers of the interosseus membrane run from the radius obliquely distad toward the ulna.

PRACTICAL CONSIDERATIONS. Fractures of the radius and ulna are not infre-quent, and the two bones are usually broken together. Occasionally only one is broken, in which case the bone fractured depends upon the character of the injury received. Thus when an injury is received by the forearm in the act of warding off a blow, it is usually the ulna that is fractured, since the ulnar side of the arm is directed against the approaching object. A fall on the hand, however, is more apt to produce a fractured radius, since this bone is the one most intimately con-nected with the bones of the hand and wrist. Such falls not infrequently produce a special type of fracture of the lower end of the radius known as Colles' frac-ture.[76] The broken lower fragment is driven into the distal end of the proximal portion, and the hand is forced into a peculiar position known as the "silver fork" deformity.

---

[76] Colles' fracture: from Abraham Colles, Irish surgeon and professor of anat-omy at Dublin, early nineteenth century. Like anatomic structures, lesions and diseases have been named for the person who first identified or described them.

Dislocation of the elbow joint is rare because of the way in which the head of the ulna fits around the humerus. Joints depend for their security upon three factors: (1) closely fitting bony parts, (2) strong ligaments, and (3) the tension of overlying muscles. The elbow joint depends chiefly upon the first factor and is rarely dislocated. The shoulder joint depends chiefly on the third and, although it has the advantage of much more mobility than the elbow joint, is much less secure.

An interesting type of dislocation of the upper end of the radius occasionally occurs in children. Its cause is a sudden jerk on the hand which lifts the child off its feet, as when the mother swings it to the side of the street out of the way of a passing automobile. The radius, being directly fixed to the bones of the hand, is pulled distally while the ulna remains with the humerus. In this way the head of the radius is pulled out of the annular ligament.

The Joints of the Hand.   There are synovial cavities between the carpals (Fig. 39). However, the bones of the proximal row, scaphoid, lunate and triangular, are so closely bound together by ligaments that only a little movement is possible. This movement is a gliding of one approximately flat surface over another, comparable to the movement at the synovial joints between the articular processes of the vertebrae. The same state of affairs exists for the distal row, trapezium, trapezoid, capitate and hamate. The joint between these two rows of bones, the *transverse carpal joint,* permits some flexion and is responsible for the fact that flexion at the wrist is greater than extension; at the radio-carpal joint flexion and extension are about equal.

The movements which the first metacarpal can perform, the movements that permit the thumb to touch each of the fingers and, in the other direction, to "thumb a ride," would lead one to expect a ball and socket joint between this metacarpal and the trapezium. Instead, there is a *saddle joint.* The two articular surfaces are saddle-shaped and fit together at a right angle to one another. An imperfect model can be made by putting the hands together in such a way that the notch between the thumb and palm of one hand lies across that of the other. This is the only joint of its kind in the body except a flattened one between the fifth metacarpal and the hamate.

There is a single synovial cavity between the remaining four metacarpals and the distal row of carpals. There is almost no movement, however, by the second and third metacarpals at the joint, a little by the fourth, and more by the fifth. The fifth can, to a limited degree, move like the first. This can be most clearly seen by observing the back of the hand while touching the tips of each finger with the tip of the thumb.

The metacarpo-phalangeal articulations are called *condyloid*[77] *joints.* These are basically ball and socket joints, but sideways

---

[77] Condyloid: G. *kondylos,* knuckle, plus *eidos,* resemblance.

movement is limited by ligaments. When the fingers are extended, sideways movement is possible, but the lateral ligaments are so attached that when the fingers are flexed they tighten and prevent any such movement at all. When the fist is clenched, the knuckles are formed by the ends of the metacarpals.

The interphalangeal joints are hinge joints.

THE BONES OF THE LOWER EXTREMITY

The foot and leg resemble in many ways the hand and arm, but instead of being adapted for the great variety of uses to which the upper extremity can be put, the lower is adapted for standing, walking, running and jumping, and for little else.

Like the hand, the foot (L. *pes*) has five digits, four of which consist of three segments and one, the big toe, or *hallux*, of two. Like the fingers, the toes can be flexed and extended, extension being greater than is possible for the fingers. This greater extension permits standing, running, and landing from a jump, "on the toes" or, more accurately, on the toes and the anterior part of the sole.

The sole is long, narrow at the heel and wider behind the toes. Though a large part of the sole is in contact with the ground when standing, three parts bear most of the weight: (1) the heel, (2) the ball of the foot (the sole just behind the big toe), and (3) the part of the sole behind the fourth and fifth toes. These three points, a tripod, form a stable support readily adaptable to irregularities of the ground. The foot has three arches between these three points, the highest being between the ball of the foot and the heel. These arches are by no means rigid, however, and should be thought of also as springs.

When one stands "on the toes," another tripod is formed. Two points are the same as when standing on the sole, but the third is formed by the first two or three toes, instead of by the heel.

The joint at the ankle is a hinge joint, permitting the foot to be raised (*dorsiflexion*), as when standing on the heels, and lowered (*plantarflexion*), as when standing on the toes. The foot can be turned inward (medially), *inversion*, and, to a lesser extent, outward, *eversion*. Inversion and eversion take place, not at the ankle joint, but at joints within the foot. There is no appreciable rotation of the foot around the axis of the lower leg.

The word "leg"[78] in ordinary speech refers to the whole lower extremity, but in anatomic terminology it refers only to that part of the lower extremity between the ankle and the knee.

---

[78] Leg. The Latin word is *crux;* the anglicized form, crus, and the adjective, crural, are not much used in connection with the leg, but are used for structures elsewhere in the body that resemble a leg or, in the plural, crura, for a pair of dividing structures.

The knee[79] is a hinge joint, but with some modifications. When the knee is bent, the leg can, to a limited degree, be rotated. When the leg is straight, however, this is not possible. Actually, in order to extend the knee completely, a light lateral rotation of the leg is necessary because of the structure of the joint, but this is hardly noticeable.

The thigh[80] is the segment of the leg between the knee and the hip.

The hip joint is a ball and socket joint, but does not permit the range of movement found at the shoulder. Rotation of the foot when the knee is straight is rotation of the whole extremity, permitted by the hip joint.

The girdle of bones with which the thigh bones articulate is firmly attached to the sacrum, and, with the sacrum, forms a complete ring. It is called the *pelvic girdle*.

The Os Coxae or Hip Bone.   The os coxae[81] or hip bone (O.T., innominate[82] bone) (Figs. 40, 10, 20) is large and complicated. It represents the fusion of three elements, the ilium, the pubis and the ischium, which are separate in early life (Fig. 41). The *ilium*[83] is the largest of the three and forms the large, upper expanded area of the hip bone. The *pubis*[84] and the *ischium*[85] are below the ilium and form the boundaries of a large opening known as the *obturator*[86] *foramen,* the pubis being anterior and the ischium posterior. On the lateral surface of the hip bone is a circular depression called the *acetabulum,*[87] which forms the socket for the head of the femur. The three elements, ilium, pubis and ischium, meet in the center of this cavity. Their lines of fusion radiate from the center like the spokes of a wheel and may be easily seen in the child (Fig. 41), although in the adult they are no longer evident.

---

[79] Knee. The Latin word is *genu,* used chiefly for bent structures elsewhere in the body.

[80] Thigh: the Latin word is *femur.* The noun is applied to the bone of the thigh, but the adjective, femoral, is used to indicate relation to the thigh, not to the bone.

[81] *Os coxae:* L., the bone of the hip.

[82] Innominate: L., unnamed. Galen, the great anatomist of ancient times, wrote that no name had been given to the bone as a whole. It was later called the innominate or unnamed bone.

[83] *Ilium* (plural *ilia*): L., the flank.

[84] Pubis (plural pubes), from pubes, the hair that develops in the region at puberty; L. *pubis,* adult.

[85] *Ischium* (plural *ischia*): G., the buttock. The adjective derived from it, ischiadic, has been shortened to sciatic.

[86] Obturator, from L. *obturare,* to close up. The foramen in life is almost completely closed by a membrane.

[87] Acetabulum: L., a little cup of vinegar; from *acetum,* vinegar. Cf. acetic acid.

Figure 40   **The Bones and Joints   57**

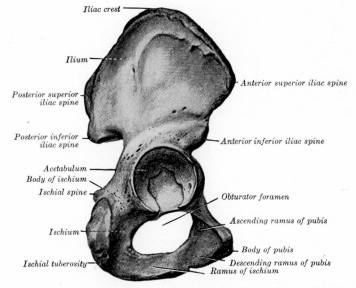

Figure 40.   Right hip bone (os coxae), lateral view. (Reduced from Warren: Handbook of Anatomy. Harvard University Press.)

There are several points of interest on the ilium. Its large, smooth medial surface is called the *iliac fossa* (Fig. 10, marked *ilium*). This fossa is limited posteriorly by a rough area through which the hip bone articulates with the sacrum in the *sacro-iliac joint*. It is limited inferiorly by a prominent ridge, the *iliopectineal*[88] *line* (Fig. 10), which runs from the rough area on the ilium to the pubic bone. The long upper border of the ilium, easily felt in the living subject, is called the *iliac crest* (Fig. 40). It terminates anteriorly in a small tubercle, the *anterior superior spine*.

The pubis consists of a body and two arms or rami. The *body* unites with its fellow in the midline anteriorly to form a joint known as the *symphysis pubis* (Fig. 10). The upper border of the body forms an easily palpated landmark, the *pubic crest*. Of the two rami (Fig. 40), one, the *ascending ramus,* extends upward and backward to the ilium; the other, the *descending ramus,* passes downward to the ischium.

The ischium (Figs. 40, 20) consists of a body and a ramus. On the under surface of the body is a large, rough area which forms the resting point of the body in sitting, and is known as the *ischial tuberosity*. The pointed projection above the tuberosity is called the *ischial spine*. The *ramus of the ischium* projects forward and upward to meet the descending ramus of the pubis.

---

[88] Pectineal, from L. *pecten,* a crest or comb.

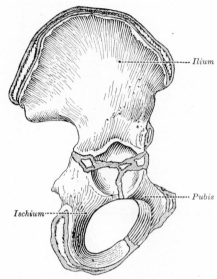

Figure 41. The right hip bone at 12 or 13 years of age, showing the three separate bones united by cartilage with several secondary centers of ossification in the cartilage. (Cunningham's Textbook of Anatomy.)

The Pelvis. The complete bony ring formed by the two hip bones anteriory and laterally and the sacrum and coccyx posteriorly is known as the *pelvis*[89] (Fig. 42). (The term "pelvis" is also applied to the lower part of the abdomen.) The cavity inside can be readily divided into two portions, a smaller, inferior cavity called the *true pelvis,* and a larger, superior one called the *false pelvis.* The line of separation between them is the *iliopectineal line* (Fig. 10). The side walls of the true pelvis are formed largely by the pubes and ischia, while the side walls of the false pelvis are formed by the ilia.

The shape of the bony pelvis shows certain differences in the two sexes, the essential characteristics of which are found in the structure of the true pelvis. In the male this cavity is deeper, narrower and more funnel-shaped, while in the female it is wider, shorter and straighter at the sides. In the female the acetabula, and therefore the thigh bones, are placed farther apart, and the angle formed by the two descending rami of the pubic bones is greater. The inlet to the true pelvis is heart-shaped in the male, and kidney-shaped in the female. The measurements of both the pelvic inlet and the pelvic outlet are greater in the female.

The Joints of the Pelvis. The joints of the pelvis are the two

---

[89] *Pelvis:* L., a basin.

Figure 42   The Bones and Joints   59

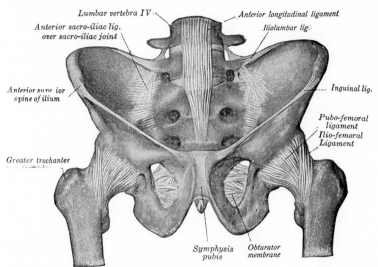

Figure 42. The male pelvis with its ligaments, seen from in front. (Sobotta and McMurrich.)

sacro-iliac joints and the symphysis pubis. The *sacro-iliac joint* (Figs. 10, 42, 43) is an important structure, for through it the weight of the body is transferred from the vertebral column to the pelvic girdle. It is formed by the lateral mass of the sacrum and the rough area of the ilium, and is firmly bound with many ligaments, most of which are found on the posterior aspect of the joint. Each bony surface is covered with hyaline cartilage, and there is a synovial capsule. Since the irregularities of the two surfaces interlock to some extent, however, only slight movement is possible. After middle life fibrous adhesions develop and partly or wholly obliterate the joint cavity. The *symphysis*[90] *pubis* (Fig. 42) is the median joint between the pubic bones. The articular surface of each is covered with hyaline cartilage, and the two are united by a thick disk of fibrocartilage. The joint is strengthened all around by ligaments.

DISORDERS OF THE SACRO-ILIAC JOINT. The sacro-iliac joint, because of the great weight it receives, may become strained. This is particularly apt to occur in pregnancy, partly because of the increased weight of the parts above, and partly because the ligaments of the joint tend to become somewhat relaxed. The pain produced usually radiates down the back of the thigh and is often labelled "sciatia." Tuberculosis not infrequently affects the joint.

The true pelvis is of great importance in childbirth. It is the canal through which the child must pass, and if it is too small or is abnormally shaped, serious difficulties may arise. One of the factors which tend to deform the pelvis is

---

[90] Symphysis: from G., to make grow together.

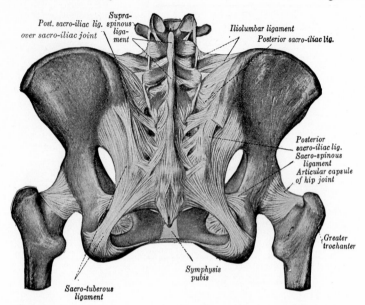

Figure 43. The female pelvis with its ligaments, seen from behind. (Sobotta and McMurrich.)

rickets; hence the importance of preventing this disease of childhood in order to lessen the difficulties and dangers of maternity in later life.

The Femur.   The femur,[91] or thigh bone (Figs. 44, 10), is the longest and strongest bone in the body. It is in many ways similar to the humerus. Proximally, there is a *head* which points upward and inward toward the acetabulum. It is attached to the *shaft* by a relatively long *neck*. At the top of the shaft and on the posterior aspect of the bone are two prominent elevations connected by a ridge or crest. The larger lateral elevation is known as the *greater trochanter*,[92] the smaller medial one, the *lesser trochanter*. Extending the length of the shaft and on its posterior aspect is a ridge, the *linea aspera*.[93] The distal end of the femur widens out into two large masses, the *medial* and *lateral condyles*. On the under surface of the distal end is a large articular area for the head of the tibia. This area is shaped like a letter **U**, with its arms projecting backward and upward on the two condyles. The space enclosed by the arms is called the *intercondylar notch*.

The Hip Joint.   The hip joint (Figs. 43, 44) is in many ways

---

[91] *Femur:* L., the thigh.

[92] Trochanter, from G., a wheel or pulley. The muscles attached to the trochanters produce the rotatory motion of the thigh. Cf. trochlea, page 47.

[93] *Aspera:* L., rough.

Figure 44   **The Bones and Joints 61**

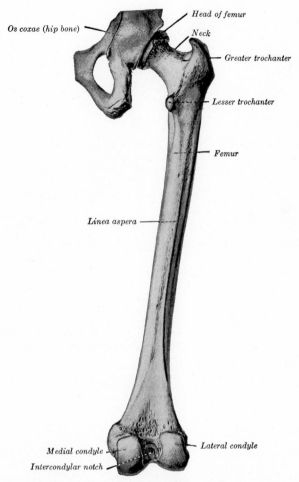

Os coxae (hip bone)

Head of femur

Neck

Greater trochanter

Lesser trochanter

Femur

Linea aspera

Medial condyle

Lateral condyle

Intercondylar notch

Figure 44. Right femur, posterior view, with fragment of pelvis. (Reduced from Warren: Handbook of Anatomy. Harvard University Press.)

similar to the shoulder joint, but is more stable and less freely movable. The socket for the head of the femur, i.e., the acetabulum, is deeper than the glenoid fossa, and in addition there is a ligament (the *ligamentum teres*[94]) which runs from a pit in the head of the femur to the center of the acetabulum. The fibrous capsule is strengthened by many ligamentous bands.

The Tibia. The tibia,[95] or shin bone (Fig. 45), is the medial and larger of the two bones of the leg. Its proximal end or *head* is wide

[94] *Teres:* L., round.
[95] *Tibia:* L., the shin bone.

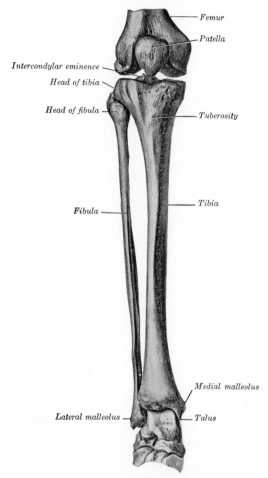

Figure 45. Bones of the right knee and leg, anterior view. (Reduced from Warren: Handbook of Anatomy. Harvard University Press.)

and is flattened on top for articulation with the femur. From the center of this upper surface an elevation, the *intercondylar eminence* (O.T., spine), projects upward. On the anterior surface of the head near its attachment to the shaft is a low projection, easily felt in the living subject, called the *tuberosity*. The sharp anterior border of the shaft can also be easily palpated. The lower end widens out to form on its under surface an articulation for the ankle joint. Medially, it projects downward as the prominent *medial malleolus*.[96]

———————————
[96] *Malleolus:* L., a little hammer.

Figure 46 **The Bones and Joints** 63

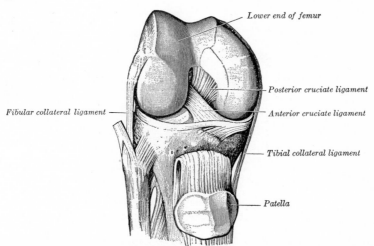

Lower end of femur

Posterior cruciate ligament

Fibular collateral ligament

Anterior cruciate ligament

Tibial collateral ligament

Patella

Figure 46. Dissection of the right knee joint from the front. The knee is flexed and the patella thrown down so that the distal end of the femur is shown. Note the broad groove on the anterodistal surface of the femur in which the patella glides. (Cunningham's Textbook of Anatomy.)

The Fibula. The fibula[97] (Fig. 45) is a long and slender bone attached above and below to the lateral aspect of the tibia. The upper end is expanded slightly to form the *head,* while the lower end projects downward below the level of the ankle joint to form the *lateral malleolus.* The two malleoli are the bony prominences on the sides of the leg just above the ankle joint.

The Patella. The patella[98] (Figs. 45, 46) is a small, flat, triangular bone that lies in front of the knee joint with its apex downward. It is *in* the heavy tendon that attaches the large muscle on the front of the thigh to the tuberosity of the tibia. The patella and the tendon above and below it are easily palpated, especially when the knee is straight.

The Knee Joint. The *knee joint* (Figs. 46, 47) is a complicated structure. The femur rests on the practically flat upper surface of the head of the tibia; hence strong ligaments are needed to prevent it from slipping off. These are provided in part by the usual fibrous bands in the capsule, and in addition there are strong ligaments outside this structure. Furthermore, two other ligaments are found inside the joint itself, which pass from the intercondylar eminence of the tibia to the intercondylar notch of the femur. These cross each other in the form of an X, and are, therefore, called the *cruciate ligaments.* Other support is provided by the surrounding

---

[97] *Fibula:* L., a pin or skewer.
[98] *Patella:* L., a little pan.

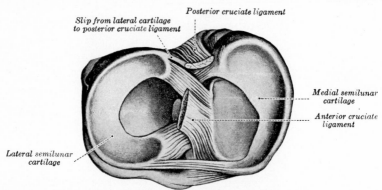

Figure 47. Upper end of right tibia with semilunar cartilages and attached portions of cruciate ligaments. (Cunningham: Textbook of Anatomy.)

muscle tendons. Fitted in between the bones are two *semilunar cartilages* or *menisci* which move backward and forward during flexion and extension of the joint.

PRACTICAL CONSIDERATIONS. Fractures of the femur are common, two frequent sites being the neck and the middle of the shaft. Neck fractures are particularly prone to occur in the aged, for them in the head of the bone is set more transversely to the shaft. In youth the angle formed by these two parts is approximately 140 degrees, while in the old it is reduced to about 120 degrees, and is therefore more vulnerable when a misstep is taken. Shaft fractures tend to produce characteristic deformities such as those described for the humerus.

The tibia and fibula are usually broken together; if one only is broken, it is usually the slender fibula. A particularly common fracture of both bones, called Pott's fracture, is due to a forceful turning of the ankle. The lower end of the shaft of the fibula and the tip of the medial malleolus of the tibia are broken.

Dislocation of the hip is relatively rare because of the great strength of the articulation; when it occurs in a healthy joint, it is always the result of severe violence. The head of the femur may be displaced in any one of several directions, the most common being upward and backward on the ilium. Congenital dislocation is of a different character and is due to a failure of development of the rim of the acetabulum. It thus happens that when the weight of the body is put upon the foot, the femur slides upward on the ilium.

Dislocation of the knee joint is still more rare. What is more common is a tear of one of the semilunar cartilages from a sudden and forceful twisting of the leg. Tuberculosis is relatively common at both hip and knee joints.

The Bones of the Foot.   The *tarsal*[99] *bones* in the foot (Fig. 48) correspond to the carpals in the hand. They consist of seven bones of different size and shape.

The *talus*[100] (O.T., astragalus[101]), the highest of the group, is

[99] Tarsal, from G. *tarsos,* the flat of the foot.

[100] *Talus:* L., a die. The analogous bones of the sheep were used in ancient times as dice.

[101] Astragalus: the Greek equivalent of talus.

Figure 48   **The Bones and Joints** 65

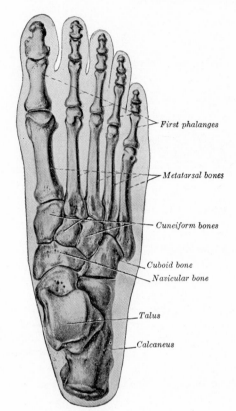

First phalanges

Metatarsal bones

Cuneiform bones

Cuboid bone

Navicular bone

Talus

Calcaneus

Figure 48. Bones of the right foot, dorsal view. (Reduced from Warren: Handbook of Anatomy. Harvard University Press.)

relatively large and articulates with the under surface of the tibia. Below and behind it is the still larger *calcaneus*[102] (O.T., os calcis), which is shaped like a revolver handle and forms the base of the heel. Attached to the anterior end of the talus is the smaller *navicular* (O.T., scaphoid), and anterior to the navicular are the three small *cuneiform*[103] bones bearing the three medial *metatarsals*. The cuneiforms and metatarsals are known by number, counting from the medial side. On the lateral side of the foot the *cuboid* bone can be found attached to the anterior end of the calcaneus. Anterior to the cuboid are the two lateral metatarsals.

The *metatarsals* and *phalanges* are built upon the same general plan as the corresponding bones in the hand.

The Arches of the Foot. There are three arches in the foot, a

---

[102] *Calcaneus, calcis:* L., pertaining to the heel.
[103] Cuneiform: L., wedge-shaped.

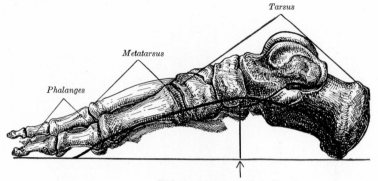

Highest point of the longitudinal arch

Figure 49. Medial longitudinal arch of the foot. (Callander.)

medial and a lateral longitudinal arch, and a transverse arch. Of the two longitudinal arches, the *lateral arch* is the simpler and lower. It consists of only three elements, which named from behind forward are the calcaneus, the cuboid and the two lateral metatarsals (the last being counted as one unit). If we liken the arches to a bridge with pillars and a central keystone, the cuboid bone is the keystone of this arch. The *medial arch* (Fig. 49) is higher and more complicated. It consists of five elements, which named from behind forward are the calcaneus, the talus, the navicular, the three cuneiforms and the three medial metatarsals. The talus is the keystone of this arch. The posterior pillar consists of only one element and gives firm support to the weight of the body. The anterior pillar contains three elements.

The *transverse arch,* sometimes called the metatarsal arch, which runs across the foot, is most clearly seen at the level of the three cuneiforms and the cuboid. The middle cuneiform forms the keystone of this arch.

Although the bones of the foot provide the general form of the arches, the chief factors which maintain their shape when the weight of the body is put upon the foot are the ligaments and muscles. When one is standing on the foot, using it as a stable tripod, the concept of arches is appropriate, but the foot is designed for walking, running and jumping, and in this connection the arches are more appropriately thought of as springs. There are movable joints between all the bones of the foot, much like those of the hand, and ligaments, tendons and muscles give the foot its characteristic resilience and mobility, as well as contributing to its strength and stability. Of the numerous ligaments, we shall mention only two. The *plantar calcaneonavicular ligament* (Fig. 50) passes between the calcaneus and the navicular bone and is an

Figure 50   **The Bones and Joints** 67

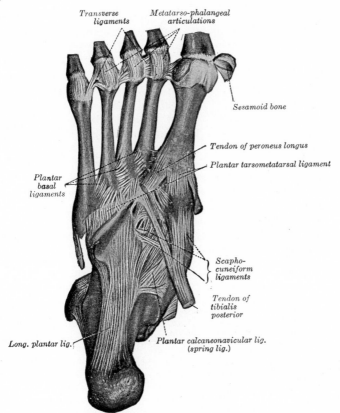

Transverse
ligaments

Metatarso-phalangeal
articulations

Sesamoid bone

Tendon of peroneus longus

Plantar tarsometatarsal ligament

Plantar
basal
ligaments

Scapho-
cuneiform
ligaments

Tendon of
tibialis
posterior

Long. plantar lig.

Plantar calcaneonavicular lig.
(spring lig.)

Figure 50. The ligaments of the right foot, seen from the plantar surface. (Sobotta and McMurrich.)

important factor in the support of the medial arch. It is sometimes called the *spring ligament*. The *long plantar*[104] *ligament* passes from the calcaneus to the cuboid and supports the lateral arch. The muscles concerned in maintaining the arches will be described later.

The Ankle Joint.   The *ankle joint*, formed by the articulation of the talus with the tibia, is a synovial joint of the hinge type (Fig. 45). Note how the two malleoli come down on each side of the talus to clasp it firmly. The joint is strengthened by medial and lateral ligaments which pass from the malleoli to the bones of the foot. Flexion and extension of the foot take place at this joint.

The Joints of the Foot.   Limited inversion and eversion of the heel are necessary for resilience and accommodation to uneven-

---

[104] Plantar, from L. *planta,* the sole of the foot.

nesses of the ground, but a much greater degree of movement is necessary for the anterior part of the foot if the two forward points of the tripod are to be accommodated to irregularities. Inversion and eversion of the heel are permitted by the rather complex *talo-calcanean joint*. The greater degree of inversion and eversion permitted the forward part of the foot takes place largely at the midtarsal joint. This consists of two parts, the *talo-navicular* and the *calcaneo-cuboid joints*. The rest of the joints of the foot need not be described in detail. The side-to-side joints between the cuneiform and cuboid bones and between the proximal ends of the metatarsals are concerned in the transverse spring. The end-to-end joints are concerned with the longitudinal springs. The fifth metatarsal can be dorsiflexed and plantarflexed to some degree, the fourth much less. Little movement of this kind is permitted the first three metatarsals. Any that does occur is chiefly at the cuneo-navicular joints. The toes can be flexed and extended like the fingers, but, as was mentioned earlier, extension is greater than that permitted the fingers.

PRACTICAL CONSIDERATIONS.   The height and strength of the arches of the foot vary considerably in different persons. In some they remain firm under the most trying conditions, while in others they "fall" on the slightest provocation. The factors tending to produce fallen arches are many. Poor posture, the wearing of improper shoes, excess weight and prolonged standing are some of the contributing factors. The treatment consists in removal of the primary causes, the use of special exercises for the feet, and in some cases the wearing of artificial appliances.

CHAPTER 4

MUSCULAR TISSUE

THE FUNCTION of a muscle is to pull. When it pulls, it either moves or steadies structures to which it is attached. If one lifts a book from the table in such a manner as not to move the upper arm while doing it, numerous muscles hold the shoulder girdle and humerus steady while certain others raise the forearm and, with it, the book. All the muscles involved are pulling, each with a force nicely adjusted to the part it has to play at the moment. Those that steady the shoulder and upper arm do not shorten; those that raise the forearm do. If the book, having been lifted, is held above the table, the muscles that raised it cease to shorten and now hold it steady. If someone unexpectedly adds another book to the load, these muscles lengthen until they can adjust their tension to the new load. If, on the other hand, someone unexpectedly removes part of the load, the muscles shorten until they have time to readjust.

To exert its pull, the muscle sets up within itself forces that tend to change its shape, to make it shorter and thicker. These forces are always oriented in the same direction; a muscle cannot set up forces that tend to make it longer and thinner. In other words, it cannot push, it can only pull.

A muscle is elastic. This is well illustrated when one jumps and lands on his toes. The extensor muscles of the leg are tense, but their elasticity permits the leg to flex and absorbs the shock of landing. This quality of elasticity makes muscular action smoother than it otherwise would be and helps to prevent damage to the muscles and tendons and to the structures to which they are attached.

There are three distinct types of muscle which differ from one another structurally and in their physiologic characteristics. They are smooth muscle, striated muscle and cardiac muscle.

Smooth Muscle. This is the simplest of the three types. Smooth muscle cells (Fig. 51) are long and spindle-shaped. Because of this they are commonly called *muscle fibers*. Each has a single elongated nucleus. A large part of their cytoplasm consists of fine fibrils, *myofibrils*,[1] running the length of the cell. Since the myofibrils are

---

[1] Myo-, from G. *mys*, muscle.

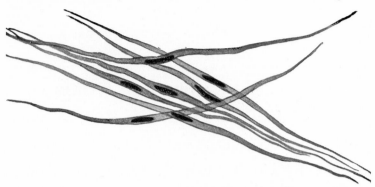

Figure 51. Isolated smooth muscle cells. × 220. (Maximow and Bloom.)

visible only in killed and fixed cells, their nature and even their existence in the living cell are not known with certainty.

The muscle cells are, of course, the active elements in muscular tissue and within their cytoplasm set up the forces that produce tension, or pull. The muscle cells also account for most of the elasticity of muscle, since the tendons are wholly of inelastic collagenous fibers. The myofibrils are generally believed to represent the contractile elements of the cell.

The muscle cells are bound together in sheets or bundles by connective tissue containing collagenous and elastic fibers and the usual connective tissue cells. Some of these fibers continue into the sheets or bundles, between the closely packed cells, and dense networks of elastic and reticular fibers, with a few thin bundles of collagenous fibers, surround the individual cells and fasten them firmly together. Fibroblasts are not found in these narrow spaces between the cells, and it appears that in smooth muscle their functions are performed by the muscle cells themselves.

Smooth muscle is found in the walls of hollow organs such as the stomach, intestine, uterus and blood vessels and in certain other parts of the body. It reacts and shortens slowly, as a rule, and often rhythmically. It has the ability to maintain a constant tension and length over long periods of time so as to maintain, for example, a constant pressure within an organ.

Striated Muscle. This tissue forms the *skeletal muscles*, that is, the muscles that are attached directly or indirectly to bones and move the arms, legs, trunk, and so forth.

Striated muscle is in most respects different from smooth muscle. Its contractions are rapid and powerful. It does not contract rhythmically. Though it normally maintains a slight tension (*tonus*) most of the time, it does not compare with smooth muscle in this regard.

Figure 52   **Muscular Tissue** 71

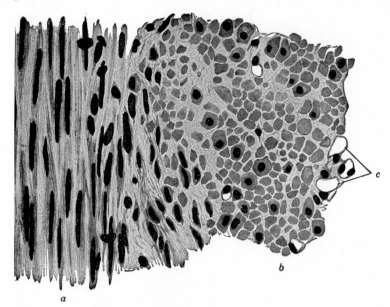

Figure 52. Section through the smooth muscle of the intestine of a dog. The muscle fibers in the two layers run at right angles to one another so that at *a* the fibers are cut longitudinally and at *b*, transversely; *c*, blood capillaries. × 470. (Maximow and Bloom.)

The muscle cells, or fibers, are much larger than those of smooth muscle. Note that Figures 51 and 53 are drawn at approximately the same magnification. In length, striated muscle fibers vary from 1 to 40 mm. (At the magnification of Figure 53 complete fibers would be from 25 to 1000 cm., or 10 inches to 33 feet, in length.) The fibers are covered with a thin, structureless, non-living membrane, the *sarcolemma*, shown in Figure 53, where the upper fiber has been crushed. Each fiber contains a large number of nuclei. As in smooth muscle, a large part of the cytoplasm consists of myofibrils running the length of the cell. The myofibrils in striated muscle, however, instead of being homogenous threads as in smooth muscle, are made up of alternating segments that stain differently and are also distinguishable in the living cell. Corresponding segments of adjacent fibrils are lined up in such a way as to give the appearance of bands running across the cell. This characteristic gives the tissue its name, *striated*, or *striped*, *muscle*.

The muscle fibers are bound together into muscles by connective tissue. Fibroblasts and all three types of fibers are found throughout muscle. Each muscle fiber is surrounded by a fibrous capsule which is attached to its sarcolemma, and the muscle fibers are bound into bundles by loose connective tissue (Fig. 54). These

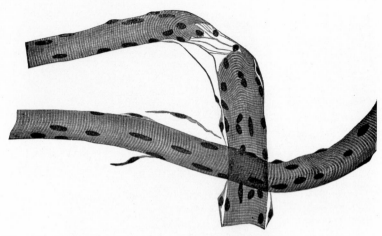

Figure 53.   Portions of two striated muscle fibers. × 250. (Maximow and Bloom.)

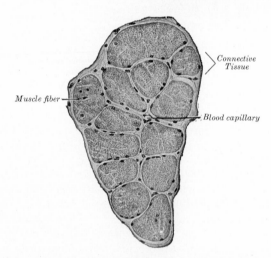

Connective Tissue

Muscle fiber

Blood capillary

Figure 54.   Cross section of a bit of striated muscle. × 110. (Maximow and Bloom.)

little bundles are, in turn, bound together to form a muscle, and the whole muscle is surrounded by a light, fibrous sheath. Where the muscle is attached to its tendon, the collagenous fibers of the muscle pass directly over into those of the tendon. Other fibers of the tendon are attached to the sarcolemma at the ends of muscle fibers.

Cardiac Muscle.   Cardiac or heart muscle (Fig. 55) has some of the features of both striated and nonstriated muscle, and some characteristics peculiar to itself. It has cross striations, although

Figure 55   **Muscular Tissue 73**

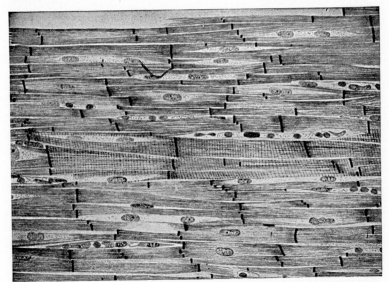

Figure 55. Section of human cardiac muscle, showing intercalated disks. About × 450. (Maximow and Bloom.)

these are less distinct than those of ordinary striated muscle. The nuclei of the individual fibers are multiple as seen in longitudinal section, and centrally placed as seen in cross section. The fibers show a marked branching and interlacing. Each has a number of transversely placed lines or stripes called *intercalated disks* which may extend wholly or partly across it. They divide it into a number of short segments, each containing a single nucleus.

CHAPTER 5

THE MUSCLES AND FASCIAE

IN THIS CHAPTER we shall discuss the skeletal or voluntary muscles of the body. As stated in the preceding chapter, these muscles are all of the striated variety. The remaining muscles, including those of the heart, stomach and other viscera, will be described in later chapters.

The skeletal muscles are connected, for the most part, to the skeleton, and their primary function is to produce movement of one bone upon another. In order to do this they must have two attachments, one to the bone that is fixed, the other to the bone to be moved. The first attachment is called the *origin* of the muscle, the second its place of *insertion*. This does not mean, however, that movement must always take place in the direction indicated, but only that it usually does so. If, for example, a muscle has its origin on bone A, and its insertion on bone B, the usual result of its contraction will be for B to move; but if B should happen to be fixed, then A will move.

The two parts of a muscle are the *fleshy part*, or *belly*, and the *tendinous part*. The fleshy part consists of the muscle fibers and the connective tissue that binds them together. Its length is usually about two and one-half times the distance through which its insertion can move, since a muscle fiber can shorten to only about 60 per cent of its extended length and since the fleshy part of a muscle is seldom longer than necessary.

The attachment of a muscle to bone may be either *fleshy* or *tendinous*. In fleshy attachment the muscle fibers appear to fasten directly to the bone, though, actually, short collagenous fibers make the connection. Such an attachment will of necessity cover a considerable area on the surface of the bone. In the tendinous attachment there is a tendon of greater or lesser length. The tendon may be round like a cord or flat like a sheet or ribbon. A flat tendon is called an *aponeurosis*. A tendon, rather than a fleshy attachment, will be found under any of the following conditions: (1) when there is not sufficient area available for a fleshy attachment; (2)

when the distance between origin and insertion is greater than the necessary length of the fleshy part; (3) where the muscle would be subject to pressure or would pass over a bony ridge. Muscle tissue cannot withstand constant pressure.

Muscles may attach to other muscles.

In the descriptions of muscles to follow it will be convenient to use the term "fiber" in a different sense from that used in the preceding chapter. Here it will mean the small bundles of muscle cells, visible without a microscope, that give the appearance of "grain" to the muscle.

It will prove of great help in visualizing and remembering the muscles, and in studying their actions, if the student will locate on his own body as many of them as possible.

Although a full discussion of the functions of the various muscles is outside the scope of this book, some account is necessary to an understanding of the anatomy.

THE MUSCLES OF THE UPPER EXTREMITY

Muscles from the Trunk to the Shoulder Girdle. The entire length of the clavicle, the acromion and the spine of the scapula can be felt beneath the skin because no muscle passes over them (except a thin sheet that will be described in connection with the muscles of the face). Extending from the acromion up to the neck is a heavy muscle that becomes tense when the shoulder is raised. This is part of the *trapezius*[1] (Figs. 56, 57), a large triangular muscle lying on the upper aspect of the back. It arises from the external occipital protuberance, the ligamentum nuchae (p. 34), and from all the thoracic vertebrae. The fibers converge laterally to be inserted into the spine of the scapula, the acromion and the lateral portion of the clavicle.

On the back, just beneath the trapezius, are the *rhomboid muscles* (Fig. 59). These constitute a sheet of muscle that has its origin on the spines of the last cervical and the first five thoracic vertebrae, and its insertion on the vertebral border of the scapula. The upper fifth of this muscle is usually distinct from the lower four fifths and is known as the *rhomboideus minor,* while the lower part is the *rhomboideus major.*

Arising from the transverse processes of the first three or four cervical vertebrae and inserting on the vertebral border of the scapula above the spine is the *levator scapulae* (Figs. 58, 59).

Arising from the third, fourth, and fifth ribs (and sometimes from the second rib) and from the fascia between them and inserting on the coracoid process of the scapula is the *pectoralis*[2]

---

[1] Trapezius: named because the two muscles form a trapezoid on the back.

[2] *Pectoralis:* L., pertaining to the breast or chest.

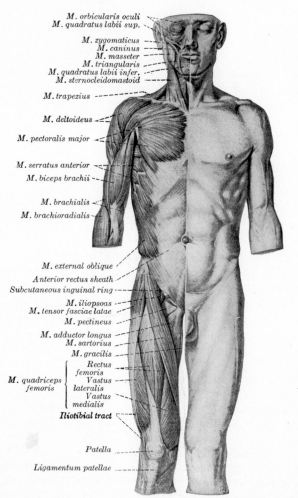

M. orbicularis oculi
M. quadratus labii sup.

M. zygomaticus
M. caninus
M. masseter
M. triangularis
M. quadratus labii infer.
M. sternocleidomastoid

M. trapezius

M. deltoideus

M. pectoralis major

M. serratus anterior
M. biceps brachii

M. brachialis
M. brachioradialis

M. external oblique
Anterior rectus sheath
Subcutaneous inguinal ring
M. iliopsoas
M. tensor fasciae latae
M. pectineus
M. adductor longus
M. sartorius
M. gracilis
Rectus femoris
M. quadriceps femoris
Vastus lateralis
Vastus medialis
Iliotibial tract

Patella

Ligamentum patellae

Figure 56. The superficial muscles of the anterior aspect of the trunk. (Braus: Anatomie des Menschen.)

minor (Fig. 58). This muscle cannot be felt on the living body because it is entirely covered by the large pectoralis major (Fig. 56).

The *serratus*[3] *anterior* (Figs. 56, 58, 59, 60) inserts on the entire vertebral border of the scapula, deep to the rhomboids and levator scapulae, and extends forward around the thorax beneath the

---

[3] Serratus: L. serrate, notched or toothed on the edge like a saw. The origin of the muscle is serrate.

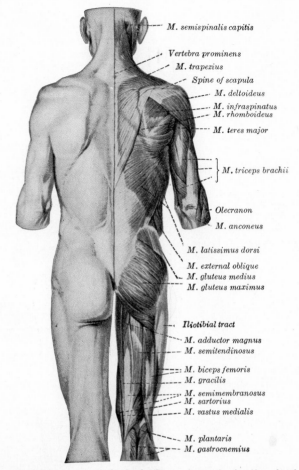

M. semispinalis capitis

Vertebra prominens

M. trapezius

Spine of scapula

M. deltoideus

M. infraspinatus
M. rhomboideus

M. teres major

M. triceps brachii

Olecranon

M. anconeus

M. latissimus dorsi

M. external oblique
M. gluteus medius
M. gluteus maximus

Iliotibial tract

M. adductor magnus
M. semitendinosus

M. biceps femoris
M. gracilis

M. semimembranosus
M. sartorius
M. vastus medialis

M. plantaris
M. gastrocnemius

Figure 57. The superficial muscles of the back. (Braus: Anatomie des Menschen.)

scapula to its origin on the upper eight or nine ribs. The muscle consists of a number of distinct slips.

The *subclavius* (Fig. 58) extends from the first rib and its cartilage upwards and laterally to the clavicle; it is hidden by the pectoralis major.

The superior fibers of the trapezius elevate the shoulder or support it when a weight is carried in the hand or on the shoulder. When a muscle is the major agent in effecting a movement—in this case the superior part of the trapezius—it is called the *prime mover*. If the trapezius is to lift the shoulder, however, the neck and head must be held upright against its pull by muscles on the other side such as the upper part of the trapezius and the sternocleidomastoid

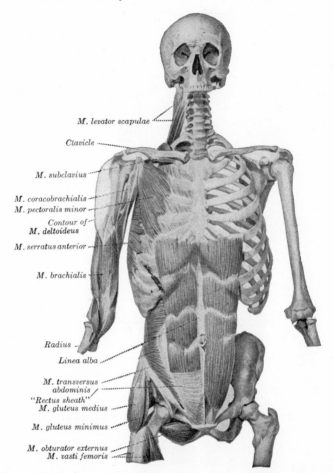

M. levator scapulae

Clavicle

M. subclavius

M. coracobrachialis
M. pectoralis minor

Contour of
M. deltoideus

M. serratus anterior

M. brachialis

Radius

Linea alba

M. transversus
abdominis
"Rectus sheath"
M. gluteus medius

M. gluteus minimus

M. obturator externus
M. vasti femoris

Figure 58.   The deep muscles on the anterior aspect of the trunk. (Braus: Anatomie des Menschen.)

(Fig. 56). When muscles thus hold a part steady so another muscle can act as a prime mover, they are called *fixators*. If, instead of the neck, the shoulder is fixed, the upper part of the trapezius will bend the neck to one side. In this case such muscles as the pectoralis minor and the latissimus dorsi (Figs. 56, 57, 63) will be the fixators. These two different actions of the upper part of the trapezius also illustrate the fact, mentioned earlier, that the "origin," or fixed point, may, under certain circumstances, become the "insertion," or movable point. The posterior fibers of the trapezius pull the scapula toward the vertebral column, and the inferior fibers rotate it by pulling the posterior end of the spine downward.

Figure 59   **The Muscles and Fasciae   79**

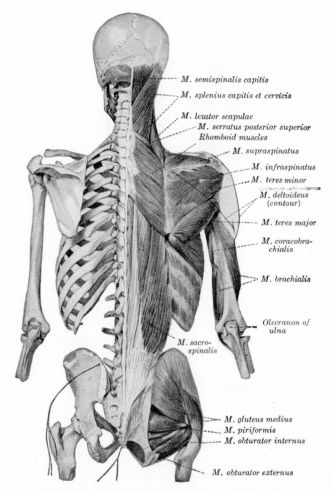

M. semispinalis capitis

M. splenius capitis et cervicis

M. levator scapulae
M. serratus posterior superior
Rhomboid muscles

M. supraspinatus

M. infraspinatus

M. teres minor

M. deltoideus
(contour)

M. teres major

M. coracobra-
chialis

M. brachialis

Olecranon of
ulna

M. sacro-
spinalis

M. gluteus medius
M. piriformis
M. obturator internus

M. obturator externus

Figure 59. The deep muscles of the back. (Braus: Anatomie des Menschen.)

The rhomboids also pull the scapula toward the vertebral column, but tend to rotate it in the opposite direction. The rhomboids and part of the trapezius may, therefore, work together in pulling the shoulders back, or they can rotate the scapula in opposite directions if the shoulder is held forward, the rhomboids and upper part of the trapezius pulling up and the lower part of the trapezius pulling down. When two muscles pull a structure in opposite directions, they are called *antagonists*, but this term is somewhat misleading because the "antagonists" do not work against one another, but, on the contrary, cooperate. Both maintain tension, but the one

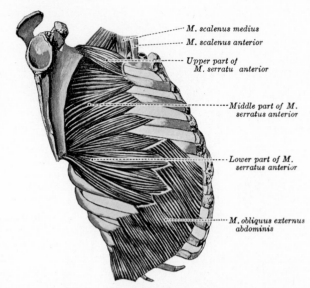

Figure 60. Serratus anterior and origin of external oblique. The scapula has been drawn away from the side of the thorax. (Cunningham's Textbook of Anatomy.)

pays out as the other shortens, thus holding the parts steady and insuring smooth, nicely regulated movement.

The levator scapulae assists the rhomboids in raising the vertebral border of the scapula and can pull it up even further. When two or more muscles pull together, the most important one may be designated the *prime mover* and the smaller ones, or those acting less directly, may be called *synergists.* In the elevation of the vertebral border of the scapula the rhomboideus might be designated as the prime mover and the levator scapulae as the synergist, but beyond a certain point the rhomboideus is no longer effective and the levator scapulae takes over as the prime mover.

The various slips of the serratus anterior pull in various directions. In general, they are antagonistic to the rhomboids and to the posterior part of the trapezius, pulling the scapula forward, but they may help to rotate the scapula in cooperation with the rhomboids and trapezius. When the arm is in a forward, horizontal position, the serratus anterior assists in pushing movements.

The pectoralis minor draws the shoulder forward and down and helps to rotate the scapula. The subclavius steadies the clavicle and helps prevent it being pulled away from the sternum.

When the arm is raised to the vertical position above the head, about half the movement takes place at the shoulder joint and about half is made possible by the rotation of the scapula, the

Figure 61   **The Muscles and Fasciae   81**

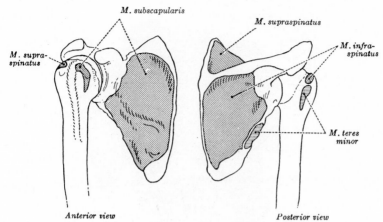

M. subscapularis

M. supraspinatus

M. supra-spinatus

M. infra-spinatus

M. teres minor

Anterior view   *Posterior view*

Figure 61. Attachments of the articular muscles of the right shoulder. (Redrawn from Grant.)

glenoid fossa moving upward and the inferior angle moving laterally. Nearly all the muscles that have been discussed either assist this movement or its reverse.

Note the manner in which the muscles have been named. The trapezius and rhomboids have been named for their shapes; the serratus, for the shape of its origin; the pectoralis and subclavius, for their positions; and the levator scapulae, for its action.

Articular Muscles of the Shoulder. This group of muscles helps to hold the head of the humerus in the glenoid fossa. The range of movement at this joint is so great that the ligaments cannot be short enough to do this effectively. These muscles also help produce movements of the joint, but they insert so close to the center of rotation of the head of the humerus that they have a great mechanical disadvantage.

The *supraspinatus* (Figs. 59, 61, 62) originates on most of the lateral surface of the scapula above the spine. It passes under the acromion and clavicle to attach to the greater tuberosity of the humerus. This muscle is entirely covered by the trapezius. It is an *abductor* of the arm; that is, it helps lift the arm away from the body.

The *infraspinatus* (Figs. 57, 59, 61, 62) originates on most of the lateral surface of the scapula below the spine. It also inserts on the greater tuberosity of the humerus. It *rotates* the humerus laterally, that is, turns it on its long axis.

The *teres minor* (Figs. 59, 61, 62) extends from the lower border of the scapula to the greater tuberosity. It is a lateral rotator, but inserts far enough distally to also act as an *adductor*, that is, to draw the arm toward the body.

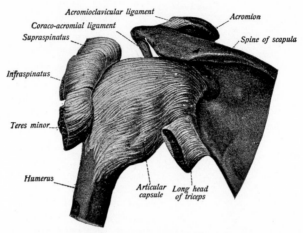

Figure 62. The left shoulder joint, seen from behind, the long head of the triceps being cut and the terminal portions of the supraspinatus, infraspinatus and teres minor muscles cut and turned outward. (Sobotta and McMurrich.)

The *subscapularis* (Fig. 61) originates on most of the costal surface of the scapula and inserts on the lesser tuberosity of the humerus. It rotates the humerus medially and, when the arm is horizontal, can help pull it forward.

Muscles That Move the Shoulder Joint.   These muscles are attached to the humerus more distally than those of the preceding group and have, therefore, greater mechanical advantage.

The *deltoid*[4] (Figs. 56, 57, 63) is a large triangular muscle which gives roundness to the upper part of the arm just below the shoulder. It takes its origin from the outer part of the clavicle, the acromion and the spine of the scapula. Its fibers converge downward to be inserted into the lateral aspect of the humerus at about its middle. Its lateral fibers abduct the arm, its anterior fibers help pull the arm forward, and its posterior fibers help pull it back. The anterior and posterior fibers are also rotators. It is apparent that the deltoid is, in some respects, an extension of the trapezius, and the two muscles frequently work together.

The *pectoralis major* (Figs. 56, 63) originates on the clavicle, sternum and ribs, and inserts on the ridge that extends down the humerus from the greater tuberosity. Its insertion is, therefore, lateral to the bicipital groove. Both its origin and insertion are continuations of those of the deltoid.

The arm pit is bordered in front by the *anterior axillary fold* and behind by the *posterior axillary fold.* (The term *axilla* means either

---

[4] Deltoid: shaped like the Greek letter *delta* (Δ).

Figure 63   **The Muscles and Fasciae**   83

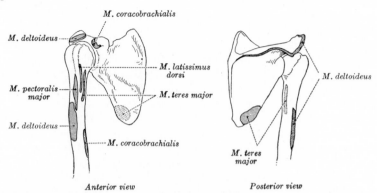

Figure 63. Attachments of muscles that move the shoulder joint (right shoulder). (Redrawn from Grant.)

the arm pit or the anatomic region just above it.) The anterior axillary fold is formed by the pectoralis major. This fold would be broader than it is were it not that the lower fibers of the pectoralis major insert high on the humerus, while the fibers from the clavicle pass in front of these to insert lower down (Fig. 56).

The pectoralis major adducts the arm, draws it across the chest, and rotates it medially. It pulls the shoulder forward and down. In birds it is the great muscle of flight.

The *latissimus dorsi*[5] (Figs. 57, 63) arises from the lower six thoracic spines and, by means of a large fibrous sheet, from the lumbar and sacral spines and the crest of the ilium. It is inserted on the humerus along the ridge that runs down from the lesser tuberosity, medial to the bicipital groove. The latissimus dorsi forms part of the posterior axillary fold. It gives a powerful downward and backward sweep to the arm, with some inward rotation, such as occurs in swimming.

The *teres major* (Figs. 57, 59, 63) extends from the scapula near its inferior angle to the humerus, where it inserts along a line parallel, and just medial to, the insertion of the latissimus dorsi. The muscle forms part of the posterior axillary fold. It acts with the latissimus dorsi, but, of course, the rhomboids and trapezius must cooperate by preventing rotation of the scapula.

The *coracobrachialis* (Figs. 58, 63) arises on the coracoid process and inserts halfway down on the humerus. It lies between the pectoralis major in front and the latissimus dorsi and teres major behind. It helps raise the arm and carry it forward across the chest. Note that this muscle is named for its attachments.

In this group of muscles that move the shoulder joint must be

---

[5] *Latissimus dorsi:* L., the broadest (muscle) of the back.

included the *biceps brachii* and the *long head of the triceps brachii,* but these have other important functions and are more conveniently described in the next section.

Deep Fascia.   Before proceeding further, it will be necessary to describe the *deep fascia.* This is a membranous investment of the limb consisting of fibrous connective tissue. It is wrapped around the muscles, nerves and blood vessels like a bandage. From it, *intermuscular septa* pass between muscles and groups of muscles. These may reach to the bone and attach there. Where the deep fascia passes over a bony ridge or protuberance, it is attached to the bone. Muscles may originate or insert on the deep fascia and on the intermuscular septa as well as on the bone. The deep fascia invests the limbs and neck. It is less well marked or absent from the chest and abdomen, since these must expand and contract, and it is absent from the face, where many of the muscles attach to the skin.

The *superficial fascia,* or subcutaneous layer of connective tissue, which lies over the deep fascia, will be described in connection with the skin.

Muscles That Flex and Extend the Elbow.   Since the elbow is a hinge joint, the muscles that cross it can be divided into flexors and extensors.[6]

Of the **flexor muscles,** two lie in the upper arm. The *biceps brachii*[7] (Fig. 56) is the large muscle on the front of the arm, the one commonly used by small boys to demonstrate their muscular prowess. It has two heads, or origins, as the name implies. The tendon of the *long head* lies in the bicipital groove of the humerus, passes through the synovial capsule of the shoulder joint (Fig. 36), and over the head of the humerus to attach to the rim of the glenoid fossa. The tendon of the *short head* runs beside the coraco-brachialis and attaches with it to the coracoid process. (In Figure 56 the two heads of the biceps are shown as distinct all the way to the distal tendon.) The two heads lie beneath the pectoralis major and the anterior part of the deltoid and in front of the latissimus dorsi and the teres major. The short head lies beside the coraco-brachialis. The lower end of the biceps is not divided into two slips, but the tendon divides (Figs. 56, 67). The main part inserts on the tuberosity of the radius (Fig. 38). The other part spreads out and is continuous with the deep fascia of the forearm. Besides

---

[6] Some writers on anatomy use the phrase "flex the elbow joint" or "flex the elbow." Others write "flex the forearm." Since flex means to bend, and since it is the joint that is bent, not the forearm, we prefer the former usage. However, *adduct,* to draw toward, and *abduct,* to draw away from, refer to the whole limb, and the phrase "adduct the arm" is proper.

[7] *Biceps brachii:* L., the two-headed (muscle) of the arm.

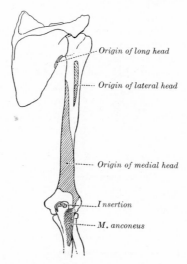

Origin of long head

Origin of lateral head

Origin of medial head

Insertion

M. anconeus

Figure 64. The M. anconeus and the attachments of the M. triceps brachii, right side, posterior view. (Redrawn from Grant.)

flexion of the elbow, the biceps brachii can help raise the arm and so belongs to the preceding group. In addition, it can turn the hand palm up and so will be included in a group to be described later.

The *brachialis* (Figs. 56, 58, 59, 62) lies between the biceps brachii and the humerus. It originates on most of the lower half of the anterior surface of the humerus and inserts on the ulna just below the coronoid process (Fig. 38). It is a powerful flexor of the elbow, and this is its only function.

Several muscles of the forearm assist in flexing the elbow, but have other functions and will be described later.

The chief **extensor muscle** is the *triceps brachii* (Figs. 57, 64, 70), which occupies the entire posterior surface of the upper arm. Its insertion is by a flat tendon to the tip of the olecranon of the ulna and to the deep fascia of the forearm on either side of it. The proximal part of the muscle is divided into three distinct heads whose attachments are shown in Figure 64. The *lateral* and *median heads* are pure extensors of the elbow. The *long head,* because of its attachment to the scapula (Figs. 62, 64), can help pull the arm back and so must be included with the muscles that move the shoulder joint.

The *anconeus*[8] (Figs. 57, 64, 70) is a small muscle that is usually described with the muscles of the forearm, but since it is continu-

---

[8] Anconeus, from L. *ancon,* the elbow.

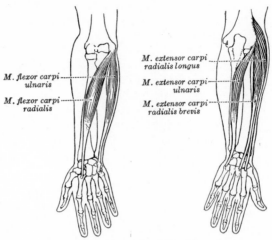

M. flexor carpi
ulnaris

M. flexor carpi
radialis

M. extensor carpi
radialis longus

M. extensor carpi
ulnaris

M. extensor carpi
radialis brevis

Figure 65.   Flexor and extensor muscles of the right wrist.

ous with the triceps brachii at both origin and insertion and since, like the triceps, it is an extensor of the elbow, it is included here.

Muscles of the Forearm.   The muscles of the forearm are primarily concerned with movements of the wrist and fingers. They can be divided anatomically and functionally into two groups: (1) an anteromedian group of flexors and pronators; (2) a posterolateral group of extensors and supinators. On the back of the forearm the ulna can be felt just beneath the skin from the elbow to the wrist. This line is the posteromedian boundary between these two groups of muscles. To locate the anterolateral boundary, flex the elbow 90 degrees and place the palm against the chest as though the arm were in a sling. Now, when the elbow is flexed against resistance, a muscle stands out prominently on the upper side of the forearm. This is the brachioradialis (Fig. 67). Its median, or ulnar, edge is the anterolateral boundary between the two groups of muscles. Most of the flexors and pronators originate on or near the median epicondyle of the humerus. Most of the extensors and supinators originate on or near the lateral epicondyle.

The table on page 87 shows the grouping of the muscles and their primary functions.

Note that the tendons of the flexors and extensors of the wrist (Figs. 65, 67, 70) pass over the carpal bones and insert on the bases of metacarpals. They are so arranged that there is at least one muscle in each "corner" of the wrist, the action of which is to pull the wrist as a whole in that direction. The flexor carpi ulnaris, for example, pulls the hand forward and to the ulnar side. If the two flexors (radial and ulnar) work together, the hand is pulled

Figure 66   **The Muscles and Fasciae   87**

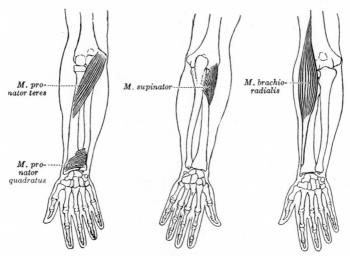

*M. pro-
nator teres*

*M. pro-
nator
quadratus*

M. supinator

*M. brachio-
radialis*

Figure 66.   The pronator and supinator muscles of the right forearm.

directly forward; if the extensors act cooperatively, the hand is pulled directly backward. If the ulnar flexors and extensors act together, the hand is pulled to the ulnar side; if the radial flexors and extensors act together, the hand is pulled to the radial side.

The two pronator muscles (Figs. 66, 67, 68) roll the radius over and across the ulna. The supinator (Fig. 66) rolls it back to a

MUSCLES OF THE FOREARM

	FLEXOR-PRONATOR GROUP (ANTEROMEDIAN)	EXTENSOR-SUPINATOR GROUP (POSTEROLATERAL)
Flexion and extension of the wrist	*Flexor carpi ulnaris* *Flexor carpi radialis*	*Extensor carpi ulnaris* *Extensor carpi radialis longus* *Extensor carpi radialis brevis*
Supination and pronation .	*Pronator teres* *Pronator quadratus*	*Supinator* *Brachioradialis**
Flexion and extension of the fingers	*Palmaris longus* *Flexor digitorum sublimis* *Flexor digitorum profundus*	*Extensor digitorum communis* *Extensor digiti quinti proprius* *Extensor indicis proprius*
Flexion, extension, and ab- duction of the thumb . . .	*Flexor pollicis longus*	*Extensor pollicis longus* *Extensor pollicis brevis* *Abductor pollicis longus*

* Functionally a semisupinator and semipronator. See text.

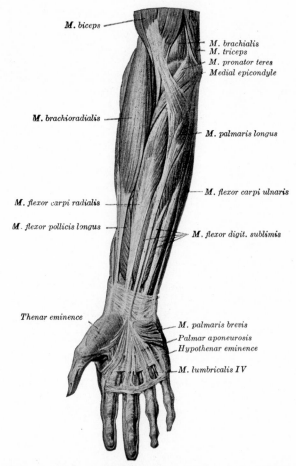

M. biceps

M. brachialis
M. triceps
M. pronator teres
Medial epicondyle

M. brachioradialis

M. palmaris longus

M. flexor carpi ulnaris

M. flexor carpi radialis

M. flexor pollicis longus

M. flexor digit. sublimis

Thenar eminence

M. palmaris brevis
Palmar aponeurosis
Hypothenar eminence
M. lumbricalis IV

Figure 67. The superficial muscles on the front of the forearm and hand. (Braus: Anatomie des Menschen.)

position parallel to the ulna. The position of the tuberosity of the radius is such that the tendon of the biceps brachii is wrapped part way around the radius when the hand is in the prone position. The biceps brachii is, therefore, a powerful supinator and must be included here, making it a member of three functional groups in all. The brachioradialis (Figs. 66, 67) has shifted its origin up the humerus from the lateral epicondyle far enough to make it an effective flexor of the elbow. Its insertion seems to have shifted from the anterior surface of the radius, where it would be a good supinator, to the lateral surface of the radius. This causes the muscle to pull the wrist to a position halfway between pronation and

Figure 68   The Muscles and Fasciae   89

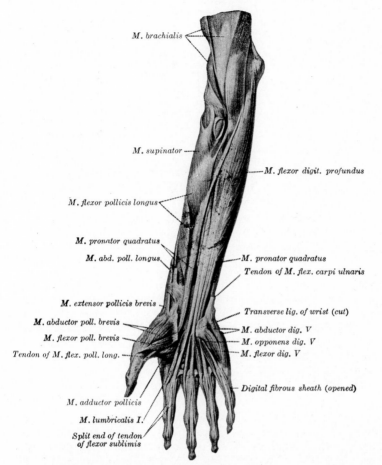

M. brachialis

M. supinator

M. flexor digit. profundus

M. flexor pollicis longus

M. pronator quadratus
M. abd. poll. longus

M. pronator quadratus
Tendon of M. flex. carpi ulnaris

M. extensor pollicis brevis
M. abductor poll. brevis
M. flexor poll. brevis
Tendon of M. flex. poll. long.

Transverse lig. of wrist (cut)
M. abductor dig. V
M. opponens dig. V
M. flexor dig. V

Digital fibrous sheath (opened)

M. adductor pollicis
M. lumbricalis I.
Split end of tendon
of flexor sublimis

Figure 68. The deep muscles of the front of the forearm and hand. (Braus: Anatomie des Menschen.)

supination. It may, therefore, be called a semisupinator or semipronator, though it belongs anatomically to the supinator group.

The tendon of the palmaris longus (Figs. 67, 69) inserts in a tough pad of connective tissue in the palm, the *palmar aponeurosis*. This, in turn, is attached to the sides of the proximal phalanges of the four fingers and runs up onto the fascia of the thumb. The palmaris longus is as much a flexor of the wrist as of the fingers. This muscle is variable and is absent in about 11 per cent of persons. If present, its tendon stands out at the wrist when the tips of the fingers are brought together and the hand and wrist are flexed forcibly.

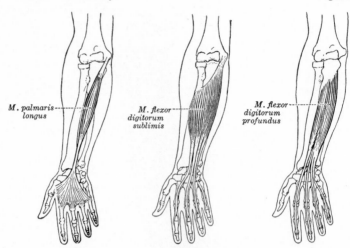

Figure 69. The flexor muscles of the fingers of the right hand.

The origin of the flexor digitorum sublimis[9] (Figs. 67, 69) is on an oblique line across the forearm starting at the median epicondyle and running laterodistad. The attachment to the radius is between the supinator and the flexor pollicis longus (Fig. 68). The muscle divides distally into four slips, each of which sends a tendon past the wrist and under the palmar aponeurosis to a finger. At the proximal phalanx of each finger the tendon splits and attaches to the sides of the second phalanx (Fig. 73).

Extending from the scaphoid and trapezium bones across the wrist to the pisiform and hamate bones is the strong *volar transverse ligament of the wrist* (Figs. 68, 73). It forms an arch beneath which the tendons of the flexor digitorum sublimis pass. This prevents them from "bow-stringing" when the wrist is flexed. The tendon of the palmaris longus passes superficial to the ligament, but is fastened to it. The volar transverse ligament is more or less continuous with the deep fascia of the forearm and with the palmar aponeurosis. The distal part of the fascia and some of the transverse ligament can be seen in Figure 67.

The flexor digitorum profundus (Figs. 68, 69), like the sublimis, divides into slips which send a tendon to each finger. Each tendon runs deep to the corresponding tendon of the sublimis, passes between its two distal slips, and attaches to the palmar surface of the distal phalanx (Fig. 73). A fibrous sheath holds both flexor tendons close to each phalanx.

---

[9] Flexor digitorum sublimis: Sublimis here means superficial. The superficial flexor of the fingers.

Figure 70   **The Muscles and Fasciae** 91

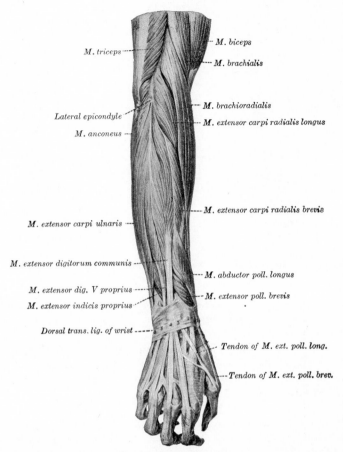

M. triceps

Lateral epicondyle

M. anconeus

M. extensor carpi ulnaris

M. extensor digitorum communis

M. extensor dig. V proprius

M. extensor indicis proprius

Dorsal trans. lig. of wrist

M. biceps

M. brachialis

M. brachioradialis

M. extensor carpi radialis longus

M. extensor carpi radialis brevis

M. abductor poll. longus

M. extensor poll. brevis

Tendon of M. ext. poll. long.

Tendon of M. ext. poll. brev.

Figure 70. The superficial muscles on the back of the forearm and hand. (Braus: Anatomie des Menschen.)

To hold the extensor tendons to the wrist there is a *dorsal transverse ligament of the wrist* (Fig. 70). It is attached chiefly to the radius and ulna and is, therefore, somewhat higher than the volar ligament.

The extensor digitorum communis (Figs. 70, 71) sends a tendon to the back of each finger. Each tendon attaches to all three phalanges. Bands interconnecting the four tendons occur just proximal to the knuckles and limit the independent action of the fingers, but the index and little fingers have, in addition to the communis, separate muscles. The extensor digiti quintis proprius (Figs. 70, 71) parallels the communis, and its tendon inserts with that of the communis. The extensor indicis proprius (Figs. 70, 71) lies deeper.

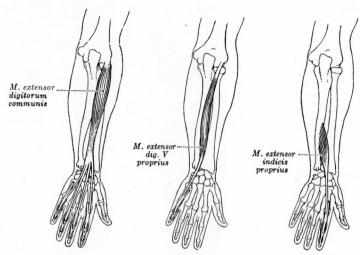

M. extensor digitorum communis

M. extensor dig. V proprius

M. extensor indicis proprius

Figure 71. The extensor muscles of the fingers of the right hand.

It originates on the ulna and on the interosseus membrane and cuts across beneath the preceding tendons to the index finger, where its tendon joins that of the communis.

All the foregoing muscles that originate on either of the epicondyles share a common tendon that is largely hidden by their fleshy parts, and they also originate in part on the deep fascia and on the intermuscular septa.

The great motility of the thumb necessitates a separate set of eight muscles: two flexors, two extensors, two abductors, one adductor and one opponens. Four of these are in the forearm: the long flexor, both extensors and the long abductor. The remaining four are in the hand. The tendon of the flexor pollicis[10] longus (Figs. 68, 72) can be felt on the palmar side of the proximal phalanx of the thumb (Fig. 73). When the thumb is abducted, a hollow appears on the radial side of the wrist at the base of the thumb. The dorsal boundary of this hollow is formed by the tendon of the extensor pollicis longus (Figs. 68, 72). Its ventral boundary is formed by the tendons of the extensor pollicis brevis and the abductor pollicis longus. These three tendons insert on the distal phalanx, the proximal phalanx and the base of the first metacarpal, respectively.

Muscles of the Hand.   On the palm are two fleshy eminences,

---

[10] Pollicis, from L. *pollex*, the thumb. The flexor pollicis longus is the long flexor of the thumb. Cf. hallux, the great toe, page 111.

Figure 72   The Muscles and Fasciae   93

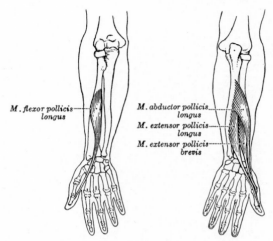

M. flexor pollicis
longus

M. abductor pollicis
longus
M. extensor pollicis
longus
M. extensor pollicis
brevis

Figure 72.   The muscles of the right thumb that lie in the forearm.

the *thenar*[11] *eminence* at the base of the thumb and the *hypothenar eminence* on the ulnar side of the hand.

The *palmaris brevis* (Fig. 67) is a quadrilateral muscle that arises from the median border of the palmar aponeurosis and the transverse ligament and is inserted on the skin on the median border of the hand. It helps deepen the palm by wrinkling the skin on the hypothenar eminence, and it probably assists the grip by preventing flattening of this part of the palm.

There are four *lumbrical*[12] *muscles* (Fig. 68). Each arises from one or two tendons of the flexor digitorum profundus in the palm, passes around the lateral side of its digit, and inserts on the tendon of the extensor digitorum communis and, with it, into the base of the terminal phalanx. These muscles flex the metacarpophalangeal joints, but extend both interphalangeal joints. In other words, they bend the knuckles while keeping the fingers straight.

The four short muscles of the thumb located in the hand are the short flexor, the short abductor, the opponens and the adductor. The first three form the thenar eminence. The *abductor pollicis brevis* (Figs. 68, 73) is straplike. Its origin is mostly from the transverse ligament of the wrist. Its insertion is on the lateral side of the proximal phalanx and into the side of the tendon of the extensor pollicis longus. In abducting the thumb it draws it forward, away from the palm. Its insertion on the extensor tendon causes it to help extend the interphalangeal joint.

Beneath the abductor pollicis brevis is the *opponens pollicis*

---

[11] Thenar: G., the palm.
[12] Lumbrical, from L. *lumbricus,* the earthworm.

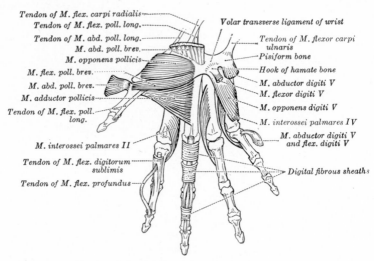

Tendon of M. flex. carpi radialis
Tendon of M. flex. poll. long.
Tendon of M. abd. poll. long.
M. abd. poll. brev.
M. opponens pollicis
M. flex. poll. brev.
M. abd. poll. brev.
M. adductor pollicis
Tendon of M. flex. poll. long.
M. interossei palmares II
Tendon of M. flex. digitorum sublimis
Tendon of M. flex. profundus

Volar transverse ligament of wrist
Tendon of M. flexor carpi ulnaris
Pisiform bone
Hook of hamate bone
M. abductor digiti V
M. flexor digiti V
M. opponens digiti V
M. interossei palmares IV
M. abductor digiti V and flex. digiti V
Digital fibrous sheaths

Figure 73.   Deep muscles of the right hand.

(Fig. 73), extending from the transverse ligament to the anterior surface of the first metacarpal. It pulls the thumb medially and forward.

The *flexor pollicis brevis* (Figs. 68, 73) extends from the transverse ligament to an insertion on the proximal phalanx near the insertion of the abductor pollicis brevis. It parallels the opponens and acts with it, but also flexes the metacarpophalangeal joint.

The *adductor pollicis* (Figs. 68, 73) has two origins, one along the third metacarpal and one on several carpals and their ligaments. The latter head is covered in Figure 73 by the flexor pollicis brevis and the opponens pollicis. It inserts on the base of the proximal phalanx. Because of its transverse position it has great mechanical advantage.

There are three short muscles of the fifth finger that form the hypothenar eminence (Figs. 68, 73). The *opponens digiti minimi* pulls the metacarpal forward to deepen the hollow of the palm. The *abductor digiti minimi* forms the lateral part of the hypothenar eminence. The *flexor digiti minimi* is thin and may be absent. It inserts with the abductor.

The interosseus muscles lie between the metacarpals, on which they originate, and pull the fingers toward or away from the middle finger. The four *palmar interossei* (Figs. 73, 74) pull the thumb and fingers toward the middle finger. The first palmar interosseus (Fig. 74) is small because its function is largely taken over by the strong adductor pollicis. The tendons insert partly on the base of the proximal phalanx and partly on the extensor tendon.

Figure 74   **The Muscles and Fasciae**   95

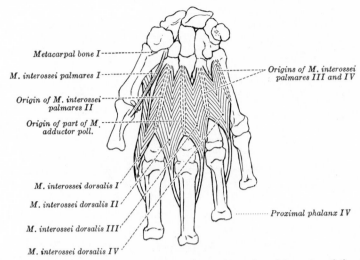

Metacarpal bone I

M. interossei palmares I

Origin of M. interossei palmares II

Origin of part of M. adductor poll.

Origins of M. interossei palmares III and IV

M. interossei dorsalis I

M. interossei dorsalis II

M. interossei dorsalis III

M. interossei dorsalis IV

Proximal phalanx IV

Figure 74. The dorsal interosseus muscles and the first palmar interosseus of the right hand.

The four *dorsal interossei* (Fig. 74) are larger than the palmar ones. The two middle muscles attach to the middle finger and pull it toward the index finger and toward the ring finger. The two lateral muscles pull the index and ring fingers away from the middle finger. The thumb and little fingers are, of course, pulled away by their abductors.

The Fasciae and Sheaths of the Hand. The *palmar aponeurosis* or the *palmar fascia* (Figs. 67, 69), mentioned earlier as the insertion of the palmaris longus, is a tough fibrous sheet which covers the palm of the hand just beneath the skin. Its presence permits of great pressure being put on the palm without injury to the nerves, blood vessels and tendons beneath.

The *digital fibrous tendon sheaths* (Fig. 73) are tunnels on the palmar aspects of the fingers through which the tendons of the long flexor muscles pass. Their function is to keep the tendons close to the bone; were they absent, the tendons would stand out during flexion of the fingers. There are no similar tendon sheaths on the backs of the fingers, but they are present on the backs of the metatarsals.

The palmar aponeurosis is a part of the deep fascia. It is continuous proximally with the volar transverse ligament of the wrist and distally with the digital fibrous sheaths. On each side it is continuous with the fascial sheaths that enclose the thenar and the hypothenar muscles.

The flexor tendons and lumbrical muscles are separated from the

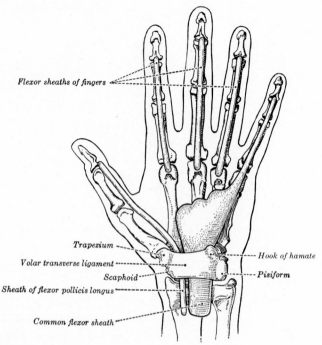

Flexor sheaths of fingers

Trapezium
Volar transverse ligament
Scaphoid
Sheath of flexor pollicis longus

Hook of hamate
Pisiform

Common flexor sheath

Figure 75. Synovial sheaths of the flexor tendons of the digits. (Redrawn from Cunningham.)

interosseus muscles and the adductor pollicis by still another sheet of connective tissue, the *deep transverse ligament of the palm.* This is especially heavy where it crosses the distal ends of the metacarpals.

The deep fascia on the back of the hand consists of two layers with the extensor tendons between them. The superficial layer is thin. It is continuous with the dorsal transverse ligament of the wrist and fuses with the tendons at the fingers.

These various fasciae divide the hand into more or less distinct compartments.

The *mucous* or *synovial sheaths* of the hand (Figs. 75, 76) are thin membranous sacs wrapped around the tendons as so to intervene between them and the fibrous sheaths in the fingers, and between the tendons and transverse ligaments and bones at the wrist. The mucous sheaths for the three middle fingers reach only about ½ inch into the palm, while those for the thumb and little finger extend to and communicate with those at the wrist.

PRACTICAL CONSIDERATIONS.   The palmar aponeurosis and the mucous sheaths are of considerable importance in infections of the palm of the hand. The palmar

Figure 76   *The Muscles and Fasciae*   97

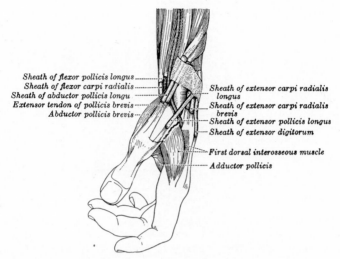

Sheath of flexor pollicis longus
Sheath of flexor carpi radialis
Sheath of abductor pollicis longu
Extensor tendon of pollicis brevis
Abductor pollicis brevis

Sheath of extensor carpi radialis longus
Sheath of extensor carpi radialis brevis
Sheath of extensor pollicis longus
Sheath of extensor digitorum

First dorsal interosseous muscle
Adductor pollicis

Figure 76. Synovial sheaths of the tendons on the radial side of the wrist. (Redrawn from Cunningham.)

fascia by its resistance helps to prevent surface infections from reaching the deeper structures; but if an infection does get beneath it, it can only with difficulty get out. Indeed, it is more likely to spread between the metacarpal bones to the back of the hand or into the wrist or fingers before breaking through the palmar fascia.

The mucous sheaths also determine the course of infection, for when pus enters one of these sacs, it can spread with relative ease throughout its entire length. For the three middle fingers this is not so serious, but in the case of the thumb and little finger the infection may rapidly travel to the wrist.

THE MUSCLES OF THE LOWER EXTREMITY

There are about twenty-five muscles in the hip, buttock and thigh. They can be divided into five groups according to their main functions: (1) flexors of the hip and extensors of the knee, on the front of the thigh; (2) extensors of the hip and flexors of the knee, on the back of the thigh; (3) abductors of the thigh; (4) adductors; and (5) lateral rotators. Before describing these, however, it will be necessary to describe the deep fascia of this region.

The Fascia Lata. The portion of the deep fascia that invests the thigh is called the *fascia lata*. Like all deep fascia, it is firmly attached to exposed bony and ligamentous prominences. At the upper end of the thigh it is attached to the anterior superior spine of the ilium (Fig. 42), the *inguinal ligament* (an important cord-like ligament stretching from this spine to the body of the pubis), to the body of the pubis, to the descending ramus of the pubis

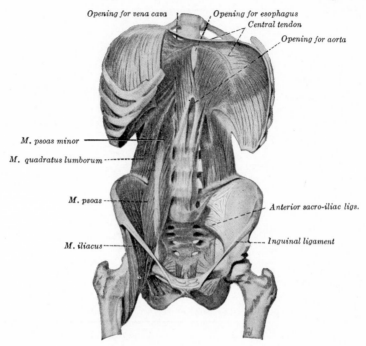

Opening for vena cava   *Opening for esophagus*
Central tendon
Opening for aorta

M. psoas minor
M. quadratus lumborum

M. psoas
Anterior sacro-iliac ligs.

M. iliacus
Inguinal ligament

Figure 77. The diaphragm and other muscles of the trunk. (Braus: Anatomie des Menschen.)

(Fig. 40), to the ischial tuberosity, to the *sacrotuberous ligament* (Fig. 43), to the sacral spines, and to the outer lip of the iliac crest. At the knee it is attached to the patella, the tuberosity of the tibia, the sides of the head (condyles) of the tibia, and to the head of the fibula. Most of the fibers of the fascia lata run more or less circularly. It is pierced by numerous small vessels and nerves, but the only large opening in it is the *saphenous opening* for the saphenous vein (Fig. 215).

Flexors of the Hip and Extensors of the Knee. The *iliacus* originates on most of the inner surface of the ilium (Fig. 77). Its fibers pass over the rim of the pelvis beneath the inguinal ligament and wind around the neck of the femur to insert on the lesser trochanter. The *psoas*,[13] or *psoas major*, arises on the lateral aspects of the lumbar vertebrae and inserts with the iliacus on the lesser trochanter. These two are powerful flexors of the hip and, in the standing posture, help to hold the body erect by keeping it from falling backward. They also tend to rotate the thigh medially at least, when standing with the foot on the ground. At first sight

---

[13] *Psoas:* G., the loin.

Figure 78   **The Muscles and Fasciae   99**

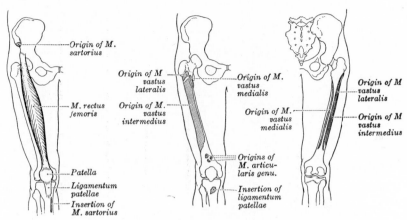

Figure 78. Muscles that flex the hip and extend the knee.

it appears that they would rotate it laterally, but the axis of rotation is not the long axis of the shaft of the femur—it is a line through the head and distal end of the bone. Such a line passes medial to the lesser trochanter (Fig. 44), so the shaft is pulled forward and medially by these muscles. Or, conversely, the opposite side of the pelvis is pulled forward in taking a step forward. Other muscles, of course, assist in this latter movement.

(The *psoas minor* [Fig. 77] is present in only about 60 per cent of persons. Its long tendon, which lies on the anterior surface of the psoas major and attaches to its fascia, inserts on the ilium so that the muscle belongs to the trunk rather than to the lower extremity.)

The *sartorius*[14] arises from the anterior superior iliac spine (Figs. 56, 78) and inserts on the anteromedian surface of the tibia. It is a weak flexor of the hip, but it also abducts the thigh and rotates it laterally, flexes the knee and rotates the leg medially. The leg below the knee can be rotated slightly when the knee is flexed or half flexed. The sartorius is the only muscle on the front of the thigh that flexes the knee. It is the longest muscle in the body. Its fleshy part is 18 inches in length. When its insertion is brought as close as possible to its origin, the distance between the two points is about 6 inches less than when the leg is extended. This is in accord with the statement at the beginning of the chapter that a muscle can shorten at most only to about two-thirds of its extended length.

Most of the front of the thigh is occupied by the *quadriceps*

---

[14] Sartorius, from L. *sartor*, tailor. The name arises from the fact that the muscle pulls the thigh into the cross-legged position of old-time tailors.

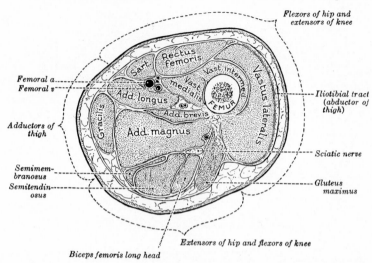

Flexors of hip and
extensors of knee

Femoral a.
Femoral v.

Adductors of
thigh

Semimem-
branosus
Semitendin-
osus

Iliotibial tract
(abductor of
thigh)

Sciatic nerve

Gluteus
maximus

Biceps femoris long head

Extensors of hip and flexors of knee

Figure 79. Cross section of the thigh through the lower corner of the gluteus maximus and just below the insertion of the pectineus. Note that of the five groups of muscles, the abductors are all above the level of this section and that the lateral rotators are not represented, since they are all in the hip. (Redrawn from Grant.)

femoris. This consists of four muscles, or heads, all of which insert on the tuberosity of the tibia by a common tendon. The patella lies in this tendon. Below the patella the tendon is known as the *ligamentum patellae.* Only one of the four muscles has its origin on the pelvic girdle. The *rectus femoris* (Figs. 56, 78) arises on the anterior inferior iliac spine (Fig. 40), which is just lateral to the iliacus where it crosses the rim of the pelvis. Like the biceps brachii and the long head of the triceps brachii, the rectus femoris crosses two joints. It is a flexor of the hip and an extensor of the knee.

The remaining parts of the quadriceps femoris are the three *vastus muscles.* The *vastus intermedius* lies beneath the rectus femoris. Its origin occupies most of the anterior and lateral surfaces of the femur (Fig. 78). The *vastus lateralis* originates on a long line extending from the greater trochanter three-fourths of the way down the posterior side of the femur. The *vastus medialis* has a similar origin on the opposite side of the femur. These two lines of origin run on each edge of the linea aspera (Fig. 44). Note how the three vastus muscles occupy nearly all the surface of the shaft of the femur except the linea aspera (Fig. 79). The vastus muscles are powerful extensors of the knee.

The *articularis genu*[15] consists of several bundles of muscle fibers

---

[15] *Genu:* L., the knee.

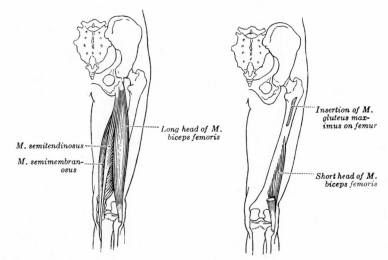

Figure 80. Muscles that extend the hip and flex the knee.

that arise from the femur (Fig. 78) and attach to the synovial capsule of the knee. They draw the capsule up when the knee is extended.

Extensors of the Hip and Flexors of the Knee. The *gluteus*[16] *maximus* (Fig. 57) is a large, coarsely fibered muscle that covers the buttock. Its origin is on the posterior part of the iliac crest, the aponeurosis of the sacrospinalis muscle (Fig. 59), the dorsal surface of the sacrum and coccyx, and the sacrotuberous ligament (Fig. 43). The lower half of its deep fibers insert on the femur (Fig. 80), while the upper half of the deep fibers and all the superficial fibers are inserted on the iliotibial tract and on the intermuscular septum (Figs. 57, 79). The *iliotibial tract* is a thickened part of the fascia lata on the lateral surface of the thigh. Most of its fibers are longitudinal, and it is, in effect, an aponeurosis which inserts on the anterolateral surface of the head of the tibia. The gluteus maximus is a strong extensor of the hip. Acting through the iliotibial tract, it is also an extensor of the knee. This is an exception to the rule that muscles on the posterior surface of the thigh are flexors of the knee. The iliotibial tract is easily palpated if, when sitting down with the leg extended straight in front, the heel is lifted from the ground. This tenses the tract, and its anterior edge can be felt a finger's breadth behind the lateral edge of the patella.

Three long muscles on the posterior aspect of the thigh, the

---

[16] Gluteus, from G., the rump or buttock.

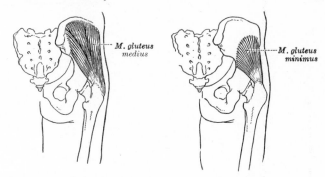

Figure 81.   Muscles that abduct the thigh.

semitendinosus, the *semimembranosus* and the *long head of the biceps femoris* (Fig. 80), are called the "hamstring muscles" because their tendons are used by butchers in hanging hams. All originate on the ischial tuberosity and insert on the leg below the knee. The long head of the biceps femoris inserts on the head of the fibula. The distal third of the semitendinosus is a cord-like tendon that inserts on the tibia just posterior to the insertion of the sartorius. The semimembranosus has at its proximal end a flat tendon (Fig. 79) which gives it its name. It inserts on the postero-median surface of the head of the tibia. The tendons of these muscles stand out prominently on the lower posterior surface of the thigh. The space between them is known as the *popliteal*[17] *fossa.*

The *short head of the biceps femoris* (Fig. 80) is a flexor of the knee. Its origin is on the linea aspera in line with the insertion of the gluteus maximus.

Abductors of the Thigh.   The *tensor fasciae latae* (Fig. 56) arises on the lateral side of the iliac crest just above the origin of the sartorius and is inserted on the iliotibial tract. It not only abducts the thigh, but also counteracts the backward pull of the gluteus maximus on the iliotibial tract and thus helps to extend the knee. It may also help to flex the hip.

The *gluteus medius* (Figs. 57, 58, 59, 81) and the *gluteus minimus,* which lies beneath it, are both strong abductors of the thigh.

Adductors of the Thigh.   The *gracilis* (Figs. 56, 57) is a long muscle that originates on the lower edge of the pubis near the pubic symphysis and inserts on the tibia between the sartorius and the semitendinosus. The remaining four adductors insert on the linea aspera to which they are confined by the vastus muscles that occupy all the rest of the surface of the femur (Fig. 79). These four adductors are arranged in three layers. The most

---

[17] Popliteal, from L., *poples,* the ham.

Figure 82   **The Muscles and Fasciae**   103

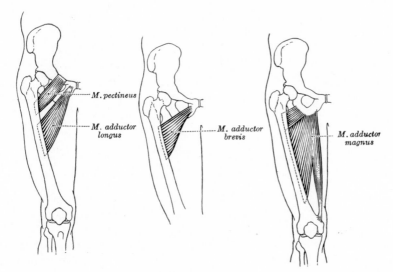

Figure 82. Muscles that adduct the thigh.

anterior consists of the *pectineus*[18] and the *adductor longus* (Figs. 82, 56). Posterior to these is the *adductor brevis* (Fig. 82). Most posterior of all, lying between the preceding muscles and the hamstring muscles, is the *adductor magnus* (Figs. 82, 79). A slip of the adductor magnus sends a tendon down to the median epicondyle of the femur, which has a projecting corner for its attachment.

Lateral Rotators of the Thigh.   There are six of these, all located in the hip. The *quadratus femoris* (Fig. 83) is a quadrangular muscle. It is low enough to assist in adduction as well as lateral rotation. The *obturator externus* (Figs. 83, 58, 59) originates on the median rim of the obturator foramen and on the adjacent part of the membrane that closes the foramen. It inserts in a pit on the posteromedian side of the greater trochanter. Like the quadratus, it can act as adductor as well as lateral rotator. The *obturator internus* (Figs. 83, 59) originates on the lateral and inferior rims of the obturator foramen and on the obturator membrane on the inside of the pelvis and makes a right-angled turn over the edge of the ilium below the sacrospinous ligament. At this point it must be tendinous to withstand the pressure. It inserts on the greater trochanter. The *gemellus*[19] *superior* and the *gemellus inferior* arise on the ischium and insert with the obturator internus. The *piri-*

---

[18] Pectineus: so called from its origin on the iliopectineal line. See page 57.
[19] *Gemellus:* L., little twin.

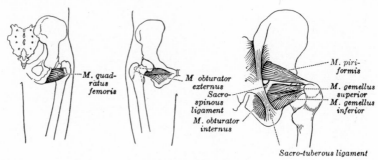

Figure 83. Muscles that rotate the thigh laterally.

formis[20] (Figs. 83, 59) originates largely on the anterior surface of the sacrum and passes out of the pelvis above the sacrospinous ligament. It and the psoas major and gluteus maximus are the only muscles of the inferior extremity that originate on the vertebral column. The piriformis inserts on the tip of the greater trochanter. The obturator internus, gemelli and piriformis can act as abductors when the hip is flexed.

Most of the muscles of the hip and thigh have some rotatory action. The chief **medial rotators** are the psoas-iliacus, gluteus medius, adductor longus and parts of the adductor magnus.

The Muscles of the Leg.   The muscles of the leg can be divided into three structural groups: (1) anterior tibiofibular, (2) posterior tibiofibular, and (3) fibular, or lateral. The tibia is approximately triangular in cross section with three borders and three surfaces. One border is anterior, and the opposite surface is posterior. The medial surface is not covered by muscles and can be palpated from the medial condyle all the way down to the medial malleolus. This surface separates the anterior and posterior tibiofibular regions. The fibula is subcutaneous only at its two ends, the remainder being covered by the lateral group of muscles. On the lateral surface of the leg the groups are separated by two intermuscular septa (Fig. 84). Between the tibia and fibula is an interosseus membrane much like that between the radius and ulna except that here there is no need for it to transmit force from one bone to the other.

The deep fascia of the leg and foot is continuous with the fascia lata. As usual, it is adherent to bony prominences, and it blends with the periosteum on the medial surface of the tibia. It is thickened around the knee, and at the ankle it contains additional fibers to form transverse ligaments that hold the tendons in place as do similar ligaments at the wrist. From its deep surface the two inter-

---

[20] Piriformis, from L. *pirum*, a pear.

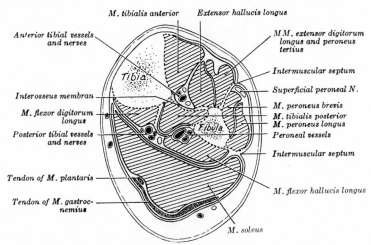

Figure 84. Cross section of the leg a little below its middle. (Redrawn from Grant.)

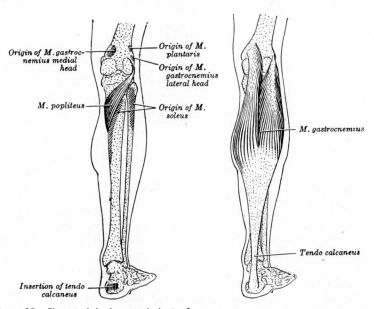

Figure 85. Flexors of the knee and plantar-flexors.

muscular septa extend inward to the fibula. A third septum separates the deeper muscles of the calf from the more superficial ones.

Flexors of the Knee and Plantar-Flexors of the Foot. As in the thigh (short head of the biceps), one muscle of the leg is devoted

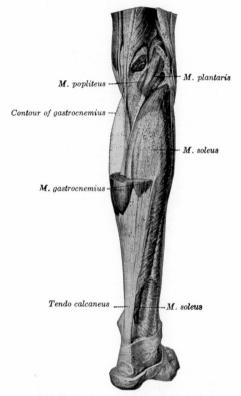

M. popliteus

Contour of gastrocnemius

M. gastrocnemius

Tendo calcaneus

M. plantaris

M. soleus

M. soleus

Figure 86. The superficial muscles of the back of the leg. Most of the gastrocnemius has been removed. (Braus: Anatomie des Menschen.)

exclusively to the knee. The *popliteus* (Figs. 85, 86) originates on the side of the lateral condyle of the femur and inserts on the median side of the tibia. It is entirely concealed by other muscles. It is a median rotator of the tibia as well as a flexor of the knee.

The *gastrocnemius*[21] (Figs. 85, 86) is the more superficial of the two large muscles of the calf. It arises on the femur by two heads that lie just median, on each side, to the hamstring tendons and form the lower boundaries of the popliteal fossa. The two heads remain separate and are inserted on the posterior surface of a broad, heavy tendon that attaches to the calcaneus.

The *plantaris*[22] (Fig. 86) is a small muscle that originates on the posterior surface of the femur above the lateral head of the gastrocnemius (Fig. 84). Its lower end is deep to the gastrocnemius, and its long, slender tendon descends obliquely to insert on the

[21] Gastrocnemius, from G., the calf of the leg.
[22] Plantaris: L. *planta,* the sole.

MUSCLES OF THE LEG

	DORSIFLEXORS OF THE FOOT		PLANTAR-FLEXORS OF THE FOOT		
Flexors of the knee			Gastrocnemius Plantaris	Posterior tibiofibular group	Popliteus
			Soleus	Posterior tibiofibular group	
Flexors of the digits			Flexor digitorum longus Flexor hallucis longus	Posterior tibiofibular group	
Invertors of the foot	Tibialis anterior	Anterior tibiofibular group	Tibialis posterior	Posterior tibiofibular group	
Evertors of the foot	Peroneus tertius	Anterior tibiofibular group	Peroneus longus Peroneus brevis	Fibular group	
Extensors of the digits	Extensor digitorum longus Extensor hallucis longus	Anterior tibiofibular group			

median side of the calcaneus or, sometimes, on the tendon of the gastrocnemius or on the posterior transverse ligament of the ankle. In lower mammals this muscle is a flexor of the toes, resembling in many respects the palmaris longus of the forearm, but in man its tendon is interrupted at the calcaneus, the distal part being represented by the plantar aponeurosis (Fig. 92, A). Like the palmaris longus, this muscle is variable in size and sometimes absent.

The *soleus*[23] (Figs. 85, 86) is the second large muscle of the calf. It originates on an oblique line on the tibia, on the fibula, and on a tendinous arch between the two that permits passage of certain blood vessels and nerves. Its fibers insert on the anterior surface of a broad, flat tendon that fuses with the tendon of the gastroc-

[23] Soleus. The usually accepted origin of this term is that it comes from *solea*, the sole of the foot. The muscle, however, does not enter the sole. According to Hyrtl, it comes from *solea*, the flatfish which it is said to resemble.

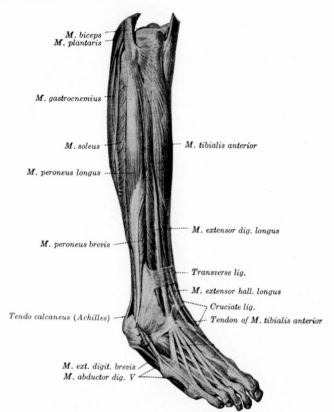

M. biceps
M. plantaris

M. gastrocnemius

M. soleus   M. tibialis anterior

M. peroneus longus

M. extensor dig. longus

M. peroneus brevis

Transverse lig.

M. extensor hall. longus

Cruciate lig.

Tendo calcaneus (Achilles)   Tendon of M. tibialis anterior

M. ext. digit. brevis
M. abductor dig. V

Figure 87. The superficial muscles of the anterior and lateral aspects of the leg. (Braus: Anatomie des Menschen.)

nemius near the calcaneus to form the tendo calcaneus (O.T., tendon of Achilles[24]). Obviously the soleus does not flex the knee.

Although some of the muscles to be described are plantar-flexors, they are not very effective as such, and it is chiefly the gastrocnemius and soleus that raise one up on his toes.

Invertors and Evertors of the Foot. The *tibilias anterior* (Figs. 87, 89) arises on the upper two-thirds of the lateral side of the tibia and from the interosseus membrane. It can be felt just lateral to the anterior border of the tibia when the foot is dorsiflexed. Its long tendon runs across the lower end of the tibia and over the median side of the foot to insert on the plantar surfaces of the median cuneiform and first metatarsal (Fig. 90, A). It is a strong dorsiflexor of the ankle, and, since its insertion is on the median

---

[24] Tendon of Achilles. From the myth that Achilles was held by the heels when being immersed in the river Styx.

Figure 88   **The Muscles and Fasciae** 109

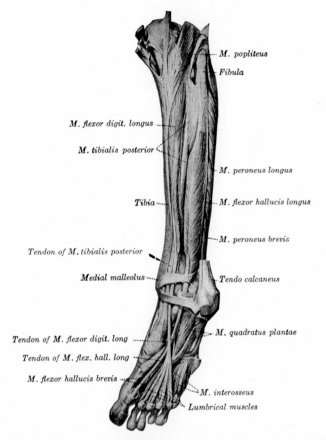

M. popliteus

Fibula

M. flexor digit. longus

M. tibialis posterior

M. peroneus longus

Tibia

M. flexor hallucis longus

M. peroneus brevis

Tendon of M. tibialis posterior

Medial malleolus

Tendo calcaneus

Tendon of M. flexor digit. long

Tendon of M. flex. hall. long

M. flexor hallucis brevis

M. quadratus plantae

M. interosseus

Lumbrical muscles

Figure 88. The deep muscles of the back of the leg. (Braus: Anatomie des Menschen.)

side of the foot and is distal to the mid-tarsal joint, it is an effective invertor.

The *tibialis posterior* (Figs. 88, 89) is the other invertor. It arises from the tibia, fibula and interosseus membrane. Its tendon passes under the medial malleolus (Fig. 90, *A*), which serves as a pulley for it, and inserts anterior to the mid-tarsal joint on the plantar surfaces of the navicular and other tarsals and metatarsals (Figs. 50, 93, *B*). Besides being an invertor, it is a plantar-flexor, and it plays an important part in maintaining the medial arch of the foot, since it passes under the spring ligament (plantar calcaneonavicular ligament).

The *peroneus*[25] *brevis* (Fig. 87) arises from the lower two-thirds of the lateral surface of the fibula and from the intermuscular

[25] Peroneus, from the Greek equivalent of fibula.

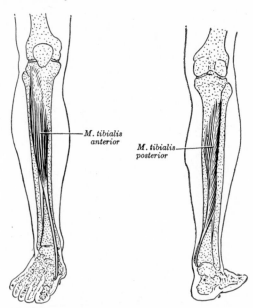

M. tibialis anterior

M. tibialis posterior

Figure 89.   The invertor muscles.

septum (Figs. 84, 91, *A*). Its tendon passes behind the lateral malleolus (Fig. 90, *B*), which serves as a pulley, and forward to insert on the projecting base of the fifth metatarsal. This muscle is an evertor, since it attaches to the lateral side of the foot and a plantar-flexor because its tendon passes beneath the lateral malleolus. The tendinous slip to the extensor tendon of the little toe, shown in Figure 87, is only occasionally present.

The *peroneus longus* (Fig. 87) arises from the lateral epicondyle of the tibia and the head and shaft of the fibula. It covers most of the peroneus brevis, and its tendon passes behind and under the lateral malleolus with the tendon of the peroneus brevis. The tendon extends medially beneath the cuboid and across the sole to the median cuneiform and the base of the first metatarsal (Fig. 91). It is an evertor and a plantar-flexor, and it helps support the transverse arch by acting as a taut bowstring across the sole.

The *peroneus tertius* (Fig. 87) is a partially separate portion of the extensor digitorum longus. It is variable in size and may be absent. Its tendon runs down the lateral side of the foot and inserts on the dorsal surface of the fifth metatarsal. It is an evertor and dorsiflexor.

Figure 91, *A*, shows the arrangement of the invertor and evertor tendons. Compare with the Table.

Extensors of the Digits.   The *extensor digitorum longus* (Fig.

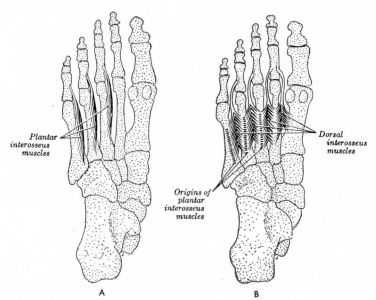

Figure 94. The interosseus muscles of the right foot.

medial edge of the sole. The muscle originates on the calcaneus and inserts on the medial side of the base of the proximal phalanx of the big toe. It is covered by a heavy fascia continuous with the plantar aponeurosis.

The *flexor hallucis brevis* (Fig. 93, *B*) lies on the plantar surface of the first metatarsal, originating on tarsals and on the tendon of the tibialis posterior. Distally it divides into two heads, the two tendons inserting on the sides of the base of the proximal phalanx. In each tendon, beneath the metacarpophalangeal joint, is a *sesamoid bone*. The two sesamoids are united by fibrocartilage and form a pulley on the plantar surface of which the tendon of the flexor hallucis longus glides.

The *adductor hallucis* (Fig. 93, *B*), which lies deep to the long flexor tendons and the lumbricales, has two distinct heads. The oblique head arises on the sheath of the peroneus longus tendon and the bases of the second, third and fourth metatarsals. The transverse head arises on the capsules of the lateral four metatarsophalangeal joints and on the deep transverse ligaments of the sole. The two heads insert with the lateral head of the flexor hallucis brevis.

The little finger has four muscles of its own, one in the forearm and three in the hand. The little toe has only two, both in the foot. The lateral edge of the sole is formed by the *abductor digiti minimi* and its tendon (Fig. 92, *B*). The muscle arises on the calcaneus and its tendon, gliding over a smooth depression on the base of the fifth metatarsal, and inserts on the lateral side of the base of the proximal phalanx. The muscle is covered by a heavy fascia continuous with the plantar aponeurosis.

The *flexor digiti minimi brevis* (Fig. 93, *B*) lies between the tendon of the preceding muscle and the fifth metatarsal. It reaches from the base of the metatarsal to the proximal phalanx.

There remains to be described only the *interosseus muscles* (Fig. 94). These are similar to the interosseus muscles of the hand except that in the foot it is the second toe instead of the third that forms the axis toward which, and away from which, the other toes are pulled.

There are a number of synovial sheaths for the tendons in the ankle and foot, and there are digital fibrous sheaths on the flexor aspects of the toes.

MUSCLES OF THE TRUNK AND NECK

Muscles of the Abdominal Wall.   The *rectus abdominis* (Fig. 58) is a long, flat muscle. It arises on the pubis and extends upward to attach to the lower costal cartilages. Each muscle is enclosed in a dense fibrous sheath formed by the aponeuroses of the muscles to be described. The medial borders of the sheaths unite in the midline to form the *linea alba,* or white line. Each muscle is crossed by three irregular tendinous lines. The recti abdominis muscles assist in bending the trunk, as when one sits up from lying flat on his back. If one, lying in this position, attempts to raise the lower extremities, the recti abdominis must fix the pelvis before flexion of the hips can be effective. The recti muscles help compress the abdomen and can be tensed to break the force of a blow and thus protect the abdominal organs from injury.

A small triangular muscle, the *pyramidalis* (Fig. 95), arising from the pubis in front of the rectus and inserting on the linea alba, is sometimes present.

Lateral to the rectus abdominis, the abdominal wall is composed of three flat muscles whose fibers run in three different directions, reminding one somewhat of the structure of plywood. The innermost is the *transversus abdominis* (Fig. 58). It arises from the lower costal cartilages, from the lumbar vertebrae by an aponeurosis, from the iliac crest, and from the lateral third of the inguinal ligament (p. 97). It inserts by a broad aponeurosis on the xiphoid process, the linea alba and the pubic symphysis. The transversus maintains constant pressure on the contents of the abdomen, playing an important part in holding the organs in place. It also helps expel the contents of the abdominal organs as in micturition, defeca-

Figure 95   **The Muscles and Fasciae**   117

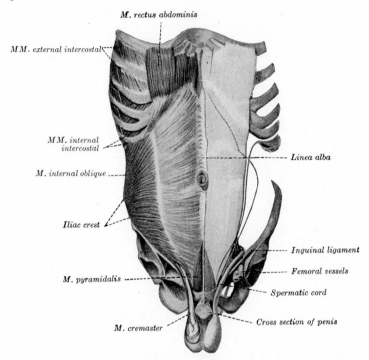

Figure 95.   The internal oblique and intercostal muscles. (Braus: Anatomie des Menschen.)

tion, vomiting and parturition. Its role in respiration is discussed in connection with the diaphragm.

The two aponeuroses of the transversus abdominis demand special attention. The one attaching to the lumbar vertebrae is called the *lumbar fascia* (Fig. 96). It splits into three parts to surround the muscles along the vertebral column. The *middle layer* attaches chiefly to the transverse processes. The *posterior layer* merges with the deep fascia of the back and with the aponeurosis of the latissimus dorsi to form a dense sheet that is often called the *lumbo-dorsal fascia.* The *anterior layer* is thin, merely covering the anterior surfaces of the muscles.

The aponeurosis that inserts on the linea alba forms part of the sheath of the rectus abdominis. Its upper two-thirds passes posterior to the muscles (Fig. 96, A), and its lower third, in front (Fig. 96, B).

Superficial to the transversus lies the *internal oblique (M. obliquus abdominis internus)* (Fig. 95). It arises from the lumbar fascia, the iliac crest and the lateral two-thirds of the inguinal ligament. Most of its fibers run obliquely forward and up, but the

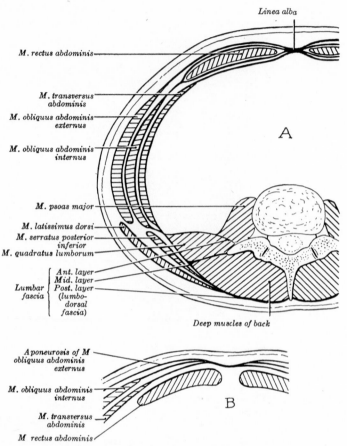

Figure 96. Diagrammatic cross section through the abdomen to show the relations of muscles and aponeuroses.

lower ones run transversely, and the lowest, obliquely downward. The upper fibers insert on the lowest costal cartilages. The rest insert by a broad aponeurosis on the xiphoid process, the linea alba and the pubis. The upper two-thirds of this aponeurosis splits, one layer going behind the rectus abdominis with the aponeurosis of the transversus and one in front. The lower third necessarily passes undivided in front of the muscle (Fig. 96).

The *external oblique (M. obliquus abdominis externus)* (Figs. 56, 57) originates on the outer surface of the lower eight ribs by slips that interdigitate with those of the serratus anterior (Fig. 60). Its fibers pass forward and down. They are short, not reaching to the edge of the rectus abdominis. The muscle inserts by a broad aponeurosis on the pubis, linea alba and xiphoid process. The lower edge of this aponeurosis, between the anterior superior iliac spine and the pubis, is thickened and folded to form the *inguinal ligament,* which has been mentioned several times before.

The two oblique muscles aid the transversus in compressing the contents of the abdomen. They also aid in respiration and in bending the trunk sideways.

Running obliquely forward through the lower portion of the abdominal muscles and just above the inguinal ligament is a canal called the *inguinal canal.* It has two openings, one superficial, the other deep. The superficial opening is in the aponeurosis of the external oblique close to the body of the pubis (Fig. 56, subcutaneous inguinal ring); the deep opening lies more laterally and opens into the abdominal cavity. The canal and the structures it transmits (round ligament of the ovary or spermatic cord), as well as the muscles of the scrotum, will be described in the chapters on the reproductive system.

Deep to the transversus abdominis muscle is a fibrous sheet, the *transversalis fascia,* and internal to it a thin membrane called the *peritoneum.* The latter will be discussed in detail later.

PRACTICAL CONSIDERATIONS. The frequency of occurrence of abdominal operations makes the nature of their incisions of some interest. Probably the majority are made over some part of the rectus sheath, although the underlying rectus muscle may be pulled to one side or the other during the operation. The more lateral incisions must pass through the external oblique, internal oblique and transversus muscles.

Muscles of the Thoracic Wall. There are two relatively independent mechanisms for respiration: the muscles and skeleton of the thoracic wall, and the diaphragm with its antagonists, the muscles of the abdominal wall. The diaphragm is described in the next section.

The student should review at this point the section on the Bones of the Thorax where the movements of the ribs and sternum in respiration are described (see p. 30). The roles of the various muscles in producing the respiratory movements constitute a complex problem, parts of which are still the subject of controversy. An amazing number of muscles take part, especially in forced respiration. Here space permits only a brief account.

The movements are accomplished primarily by the muscles of the thoracic wall. Three layers of muscles can be identified, corresponding to the three layers of the abdominal wall.

The *external intercostal muscles* occupy the intercostal spaces from the tubercles of the ribs forward to the costal cartilages (Fig. 97). Between the costal cartilages the layer is represented by a

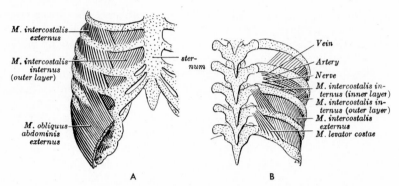

M. intercostalis externus

M. intercostalis internus (outer layer)

ster-num

M. obliquus abdominis externus

Vein

Artery

Nerve

M. intercostalis internus (inner layer)

M. intercostalis internus (outer layer)

M. intercostalis externus

M. levator costae

A   B

Figure 97. Muscles of the thoracic wall. A, Anterior aspect of inferior part of wall. B, Posterior aspect of four intercostal spaces. From the upper two spaces the levator costae and the external intercostal have been removed, disclosing parts of both layers of internal intercostals and the intercostal vessels and nerve.

ABDOMEN	THORAX
External oblique	External intercostals Levatores costarum
Internal oblique	Internal intercostals, outer layer
(Blood vessels and nerves)	(Blood vessels and nerves)
Transversus abdominis	Internal intercostals, inner layer Subcostals Transversus thoracis

fibrous membrane. The fibers of the external intercostals, like those of the external oblique, run forward and down.

There are twelve pairs of *levatores costarum* (Fig. 97). Each extends from a transverse process to the rib next below.

Two layers of *internal intercostals* can be distinguished (Fig. 97). The *outer layer* occupies the intercostal spaces from the sternum back to the angles of the ribs and is represented from there to the tubercles by a fibrous membrane. The *inner layer* is more variable in extent. It usually lies farther posterior, the two layers overlapping to some extent. Between the two lie the intercostal blood vessels and nerves; the corresponding blood vessels and nerves of the abdominal wall lie between the internal oblique and the transversus. The fibers of both layers run at approximately a right angle to those of the external intercostals and in the same direction as the upper fibers of the internal oblique of the abdomen.

The *subcostals* are slips of the inner layer of the internal intercostals at their posterior edges that pass over two or more intercostal spaces.

Figure 98   **The Muscles and Fasciae**   121

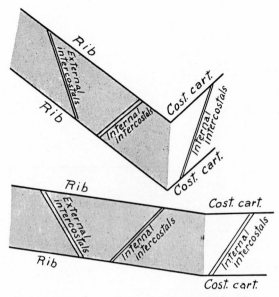

Figure 98.   Diagram to show the mechanics of the intercostal muscles.

Figure 98 shows how the external intercostals and that portion of the internal intercostals between the costal cartilages elevate the ribs and are, therefore, muscles of inspiration. Most of the force for expiration is provided by the elasticity of the cartilages and by gravity, but the internal intercostals between the ribs pull the ribs downward.

Working together, the intercostals of either side can help bend the body sideways. This motion in the thoracic region is limited, of course, by the ribs.

The *transversus thoracis* (Fig. 99) is an incomplete and variable layer on the anterior wall of the thorax, continuous with the transversus abdominis. Its slips assist in expiration by pulling the costal cartilages toward the sternum.

The *serratus posterior superior* and *serratus posterior inferior* (Fig. 100) appear to be parts of the outer layer that have spread over the deep muscles of the back to reach the spinous processes. The former assists in inspiration, and the latter steadies the lower ribs upon which various other muscles are pulling.

The Diaphragm.   The thoracic and abdominal cavities are separated from one another by a dome-shaped sheet of tissue, the *diaphragm*[27] (Fig. 77). The roof of the dome is made of fibrous tissue, while the sides are made of muscle. The fibrous roof is called

---

[27] Diaphragm, from G., to fence across.

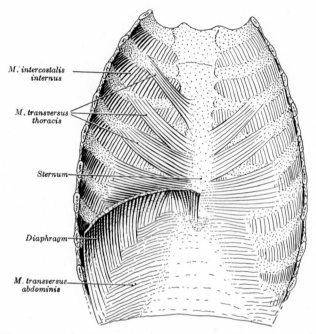

M.' intercostalis
internus

M. transversus
thoracis

Sternum

Diaphragm

M. transversus
abdominis

Figure 99. Muscles of anterior wall of thorax, internal aspect. (Redrawn from Grant.)

the *central tendon.* The muscle forming the sides arises by a series
of slips from the sides of the body cavity. They are attached anteriorly to the xiphoid process of the sternum, laterally to the costal
margins, and posteriorly to the vertebral column. The diaphragm
contains three large openings, one for the esophagus, one for the
aorta, and one for the inferior vena cava.

The diaphragm, together with the muscles of the abdominal wall,
constitutes a second mechanism of respiration relatively independent of that described before. When the muscle fibers of the
diaphragm contract, its dome is lowered and the volume of the
thoracic cavity is increased. Since the contents of the abdominal
cavity are not compressible, the muscles of the abdominal wall
must relax as the diaphragm flattens. In expiration the muscles of
the abdominal wall contract, forcing the viscera up against the
diaphragm and raising its dome. The muscles of the abdominal
wall and the diaphragm are, therefore, antagonists in respiratory
movements. The two mechanisms of respiration, thoracic and abdominal, are used together, the relative part played by each depending on circumstances.

In forcing out of the body the contents of any abdominal organ,
the diaphragm must contract with the abdominal muscles to bring

Figure 100   *The Muscles and Fasciae*   123

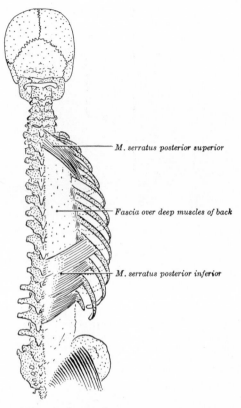

M. serratus posterior superior

Fascia over deep muscles of back

M. serratus posterior inferior

Figure 100. The serratus posterior muscles.

pressure on the organs. The diaphragm is usually assisted by filling the lungs with air and closing the throat so that the diaphragm is backed up by the air held in the lungs.

The Muscles of the Pelvic Floor. The muscles of the pelvic floor are an important group, for on them rests part of the weight of the abdominal and pelvic viscera. They consist of the levator ani and coccygeus, both paired muscles (Figs. 101, 178).

The *levator ani* arises anteriorly from the body of the pubis, posterolaterally from the spine of the ischium, and from a line connecting these two points along the lateral pelvic wall. The fibers are directed downward, backward and toward the midline. The most posterior fibers are inserted into the coccyx, while the more anterior ones unite with those of the opposite muscle. In the interval between the two muscles anteriorly the urethra, the rectum and, in the female, the vagina pass through. These structures will be described later.

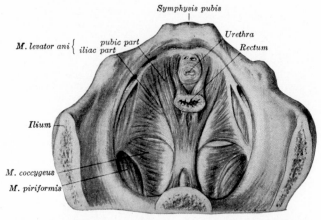

Figure 101. The muscles of the pelvic floor as seen from above. (Callander.)

The *coccygeus* is essentially the posterior continuation of the levator ani. Its fibers arise from the spine of the ischium and pass backward to be inserted into the sides of the coccyx and sacrum.

PRACTICAL CONSIDERATIONS. The muscles of the pelvic floor are of great importance, for they are sometimes torn during the process of childbirth. If the tear is not repaired, the pelvic floor becomes lax and the organs resting upon it begin to drop. This is the common cause of falling of the uterus or, as it is popularly called, "falling of the womb." It leads to many uncomfortable symptoms and requires either the repair of the pelvic floor or the support of the affected organs by some other method.

The Deep Muscles of the Back. On each side of the back, beneath the muscles of the upper limb, filling the gutter between the spinous processes and the angles of the ribs, and extending up to the skull, lies a heavy column of muscles whose function is to bend the vertebral column backward and laterally, to twist it, to help maintain erect posture and to assist in walking. Each column is subdivided into numerous smaller columns, separate muscles, and slips.

The *splenius*[28] (Fig. 59) arises on the spines of the lower cervical and upper thoracic vertebrae and inserts on the transverse processes of the upper cervicals (*splenius cervicis*) and on the skull (*splenius capitis*). Its lower end lies beneath the serratus posterior superior.

The *sacrospinalis* (Fig. 59) is a complex series of muscle bundles. It originates on the posterior layer of the lumbar fascia, the dorsal surface of the sacrum, the ilium, and the ligaments of the area. In the lumbar region it divides into three columns which can be distinguished in Figure 59. The lateral column, the broadest on the

[28] *Splenius:* L., a bandage.

Figure 102   **The Muscles and Fasciae** 125

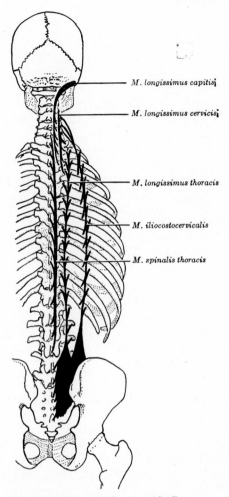

M. longissimus capitis

M. longissimus cervicis

M. longissimus thoracis

M. iliocostocervicalis

M. spinalis thoracis

Figure 102. The origins and insertions of the sacrospinalis.

surface, is the *iliocostalis*. It inserts on the angles of the lower six ribs. Median to each insertion is the origin of another slip which, in turn, inserts about six segments farther up. Thus the muscle is continued by relays up onto the transverse processes of the lower cervical vertebrae. Its origins and insertions are shown diagrammatically in Figure 102.

The medial column is the *spinalis thoracis*. It originates on the spinous processes of the upper lumbar and lower thoracic vertebrae and inserts on the spinous processes of the upper thoracics and, sometimes, the lower cervicals.

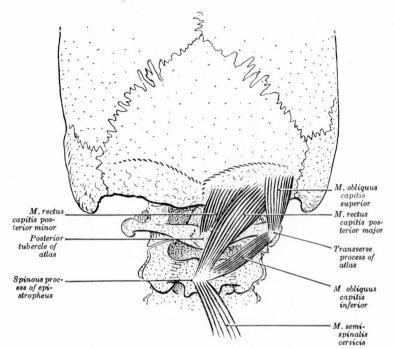

M. rectus capitis posterior minor

Posterior tubercle of atlas

Spinous process of epistropheus

M. obliquus capitis superior

M. rectus capitis posterior major

Transverse process of atlas

M obliquus capitis inferior

M. semispinalis cervicis

Figure 103. The suboccipital muscles.

Between these two lies the *longissimus,* the longest and heaviest of the three. It is inserted on the transverse processes of the lumbars and the transverse processes and ribs in the thorax. Additional bundles, arising on the upper thoracics, insert on the cervicals (*longissimus cervicis*), and still others, originating on the upper thoracics and cervicals, insert on the skull (*longissimus capitis*) beneath the splenius.

Another column of muscles lies beneath the sacrospinalis. Its slips run from transverse processes upward to spinous processes, thus having consistently an oblique direction. Three layers can be distinguished, semispinalis, multifidis, and rotatores. The *semispinalis* (*semispinalis thoracis, semispinalis cervicis, semispinalis capitis*) (Fig. 59) extends from the lower thoracic region to the skull, each slip spanning, as a rule, five vertebrae. The *multifidus*[29] lies deeper, and its slips span three segments. It extends from the sacrum to the epistropheus. The *rotatores,* deepest of all, are very short, from one vertebra to the next. They are best developed in the thoracic region.

In the lumbar and cervical regions are small, paired *interspinales*

---

[29] *Multifidus,* from L. *multi-,* many, and *findere,* to split.

Figure 104   The Muscles and Fasciae   127

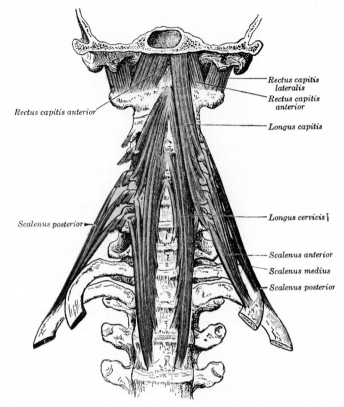

Rectus capitis anterior

Scalenus posterior

Rectus capitis
lateralis
Rectus capitis
anterior

Longus capitis

Longus cervicis

Scalenus anterior
Scalenus medius
Scalenus posterior

Figure 104. The scalene muscles and the prevertebral muscles of the neck. (Cunningham's Textbook of Anatomy.)

between adjacent spinous processes, and *intertransversales* between adjacent transverse processes.

The *rectus capitis posterior major, rectus capitis posterior minor, obliquus capitis superior* and *obliquus capitis inferior* are shown in Figure 103. They assist in the specialized movements between epistropheus and atlas and between atlas and skull. From the anterior surface of the atlas two more pairs of short muscles go to the skull, the *rectus capitis anterior* and the *rectus capitis lateralis* (Fig. 104).

Prevertebral Muscles. Prevertebral muscles are not numerous because opposition to the deep muscles of the back is mostly by the muscles on the anterior surface of the neck and trunk. The last two muscles mentioned would properly belong in this group. Lower in the neck are the *longus cervicis* and *longus capitis* (Fig. 104). In the thorax the ribs and sternum would render such muscles

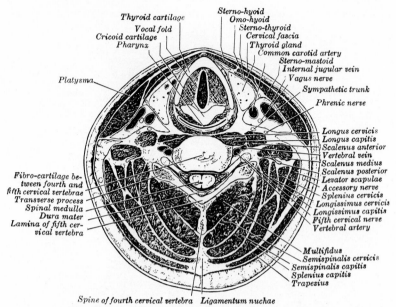

Thyroid cartilage
Vocal fold
Cricoid cartilage
Pharynx

Sterno-hyoid
Omo-hyoid
Sterno-thyroid
Cervical fascia
Thyroid gland
Common carotid artery
Sterno-mastoid
Internal jugular vein
Vagus nerve
Sympathetic trunk
Phrenic nerve

Platysma

Longus cervicis
Longus capitis
Scalenus anterior
Vertebral vein
Scalenus medius
Scalenus posterior
Levator scapulae
Accessory nerve
Splenius cervicis
Longissimus cervicis
Longissimus capitis
Fifth cervical nerve
Vertebral artery

Fibro-cartilage be-
tween fourth and
fifth cervical vertebrae
Transverse process
Spinal medulla
Dura mater
Lamina of fifth cer-
vical vertebra

Multifidus
Semispinalis cervicis
Semispinalis capitis
Splenius capitis
Trapezius

Spine of fourth cervical vertebra   Ligamentum nuchae

Figure 105.   Cross section through the neck between the fourth and fifth cervical vertebrae. (Cunningham's Textbook of Anatomy.)

ineffective, and none exist. In the abdomen there is the *quadratus
lumborum* (Fig. 77), arising on the posterior parts of the iliac crest,
the iliolumbar ligament and the transverse processes of the lower
lumbar vertebrae, and inserting on the transverse processes of the
upper lumbar vertebrae and on the last rib. The *psoas minor* (p.
99), when present, flexes the vertebral column, as does the *psoas
major.*

Muscles of the Neck.   The following muscles are to be found in
the neck in addition to those described under deep muscles of the
back and those attached to the hyoid bone described below. Extending from the first rib to the transverse processes of cervical
vertebrae are the slips of the *scalenus*[30] *anterior* and *scalenus
medius* (Fig. 104). The *scalenus posterior* extends up from the second rib. These flex and rotate the neck and help in inspiration by
raising the ribs.

Lying superficially in the anterior and lateral aspects of the neck
is the *sternocleidomastoid muscle* (O.T., sternomastoid) (Fig. 56).
It arises from the upper border of the sternum and clavicle and
passes obliquely upward and backward to the mastoid process of
the temporal bone. Its action is to rotate the head, the left muscle

---

[30] *Scalenus:* G., uneven.

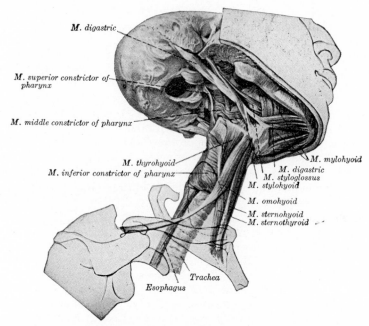

M. digastric

M. superior constrictor of pharynx

M. middle constrictor of pharynx

M. thyrohyoid
M. inferior constrictor of pharynx

M. mylohyoid
M. digastric
M. styloglossus
M. stylohyoid
M. omohyoid
M. sternohyoid
M. sternothyroid

Trachea
Esophagus

Figure 106. The muscles attached to the hyoid bone. (Braus: Anatomie des Menschen.)

turning it to the right and the right muscle turning it to the left. Acting together, the two bend the head directly forward. If the head is fixed, they act as muscles of forced inspiration and elevate the sternum.

The Muscles Attached to the Hyoid Bone. A further group of muscles in the neck are those attached to the hyoid bone (Fig. 106). They can be divided into four groups as follows:

1. A group, called the depressors of the hyoid bone, which pass downward to the clavicle, scapula, and so on (the *sternohyoid, thyrohyoid, omohyoid*).

2. A group passing upward and forward to the mandible. They form part of the floor of the mouth (the *mylohyoid, geniohyoid,* part of *digastric,* and so forth).

3. A group passing upward and backward toward the base of the temporal bone (the *stylohyoid,* part of the *digastric*).

4. One muscle passing upward to the tongue (the *hyoglossus*).

These muscles act in many ways. Thus, if the muscles of Group 1 are contracted and the hyoid bone is depressed, then the muscles of Group 2 will pull the mandible downward and open the mouth. If, however, the muscles of Group 1 are relaxed, then the contraction of Group 2 will pull the hyoid bone, and with it the tongue, forward. The muscles of Group 3 assist in the retraction of the tongue; those of Group 4 depress it. They play an important role in the mechanism of speaking and swallowing.

The Muscles of Facial Expression. The muscles of facial expression (Figs. 56, 107, 108) are a complex group and have many individual origins and insertions. We shall describe only a few.

The *epicranius* (O.T., occipito-frontalis) consists of two separate muscular portions, the occipitalis muscles lying over the occipital bone and the frontalis lying over the frontal. Connecting the two is a fibrous sheet, the *galea aponeurotica*[31] (O.T., epicranial aponeurosis). The galea is but loosely attached to the skull; if it is cut through, the whole scalp can be stripped off like the peel of an orange. The epicranius muscle as a whole raises the eyebrows and moves the scalp.

The *corrugator supercilii muscle* (Fig. 108) arises just above the nose and passes upward into the skin of the forehead. In action it wrinkles the skin of the forehead vertically, as in frowning.

The *orbicularis oculi muscle* (O.T., orbicularis palpebrarum) (Fig. 107) encircles the eyelids. It closes the eye.

The *orbicularis oris muscle* (Figs. 107, 108) encircles the mouth and functions in closing the lips. A number of small muscles (the *zygomaticus, caninus* and others) converge upon it to pull the corners of the mouth in various directions.

The *buccinator*[32] *muscle* (Fig. 108) is the muscle of the cheek. It arises from the maxilla and mandible and passes forward to the side of the mouth. It retracts the corner of the mouth, or, if the lips are closed by the contraction of the orbicularis oris muscle, it flattens the cheek.

The *platysma*[33] (Fig. 107) is a long flat muscle which originates on the skin and superficial fascia of the deltoid and pectoral regions and passes upward on the anterior aspect of the neck to be inserted into the mandible and the skin around the mouth. It draws the mandible and the corners of the mouth downward. It is the thin muscle that lies over the clavicle.

A number of small muscles are attached to the ala or movable margins of the nose (Figs. 107, 108). They act in dilating and constricting the nostrils. A few are also attached to the ear, but only exceptionally can they be activated.

The muscles, as a group, not only produce gross movement, but by their constant activity they also give expression to the face. If for any cause they are rendered inactive, the face becomes smoothed out and bland.

---

[31] *Galea aponeurotica:* L., aponeurotic helmet.

[32] *Buccinator:* L., a trumpeter.

[33] *Platysma:* G., a flat piece.

Figure 107   **The Muscles and Fasciae**   131

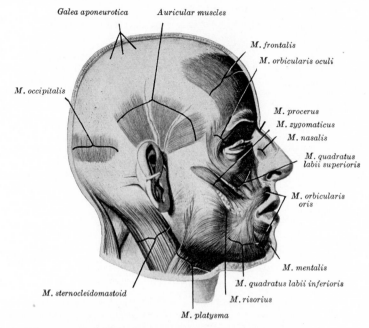

Galea aponeurotica   Auricular muscles

M. frontalis

M. orbicularis oculi

M. occipitalis

M. procerus
M. zygomaticus
M. nasalis

M. quadratus labii superioris

M. orbicularis oris

M. mentalis

M. sternocleidomastoid

M. quadratus labii inferioris

M. risorius

M. platysma

Figure 107. The muscles of facial expression. (Sobotta and McMurrich.)

The Muscles of Mastication. The muscles of mastication include the masseter, the temporal, the external pterygoid and the internal pterygoid muscles.

The *masseter*[34] *muscle* (Fig. 56) arises from the zygomatic arch and passes downward over the external aspect of the ramus of the mandible. It can easily be felt in action when the jaws are vigorously closed.

The *temporal muscle* (Fig. 108) arises from the temporal region of the skull and passes downward beneath the zygomatic arch to be inserted into the coronoid process of the jaw. It closes the jaws.

The *external* and *internal pterygoid muscles* (Fig. 108) are deeply placed and pass from the under aspect of the skull to the medial surface of the ramus of the mandible. The internal pterygoid assists in closing the jaws, while the external pterygoid helps to open them. Side-to-side movements, such as occur in grinding the teeth, are produced by the pterygoid muscles on the two sides acting alternately. Acting together, they pull the jaw forward.

PRACTICAL CONSIDERATIONS. Acute myositis, or inflammation of the muscles, is a rare condition. Fibrositis, a subacute or chronic inflammation of the connective tissue of the muscles, on the other hand, is common. It is sometimes called

[34] Masseter: G., a chewer.

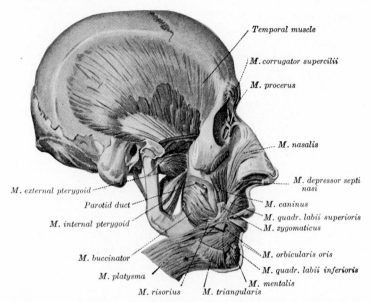

Temporal muscle

M. corrugator supercilii

M. procerus

M. nasalis

M. depressor septi nasi

M. external pterygoid

Parotid duct

M. internal pterygoid

M. caninus

M. quadr. labii superioris

M. zygomaticus

M. buccinator

M. orbicularis oris

M. quadr. labii inferioris

M. platysma

M. mentalis

M. risorius   M. triangularis

Figure 108. The muscles of mastication and of facial expression. Part of the mandible has been removed in order to expose the external and internal pterygoid muscles. (Braus: Anatomie des Menschen.)

myalgia, myositis, or muscular rheumatism. When confined to the lumbar region, it is often called lumbago; when affecting the intercostal muscles, it is known as pleurodynia. The pain and stiffness in the muscles of the back and sides of the neck resulting from a ride in a draughty car is another example of the condition.

A muscular strain is a tear of a number of muscular fibers brought on by over-exertion. "Tennis arm" is a strain of the pronator teres muscle; the "glass arm" of baseball players is a strain of the biceps muscle.

Progressive myositis ossificans is a rare disease in which the connective tissue of many of the muscles, tendons and fasciae is gradually replaced by bone. The familiar ossified man of the circus, who is often exhibited resting horizontally on a central pedestal, is an example of this disease.

Muscular paralysis is a condition which can be more profitably discussed in connection with the nervous system, where its cause usually lies. Here, however, we may note one of the procedures sometimes used for its relief, namely, tendon transplantation. This is the functional replacement of a paralyzed muscle by a nearby normal one. For example, if the anterior tibial muscle is paralyzed, the tendon of the peroneus longus may be released from its normal insertion and brought across the dorsum of the foot to act in its stead.

THE CERVICAL FASCIA

The cervical fascia (Fig. 109) is a dense fibrous sheet which not only encircles the neck just beneath the skin, but also sends fibrous partitions across the neck to divide it into a number of compartments. It extends upward to the zygomatic arch and downward to

Figure 109   *The Muscles and Fasciae*   133

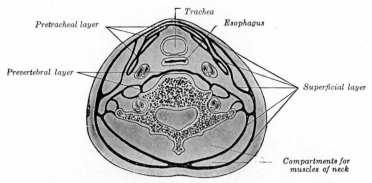

Figure 109. Cross section of the neck to show the relations of the cervical fascia. (Callander.)

the clavicle. It covers and encloses the parotid gland, a large salivary gland lying in front of and below the ear.

PRACTICAL CONSIDERATIONS. The cervical fascia is of practical importance for two reasons. First, it determines the course of purulent (pus-containing) material lying beneath it, as does the palmar fascia in the hand. Thus pus in one of the deeper compartments cannot readily break through to the surface, and if it is not released artificially, it may track down into the thorax and lungs. Second, the fascia is of importance in that well known infection of the parotid gland, mumps. In this disease the inflammatory process tends to produce a swelling of the gland, and this swelling is hindered by the unyielding cervical fascia which encloses it. The pressure produced is the cause of the severe pain characteristic of the condition.

THE BURSAE

Bursae[35] are synovial sacs containing small amounts of fluid, which lie scattered throughout the body in regions where moving parts are subject to pressure. They are frequently found where a muscle crosses a bony margin, and they sometimes intervene between the skin and a bone in regions subject to pressure, such as the knee. Perhaps the most important are the following:

1. The *subacromial bursa,* beneath the acromion process and the deltoid muscle and above the head of the humerus.

2. The *olecranon bursa,* superficial to the olecranon.

3. The *radiohumeral bursa,* lying over the radiohumeral articulation below the lateral epicondyle.

4. The *ischial bursa,* over the ischial tuberosity.

5. The *prepatellar bursa,* superficial to the patella.

PRACTICAL CONSIDERATIONS. Under certain conditions a bursa may become irritated and inflamed (bursitis), with the result that its cavity becomes filled with fluid and a large watery swelling is produced. Movement of the part to

---

[35] Bursae: plural of *bursa,* L., a purse.

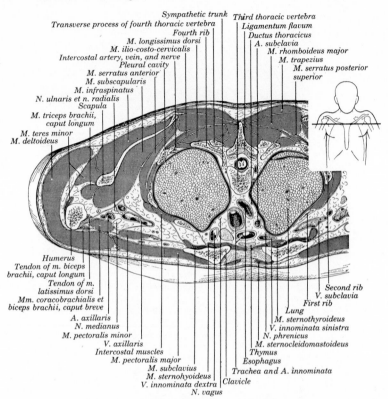

Sympathetic trunk
Transverse process of fourth thoracic vertebra
Fourth rib
M. longissimus dorsi
M. ilio-costo-cervicalis
Intercostal artery, vein, and nerve
Pleural cavity
M. serratus anterior
M. subscapularis
M. infraspinatus
N. ulnaris et n. radialis
Scapula
M. triceps brachii, caput longum
M. teres minor
M. deltoideus

Third thoracic vertebra
Ligamentum flavum
Ductus thoracicus
A. subclavia
M. rhomboideus major
M. trapezius
M. serratus posterior superior

Humerus
Tendon of m. biceps brachii, caput longum
Tendon of m. latissimus dorsi
Mm. coracobrachialis et biceps brachii, caput breve
A. axillaris
N. medianus
M. pectoralis minor
V. axillaris
Intercostal muscles
M. pectoralis major
M. subclavius
M. sternohyoideus
V. innominata dextra
N. vagus

Second rib
V. subclavia
First rib
Lung
M. sternothyroideus
V. innominata sinistra
N. phrenicus
M. sternocleidomastoideus
Thymus
Esophagus
Trachea and A. innominata
Clavicle

Figure 110.　Cross section of thorax and shoulders at the level of the upper end of the sternum and the third thoracic vertebra. The shoulders are held higher and the clavicles are more slanting than in Figure 10. (Redrawn from Eycleshymer and Schoemaker.)

which it is connected may then be the cause of severe pain. Inflammations of certain bursae have been given special names. Thus inflammation of the olecranon bursa is called "miner's elbow" or "student's elbow"; of the radiohumeral bursa, "tennis elbow"; of the ischial bursa, "weaver's bottom" or "tailor's bottom"; and of the prepatellar bursa, "housemaid's knee."

Constant pressure in a region where normally no bursae are present may cause one to develop. A common site for this to occur is over the metatarsophalangeal joint of the great toe, where it forms the swelling known as bunion. The cause is usually pressure from poorly fitting shoes.

Figure 111   The Muscles and Fasciae   135

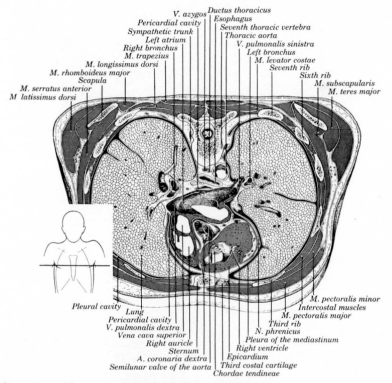

V. azygos Ductus thoracicus
Pericardial cavity Esophagus
Sympathetic trunk Seventh thoracic vertebra
Left atrium Thoracic aorta
Right bronchus V. pulmonalis sinistra
M. trapezius Left bronchus
M. longissimus dorsi M. levator costae
M. rhomboideus major Seventh rib
Scapula Sixth rib
M. serratus anterior M. subscapularis
M latissimus dorsi M. teres major

M. pectoralis minor
Intercostal muscles
M. pectoralis major
Pleural cavity Third rib
Lung N. phrenicus
Pericardial cavity Pleura of the mediastinum
V. pulmonalis dextra Right ventricle
Vena cava superior Epicardium
Right auricle Third costal cartilage
Sternum Chordae tendineae
A. coronaria dextra
Semilunar valve of the aorta
Pleura of the mediastinum

Figure 111. Cross section of thorax through the heart and the seventh thoracic vertebra. (Redrawn from Eycleshymer and Schoemaker.)

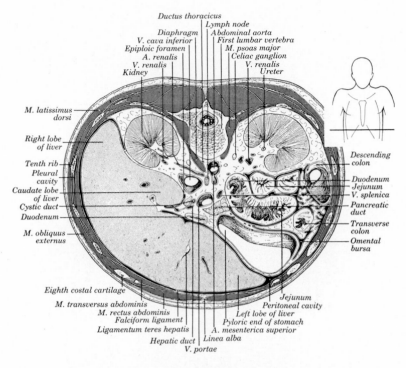

Ductus thoracicus
Lymph node
Diaphragm
Abdominal aorta
V. cava inferior
First lumbar vertebra
Epiploic foramen
M. psoas major
A. renalis
Celiac ganglion
V. renalis
V. renalis
Kidney
Ureter

M. latissimus dorsi

Right lobe of liver

Tenth rib
Pleural cavity
Caudate lobe of liver
Cystic duct
Duodenum

M. obliquus externus

Descending colon

Duodenum
Jejunum
V. splenica
Pancreatic duct

Transverse colon
Omental bursa

Eighth costal cartilage
M. transversus abdominis
M. rectus abdominis
Falciform ligament
Ligamentum teres hepatis
Hepatic duct
V. portae

Jejunum
Peritoneal cavity
Left lobe of liver
Pyloric end of stomach
A. mesenterica superior
Linea alba

Figure 112. Cross section of abdomen through the kidneys, the twelfth thoracic vertebra, and the lower edges of the diaphragm. (Redrawn from Eycleshymer and Schoemaker.)

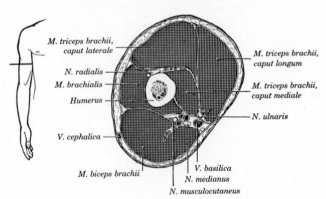

M. triceps brachii, caput laterale

N. radialis
M. brachialis
Humerus

V. cephalica

M. biceps brachii

M. triceps brachii, caput longum

M. triceps brachii, caput mediale

N. ulnaris

V. basilica
N. medianus
N. musculocutaneus

Figure 113. Cross section through the middle of the arm. (Redrawn from Eycleshymer and Schoemaker.)

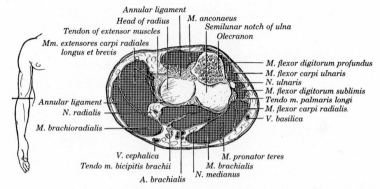

Figure 114. Cross section through the elbow. (Redrawn from Eycleshymer and Schoemaker.)

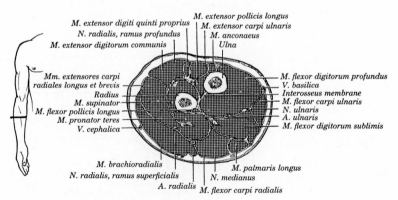

Figure 115. Cross section through the upper half of the forearm. (Redrawn from Eycleshymer and Schoemaker.)

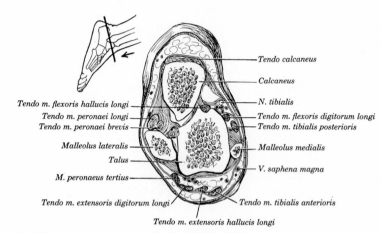

Tendo calcaneus

Calcaneus

N. tibialis

Tendo m. flexoris hallucis longi

Tendo m. peronaei longi

Tendo m. peronaei brevis

Tendo m. flexoris digitorum longi

Tendo m. tibialis posterioris

Malleolus lateralis

Malleolus medialis

Talus

V. saphena magna

M. peronaeus tertius

Tendo m. extensoris digitorum longi

Tendo m. tibialis anterioris

Tendo m. extensoris hallucis longi

Figure 116.   Cross section through the ankle joint. (Redrawn from Eycleshymer and Schoemaker.)

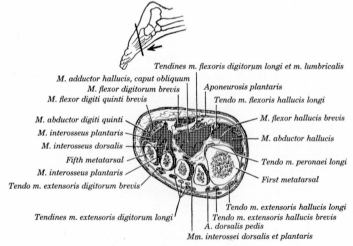

Tendines m. flexoris digitorum longi et m. lumbricalis

M. adductor hallucis, caput obliquum

M. flexor digitorum brevis

M. flexor digiti quinti brevis

Aponeurosis plantaris

Tendo m. flexoris hallucis longi

M. abductor digiti quinti

M. interosseus plantaris

M. interosseus dorsalis

Fifth metatarsal

M. interosseus plantaris

Tendo m. extensoris digitorum brevis

M. flexor hallucis brevis

M. abductor hallucis

Tendo m. peronaei longi

First metatarsal

Tendines m. extensoris digitorum longi

Tendo m. extensoris hallucis longi

Tendo m. extensoris hallucis brevis

A. dorsalis pedis

Mm. interossei dorsalis et plantaris

Figure 117.   Cross section of the foot through the proximal ends of the metatarsals. (Redrawn from Eycleshymer and Schoemaker.)

CHAPTER 6

EPITHELIUM, EPITHELIAL
MEMBRANES⌉AND SKIN

EPITHELIUM

EPITHELIUM[1] is a tissue that covers surfaces, and there are but few free surfaces in the body that are not covered by epithelium of one kind or another. Epithelial tissue consists of layers of cells firmly and closely fastened together with a minimum of intercellular substance.

Epithelial cells are typically short prisms (Fig. 119). If the height is about equal to the diameter, the epithelium is called *cuboidal*. If the cells are tall, it is called *columnar* (Fig. 120). Frequently the cells have the form of thin plates, and such epithelium is referred to as *squamous epithelium* (Fig. 118). Epithelium may be one cell thick, *simple epithelium* (Figs. 119, 120, 122), or several cells in thickness, *stratified epithelium* (Fig. 121). *Simple squamous epithelium*, then, would consist of a single layer of flattened cells. Stratified epithelium is named for the cells of its uppermost layer, since the cells may not be uniform throughout its thickness.

The lower surface of the epithelium, next to the underlying connective tissue, is supported by a *basement membrane* which appears in sections as a fine line (Figs. 120, 121). The basement membrane is probably a condensation of the intercellular substance of the connective tissue.

Epithelium has many functions. It may protect underlying tissues from mechanical injury, from harmful substances and from infection. It may absorb certain substances from the cavity it lines and reject others. Nearly all substances which are taken into, or given off from, the body pass through epithelium. It may contain nerve endings or special sensory cells and thus serve as a sense organ. The free surfaces of its cells may be equipped with cilia. These are fine,

---

[1] Epithelium: G., upon the nipple. Nipple refers here to the papillae or finger-like processes which were found projecting upward from the underlying tissue in the region where it was first discovered.

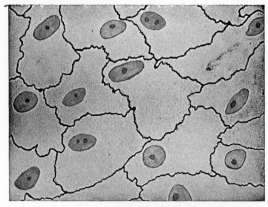

Figure 118. Surface view of simple squamous epithelium. (Maximow and Bloom.)

Figure 119. Simple cuboidal epithelium. (Maximow and Bloom.)

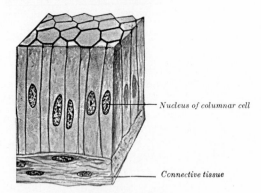

Nucleus of columnar cell

Connective tissue

Figure 120. Simple columnar epithelium. (Maximow and Bloom.)

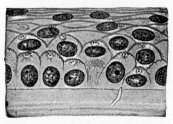

Figure 121. Stratified squamous epithelium of the cornea of a monkey. (Maximow and Bloom.)

Figure 122   **Epithelium, Epithelial Membranes and Skin**   141

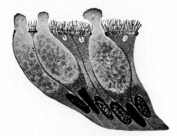

Figure 122. Goblet cells and ciliated columnar epithelium. (Maximow and Bloom.)

protoplasmic, hair-like processes (Fig. 122) that, by their rhythmical beating, transport substances over the surface. Its cells may manufacture substances needed by the body—mucus, enzymes, hormones, and the like. Epithelial cells engaged in manufacturing are called *gland cells* or *goblet cells* (Fig. 122).

Glands

Gland cells usually pour their products, or secretions, out on the surface of the epithelium. If a relatively small amount of material is needed at any one point, the secreting cells will be scattered singly or in small groups over the area. If large amounts must be produced in a small area, however, the epithelium will grow down beneath the surface as a tube or sac, and the combined product of the cells can be poured out on the surface at one point. Such an arrangement is called a *gland.*[2]

The numerous glands of the body are named according to the configuration of their glandular epithelium (Figs. 123, 124). There are *simple tubular glands* in the form of slender tubes which may be either straight or coiled, and simple saccular or *alveolar glands,* shaped like small round sacs. The sweat glands of the skin belong to the first type; the sebaceous or oil glands attached to the hair belong to the second. In the larger glands there are various degrees of branching, and in the largest ones, such as the salivary glands, complicated branching patterns are produced. These more complex structures are designated as *compound tubular, compound alveolar* or *compound tubulo-alveolar glands,* depending upon their fundamental type. All these glands contain an active secreting portion, or fundus, and a collecting portion, a duct or system of ducts. The epithelial part of the gland is always supported by connective tissue. The whole gland, therefore, consists of the epithelial parts (fundus and ducts) and the supporting connective tissue.

---

[2] Gland, from L. *glandula,* diminutive of *glans,* acorn.

Figure 123. Diagram of simple glands. The secretory portions are black. *a,* Simple tubular; *b,* simple coiled tubular; *c, d,* simple branched tubular; *e,* simple alveolar; *f, g,* simple branched alveolar. (Maximow and Bloom.)

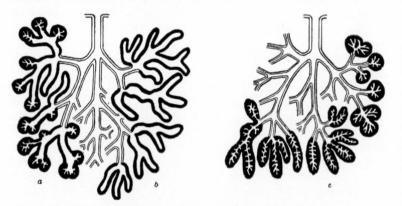

Figure 124. Diagram of compound glands. Secretory portions, black; ducts, double contoured. *a,* Compound tubulo-alveolar; *b,* compound tubular; *c,* compound alveolar. (Maximow and Bloom.)

EPITHELIAL MEMBRANES

The term *mucous membrane* covers all those membranes lining the canals and cavities of the body which open upon the surface of the skin, and thus includes the membranes of the mouth, the gastro-intestinal tract, the respiratory passages and the genito-urinary tract. The name comes from the fact that their surfaces are

The *sweat glands* are of the simple tubular type. Their upper ends open upon the surface of the skin. Their lower ends lie in the deeper parts of the corium or in the subcutaneous tissue and are coiled in the form of a ball. Sweat, the product of the gland, is secreted into the lumen of the tube and poured out onto the surface of the skin.

The *sebaceous* or *oil glands* (Fig. 126) are of the branched saccular type. Their ducts usually open into the sides of the hair follicles, although some of them open directly on to the surface of the skin. In cross section their walls are not seen as a single layer of cells, but the whole gland seems to be full of cells. The most centrally placed ones are in a degenerating condition, and the oily secretion of the gland is the product of this cell destruction. This secretion, called *sebum,* keeps the hair and horny layer soft and pliable and probably helps to water-proof it.

The so-called pores of the skin are the openings of the sweat and sebaceous glands.

A number of lines are found within the skin. They are of two types: (1) the larger and heavier lines, called flexion creases, found characteristically on the palms of the hand and in front of the joints of the fingers, and (2) the fine lines seen most easily on the tips of the fingers. The first are used by palmists in allegedly reading one's fortune. The second are used by the police in identifying criminals, for the pattern is different in each individual and remains constant throughout life.

DISORDERS OF THE SKIN. Acne or "pimples" is an infection of the sebaceous glands. A comedo or blackhead is essentially a plug of dried secretion inside a sebaceous duct. A boil is an infection in and around a hair follicle.

CHAPTER 7

THE DIGESTIVE SYSTEM

Food, in the condition it is taken into the mouth, is of little use to the body. To be absorbed through the walls of the digestive tract into the blood, it must be in solution, and even some soluble substances, such as table sugar, are not absorbed. It is the business of the digestive system, therefore, to change the innumerable compounds that constitute food into compounds that are soluble and are suitable for absorption, and then to absorb them.

The chemical changes are accomplished by enzymes which the digestive tract manufactures. Since these enzymes can act only on the surface of a piece of insoluble material, it greatly accelerates digestion if the food is ground into small pieces, thereby increasing the surface.

The digestive system consists of a long, muscular tube into which the food is taken and within which the digestive processes occur. The system must provide (1) means for a final testing of the food to make certain it is fit, (2) apparatus for grinding it, (3) means to transport it from point to point as the various processes are completed, (4) glands to produce the enzymes and accessory substances needed, (5) means of absorbing the useful products of digestion, and (6) a way of ridding the tract of residue that is of no use to the body. The tract can be divided into several portions: the mouth, pharynx, esophagus, stomach, small intestine, large intestine, and rectum. These, with their attendant structures, the salivary glands, liver and pancreas, will be discussed in turn.

THE DIGESTIVE SYSTEM IN THE HEAD, NECK AND THORAX

The Mouth. The mouth (Fig. 128) is the first division of the digestive tube. Its anterior boundary is formed by the lips, and posteriorly it leads into the pharynx. Its roof is the palate, its side walls are the cheeks, and its floor is formed by the tongue and its muscles. It contains the teeth, and the salivary glands open into it.

The *palate* consists of two parts: an anterior portion, the hard

Figure 127   The Digestive System   149

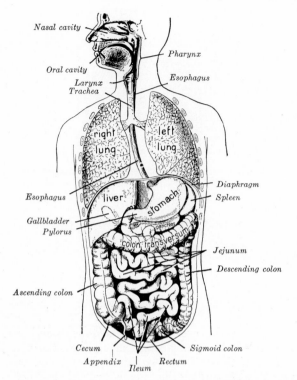

Figure 127. Diagram of the digestive and respiratory systems. (Sobotta and McMurrich.)

palate, and a posterior one, the soft palate. The *hard palate* has already been shown to be formed by the maxillae and the palatine bones. The *soft palate* is formed by muscles. From its posterior free margin a dependent portion, the *uvula,*[1] hangs downward toward the tongue.

The *cheek* forms the side wall of the mouth. Its chief muscle, the buccinator, has been previously described. The posterolateral boundary of the mouth is formed internally by a vertical muscular pillar, the *glossopalatine arch.*

The muscles of the floor of the mouth have been described with the muscles attached to the hyoid bone. The largest is the mylohyoid muscle, which runs from the hyoid bone to the mandible.

The mouth is lined with a smooth mucous membrane. Histologically, its superficial layer is composed of stratified squamous epithelium.

The Tongue. The tongue (Fig. 129) is an organ composed of

---

[1] *Uvula:* L., a little grape.

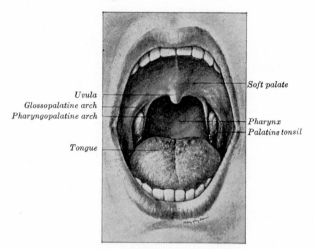

Uvula
Glossopalatine arch
Pharyngopalatine arch

Tongue

Soft palate

Pharynx
Palatine tonsil

Figure 128.   The mouth. (Callander.)

muscles and covered with mucous membrane. The muscles are divided into two groups, called extrinsic muscles and intrinsic muscles.

The *extrinsic muscles* arise outside the tongue and pass into it. Thus one muscle (the genioglossus) arises from the mandible behind the point of the chin and passes backward and upward into the tongue. It acts in pulling the tongue forward. Another (the hyoglossus) arises from the hyoid bone and passes upward into the tongue. It pulls the tongue downward. A third (the styloglossus) arises posteriorly from the styloid process of the temporal bone. It pulls the tongue backward.

The *intrinsic muscles* of the tongue both arise and insert within the tongue. They are responsible for changes in the shape of the organ.

The mucous membrane covering the tongue is made rough by the presence of numerous elevations or papillae. These papillae are of three kinds: (1) the high and narrow *filiform papillae,* (2) the low and wide *fungiform papillae,* and (3) the large *vallate*[2] *papillae* (O.T., circumvallate papillae) surrounded by a circular trough. The vallate papillae are only about twelve or thirteen in number and are arranged in the form of a **V** which lies with its apex directed toward the back of the tongue. The organs of taste, called *taste buds,* are scattered over the surface of the tongue, but are most easily found in the side walls of the vallate papillae. They will be described on page 357.

_____

[2] Vallate: L., from *vallare,* to surround with a rampart.

Figure 129   **The Digestive System**   151

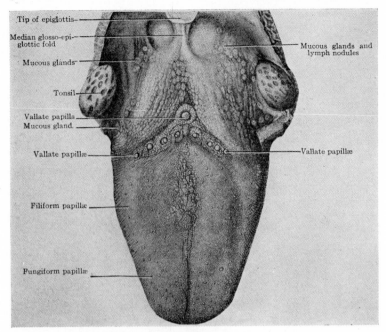

Figure 129. Upper surface of the tongue. (Sappey.)

The mucous membrane of the tongue as it is reflected on to the floor of the mouth anteriorly leaves a fold or ridge in the midline called the *frenulum*.[3]

PRACTICAL CONSIDERATIONS.   In addition to its functions with the digestive system, the tongue plays an important part in the production of speech. In tonguetie the frenulum is so short that movements of the tongue are hampered, and speech in such persons is faulty.

The Teeth.   Functionally, there are three types of teeth: (1) *incisors*,[4] designed for cutting and located in the front of the jaws; (2) *canines*,[5] pointed teeth for holding and tearing; and (3) *molars*,[6] adapted for grinding. Usually, however, four types are described: (1) *incisors*, (2) *canines*, (3) *premolars*, and (4) *molars*. The premolars of the adult are preceded by deciduous teeth (see below), the molars are not. The grinding surface of each premolar has two eminences or cusps, and the premolars are sometimes called *bicuspids*. The molars each have several cusps (*multicuspid*).

---

[3] *Frenulum:* L., a little bridle.

[4] Incisor, from *L. incidere,* to cut into.

[5] Canine, from *L. canis,* dog.

[6] Molar, from L. *molaris,* relating to a mill.

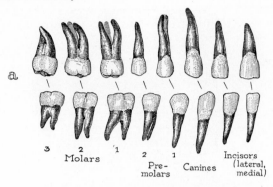

a

3	2	1	2	1		Incisors
	Molars		Pre-molars	Canines		(lateral, medial)

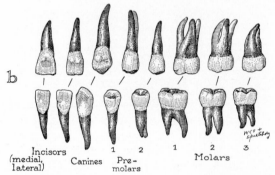

b

| Incisors (medial, lateral) | Canines | 1 | 2 | 1 | 2 | 3 |
| | | Pre-molars | | | Molars | |

Figure 130. Teeth of the right half of both jaws, seen (a) from the outer, or labial, aspect, and (b) from the inner, or lingual, aspect. (Anson: Atlas of Human Anatomy.)

The first teeth to appear are the deciduous, or milk, teeth. These are later replaced by the permanent teeth.

The *deciduous teeth* (O.T., milk teeth) are twenty in number. In each half jaw there are two incisors, one canine and two molars named in order from before backward. Their order of appearance is approximately as follows:

Lower central incisors......................	6– 9 months
Upper incisors...........................	8–10 months
Lower lateral incisors......................	15–21 months
First molars.............................	15–21 months
Canines.................................	16–20 months
Second molars...........................	20–24 months

The *permanent teeth* are thirty-two in number (Figs. 130, 24, 27, 30, 31). In each half jaw from before backward are two incisors that replace the deciduous incisors, one canine that replaces the deciduous canine, two premolars that replace the deciduous molars. and three molars that have no forerunners.

The *incisor* teeth have a sharp margin for cutting and biting. The *canines* tend to have a somewhat pointed border and may project slightly beyond the others. The upper canine is popularly known as the eye tooth, the lower as the stomach tooth. The third molar is known as the wisdom tooth.

The order of appearance of the permanent teeth is approximately as follows:

First molars	6th year
Central incisors	7th year
Lateral incisors	8th year
First premolars	9th year
Second premolars	10th year
Canines	11th or 12th year
Second molars	12th or 13th year
Third molars	17th to 21st year

As seen in the gross each tooth consists of three parts: a crown, a neck and a root or roots. The *crown* is the exposed portion not covered by the gums. The *root* is the portion embedded in the jaw. The incisors, canines and bicuspid teeth have one root each; the lower molars have two, and the upper molars three. The *neck* of the tooth connects the crown and roots.

If a tooth which has been sawed through vertically is examined (Fig. 131), it will be found to consist of a solid outer portion and a central *pulp cavity*. The cavity passes down through the roots and opens on their apices. It contains the soft *dental pulp*, which consists of connective tissue, blood vessels and nerves.

The solid portion of the tooth consists of two parts: the *dentin* or *ivory*, and the *enamel*. The *dentin* forms the main mass of the tooth. It is really a form of bone, but harder and denser. Its cells, *odontoblasts*, all lie on the inner surface next to the pulp cavity, and the calcified material is traversed by numerous tiny canals, corresponding to the canaliculi of bone, which run in a parallel direction and give a striated appearance to the whole. The *enamel* covers the crown of the tooth. It is harder than the dentin and is the most resistant substance in the body. The cells that produced it disappeared when the tooth erupted. A third substance, the *cement*, covers the dentin of the root and is composed of modified bone.

The tooth fits into a cavity in the jaw called the *socket* or *alveolus*. The socket is lined with a membrane, the *alveolar periosteum* or *peridontal membrane*, which is continuous on the margin of the jaw with the *gum*. The peridontal membrane consists of bundles of collagenous fibers that run obliquely from the wall of the socket to the cement.

PRACTICAL CONSIDERATIONS. In dental caries the enamel becomes broken or eroded and leaves the softer dentin exposed to the action of bacteria. If it is left

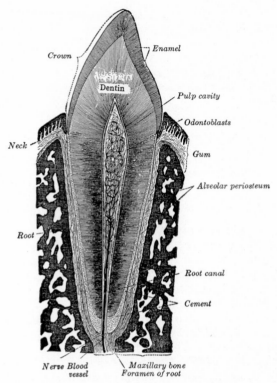

Figure 131.   Longitudinal section of a tooth in its socket (diagrammatic). (Sobotta and McMurrich.)

untreated, a large cavity is formed in the tooth which eventually extends into and involves the sensitive dental pulp. An alveolar abscess is a collection of pus at the apex of a tooth. Pyorrhea is an inflammation of the substantia ossea or cement. It results in a discharge of pus with a loosening and a subsequent falling out of the teeth.

The Salivary Glands.   There are three pairs of salivary glands, the parotid, the submaxillary and the sublingual glands.

The *parotid*[7] *gland* (Fig. 132) lies below and in front of the ear and in contact with the outer and posterior parts of the mandible. Its long duct, the *parotid duct*, runs forward to open into the mouth opposite the second upper molar tooth. The relations of the cervical fascia to the gland and its importance in mumps have been already noted (p. 133).

The *submaxillary gland* (Fig. 133) lies in the posterior part of the floor of the mouth close to the angle of the jaw. Its duct, the *sub-*

---

[7] Parotid: G., beside or near the ear.

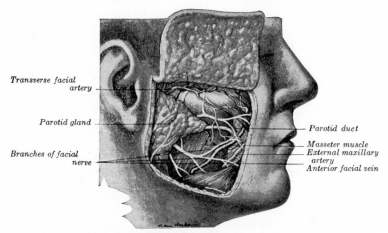

Transverse facial
artery

Parotid gland

Branches of facial
nerve

Parotid duct

Masseter muscle
External maxillary
artery
Anterior facial vein

Figure 132.   The parotid gland. (Callander.)

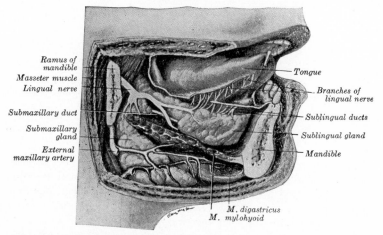

Ramus of
mandible
Masseter muscle
Lingual nerve

Submaxillary duct

Submaxillary
gland
External
maxillary artery

Tongue

Branches of
lingual nerve

Sublingual ducts

Sublingual gland

Mandible

M. digastricus
M. mylohyoid

Figure 133.   The submaxillary and sublingual glands. The body of the mandible has
been removed. (Callander.)

maxillary duct, runs forward alongside the base of the tongue to
open by the side of the frenulum.

The *sublingual gland* (Fig. 133) lies in the floor of the mouth
under the mucous membrane on either side of the tongue. Its ducts,
about twelve in number, open on a ridge in the floor of the mouth
beside the tongue or into the submaxillary duct.

The salivary glands are of the compound tubulo-alveolar type. In
a histologic section of any one of them many tubules and ducts
can be seen cut across at various angles. Between the clusters of

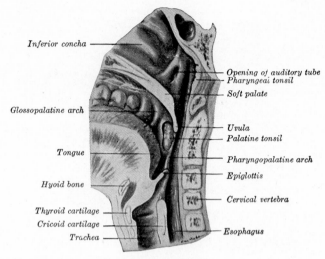

Inferior concha

Glossopalatine arch

Tongue

Hyoid bone

Thyroid cartilage
Cricoid cartilage
Trachea

Opening of auditory tube
Pharyngeal tonsil
Soft palate

Uvula
Palatine tonsil

Pharyngopalatine arch

Epiglottis

Cervical vertebra

Esophagus

Figure 134. Lateral view of the pharynx. (Callander.)

alveoli and tubules connective tissue bands or septa divide the organ into large divisions or lobes, and subdivide these again into smaller divisions or lobules.

THE SALIVARY SECRETIONS. The secretions of the salivary glands as a whole form the saliva. Saliva has four main functions. It facilitates chewing by moistening the food. It makes taste possible, for food, to be tasted, must be in solution. It contains an enzyme that accomplishes considerable digestion of carbohydrates before it is inactivated by the acid gastric juice. It contains mucus that lubricates the food so that it can be swallowed.

The Pharynx. The pharynx (Figs. 134, 155), the second portion of the digestive tube, lies in front of the upper cervical vertebrae. It can be divided into three main portions: (1) a nasal portion or nasopharynx, (2) an oral portion, and (3) a laryngeal portion. They lie behind the nose, mouth and larynx respectively.

The *nasal portion* is partially separated from the oral part by the soft palate. It will be discussed in connection with the respiratory system.

The *oral portion* has in its lateral walls two vertical muscular arches. The anterior arch is called the *glossopalatine arch* (O.T., anterior pillar of the fauces); the posterior, the *pharyngopalatine arch* (O.T., posterior pillar of the fauces). Between them lies the *tonsillar sinus* or *fossa*, which lodges the palatine tonsil (Figs. 128, 134).

The *laryngeal portion* has an opening for the larynx, anteriorly. Inferiorly it continues into the esophagus.

The pharynx as a whole is lined with mucous membrane similar

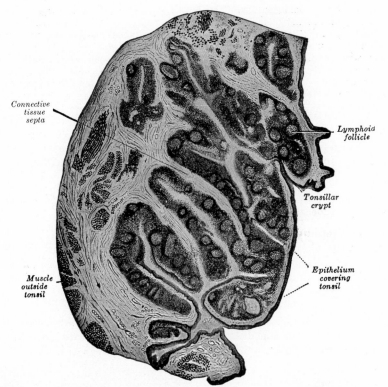

Connective
tissue
septa

Lymphoid
follicle

Tonsillar
crypt

Muscle
outside
tonsil

Epithelium
covering
tonsil

Figure 135. Section through the palatine tonsil. (After Sobotta and McMurrich.)

to that in the mouth. The muscles in its walls are called the *superior, middle* and *inferior constrictors* of the pharynx (Fig. 106) in that order from above downward. They play an important role in swallowing.

The Palatine Tonsils. The tonsils,[8] or, more correctly, the palatine tonsils (Figs. 128, 134), are two oval masses which lie in the tonsillar fossae between the glossopalatine and pharyngopalatine arches. They vary greatly in size and may be so small as to be hardly visible, or, on the other hand, they may be so large that they almost block the throat. A number of pit-like depressions, the *tonsillar crypts* (Fig. 135), may be seen on their free surfaces. The connective tissue binding each tonsil to the pharyngeal wall is called the *capsule.*

Histologically, the tonsils are composed of lymphoid tissue (Fig. 135 and p. 259). The surface is covered with stratified squamous epithelium.

---

[8] Tonsil: L. *tonsilla,* originally a peg to which boats are tied.

PRACTICAL CONSIDERATIONS. The tonsils are of considerable surgical importance on account of their liability to infection. One of their functions is to intercept and destroy bacteria, but they themselves sometimes become infected. In such a case one often sees the tonsillar crypts filled with pus and the organ as a whole completely diseased. Such tonsils are worse than useless, just as a clogged and infected strainer is worse than none at all. Their removal, as a rule, is not a matter of great difficulty. Quinsy is an abscess in the tissue around the tonsil, the peritonsillar tissue.

Accumulations of lymphoid tissue are found in other places in the throat besides the palatine tonsils. A small amount is found on the dorsal part of the tongue where it is known as the *lingual tonsil.* Another mass located on the roof of the pharynx is called the *pharyngeal tonsil* (Fig. 134).

PRACTICAL CONSIDERATIONS. Enlargement of the pharyngeal tonsil forms the well known adenoids.

The Esophagus. The esophagus[9] (Figs. 134, 198) is a muscular tube about 10 inches long leading from the pharynx to the stomach. It lies first in the neck, then in the thorax, and finally, after penetrating the diaphragm, in the abdomen. It lies directly in front of the vertebral column and behind the trachea and the heart. In cross section it is flattened anteroposteriorly (Fig. 109).

It is lined with stratified squamous epithelium throughout. In the upper part the muscle fibers are striated, but these are gradually replaced by smooth muscle in the lower part.

THE MECHANISM OF CHEWING AND SWALLOWING. The mastication of food in the mouth, practised only by mammals, is made possible by a unique combination of structures: (1) the molar teeth, which grind; (2) the cheeks and lips, which retain the food in the mouth while the jaws are opened and closed, (3) the tongue, which, with the cooperation of the muscles in the cheeks and lips, keeps the food between the teeth as they grind; (4) the peculiar joints between the mandible and the skull which permit the grinding movements of the jaws; and (5) the muscles—masseters, temporals, and pterygoids—that produce these movements.

The mechanism of swallowing is also complicated. The mass of food and saliva, technically called the *bolus,* is pushed backward into the pharynx by the tongue, and several mechanisms get into action to prevent it from "going the wrong way." The soft palate is elevated and made tense to form a curtain which prevents it from ascending into the nasopharynx and nose. The muscles attached to the larynx and its appendages prevent the bolus from passing into the trachea. The tongue prevents it from passing forward into the mouth, and the pharyngeal constrictors push it downward into the esophagus.

The progress of the bolus through the esophagus is carried out in the main by an involuntary mechanism known as *peristalsis.* A ring of contraction, preceded by a ring of dilatation, moves along the esophagus from its upper to its lower end. Several such rings proceed in waves until the bolus has entered the stomach.

---

[9] Esophagus (or oesophagus), from two Greek words meaning will carry and to eat

THE WALL OF THE DIGESTIVE TRACT

The wall of the digestive tract consists, as a rule, of eight layers of tissue. For convenience these are grouped into four structural layers as follows:

(LUMEN OF DIGESTIVE TRACT)

Epithelium, of various types. . Epithelium		
Connective tissue. . . . . .Lamina propria	}	Mucous membrane or mucosa
Smooth muscle. . . . . .Muscularis mucosae		
Connective tissue. . . . . .Submucosa		Submucosa
Smooth muscle. . . . . .Circular muscle	}	Muscularis externis
Smooth muscle. . . . . .Longitudinal muscle		
Connective tissue. . . . . .Lamina propria	}	Serous membrane or serosa
Simple squamous epithelium. . Mesothelium		(in abdomen, peritoneum)

(BODY CAVITY)

The epithelium is named from the region in which it is located, e.g., esophageal epithelium. All the glands of the digestive tract are outgrowths of the epithelium and continuous with it. Most of the glands are small and lie in the lamina propria. The liver and pancreas, however, are large and lie entirely outside the tube, their ducts penetrating the wall to open into the lumen. The muscularis mucosae is thin, and, where it is absent, there is no clear boundary between mucosa and submucosa. The muscularis externis is responsible for moving the food about in the tract. Its two layers are not always clearly distinguishable. The serous membrane was described in the preceding chapter. If at any point the tract is not next to one of the serous cavities, there is, of course, no serous membrane, but simply a layer of connective tissue, the *adventitia*, between the muscularis and adjacent structures. The variations on the plan of structure will be described for each portion of the tract.

THE DIGESTIVE SYSTEM IN THE ABDOMEN

The remainder, and by far the greatest part of the digestive system, is found within the abdominal cavity. On removing the abdominal muscles the following structures can easily be made out (Figs. 127, 136, 140): The liver lies beneath the diaphragm. The stomach lies below the left half of the liver. The ascending colon is seen on the right side of the abdominal cavity, the transverse colon crosses it from right to left below the liver and the stomach, and the descending colon passes downward toward the pelvis on the left. A large apron laden with fat, the greater omentum, hangs from the stomach and transverse colon and covers, to a greater or less extent, the coils of small intestine which fill the remainder of the exposed area. A white glistening membrane, the peritoneum,

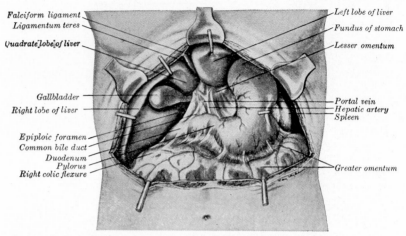

Falciform ligament
Ligamentum teres
Quadrate lobe of liver

Gallbladder
Right lobe of liver

Epiploic foramen
Common bile duct
Duodenum
Pylorus
Right colic flexure

Left lobe of liver
Fundus of stomach
Lesser omentum

Portal vein
Hepatic artery
Spleen

Greater omentum

Figure 136. The upper abdominal organs. (Callander.)

lines the abdominal cavity and covers the organs. These organs
and the deeper lying structures will be discussed in turn.

ABDOMINAL REGIONS. For convenience in gross description the abdominal
cavity is arbitrarily divided into nine regions. They are marked out as follows
(Fig. 137). A horizontal line is drawn across the body at the level of the tips
of the tenth ribs; another is drawn horizontally at the level of the tops of the iliac
crests. Two vertical lines are drawn upward from the midpoints of the inguinal
ligaments. The regions thus delimited are named on the figure.

The Stomach. The stomach[10] (Figs. 127, 136) is a bag-like organ which lies below the left costal margin and the liver. Its shape
is highly variable and differs in different persons and in the same
person at different times. In the living subject, as seen by roent-
genogram, it can perhaps be best described as that of a letter **J.** It
has two borders called curvatures, a *lesser curvature* on the right
and a *greater curvature* on the left. It contains three parts: a
centrally placed *body,* a ballooned out portion projecting to the
left called the *fundus,* and a constricted portion leading into the
small intestine, the *pylorus.*[11] The opening of the stomach into the
esophagus is called the *cardiac orifice,* since it lies under the heart;
the opening into the intestine is called the *pyloric orifice.*

The distance to which the stomach descends into the abdominal
cavity is variable and shows certain differences characteristic of
the general body type. Thus in flat-chested, lanky people, the

---

[10] Stomach, from G. *stoma,* mouth. The early Greek word for stomach was
gaster; the Latin words, *ventriculis.* The most commonly used adjective is gastric,
derived from *gaster.* Cf. gastric contents, gastric ulcer.

[11] Pylorus: G., a gate keeper.

Figure 137   **The Digestive System**   161

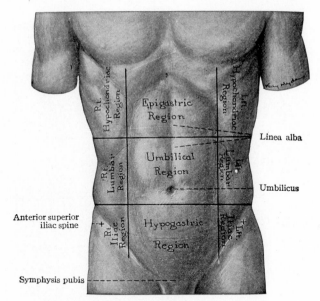

Linea alba

Umbilicus

Anterior superior
iliac spine

Symphysis pubis

Figure 137.   Regional topography of the abdominal wall. (Callander.)

stomach is normally low and may be found almost in the pelvis, while in thick-chested, buxom people the organ is much higher and lies above the umbilicus.

The walls of the stomach are composed of the usual four layers (Fig. 138). The surface of the *mucosa,* as seen in the gross specimen, is reddish and soft to the touch. It is smooth when the organ is full and thrown into folds when it is empty. The *muscular layer* consists of three coats, the fibers of which run in different directions. The fibers of the internal coat run in an oblique direction; those of the middle coat run in a circular direction; and those of the outer coat run in a longitudinal direction. These muscular coats do not completely surround the organs, so that at any one place there are, as a rule, no more than two. At the pyloric orifice the circular muscle is increased in amount and forms the *pyloric sphincter.* The *serous layer* is a smooth glistening membrane and is, of course, part of the visceral peritoneum (pp. 143, 159).

MICROSCOPIC.   The following features can be made out in the microscopic section of the stomach. The gastric epithelium is columnar. The mucosa contains large numbers of long tubular glands. These glands are somewhat different in different parts of the stomach, but in general they are simple tubes with only a small amount of branching (Fig. 139). The cells which line them in the pyloric end are uniform in structure; in the fundus two types may

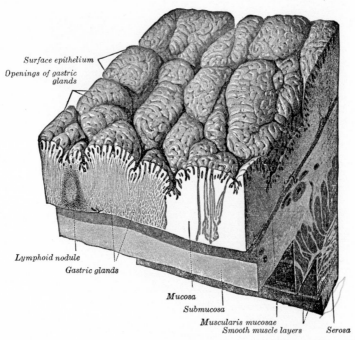

Surface epithelium
Openings of gastric
          glands

Lymphoid nodule
    Gastric glands

Mucosa
Submucosa
Muscularis mucosae
Smooth muscle layers   Serosa

Figure 138.   The layers of the stomach. In the mucosa on the left the normal distribution of the gastric glands is shown; on the right only a few are indicated. × 17. (After Braus.)

be seen. They are designated as *chief cells* and *parietal cells,* and they secrete different kinds of fluid. The chief cells are believed to elaborate the enzyme pepsin, while the parietal cells produce hydrochloric acid; both are constituents of the gastric juice.

ACTIVITIES OF THE STOMACH.   We have already described the mechanism of swallowing and the course of the bolus through the mouth, pharynx and esophagus. In the stomach the bolus comes in contact with the gastric juice secreted by the glands. The motor activity here is of two kinds. First, there is a peristaltic movement which moves the mass from the cardiac to the pyloric end and onward into the intestine. Second, there is a constant pressure exerted by the muscles, which brings the bolus into close contact with the gastric juices. The bolus is kept in the stomach by the closure of the pyloric sphincter until digestion has reached a certain stage. The sphincter is then released spasmodically, and little by little the organ is emptied.

The first stages of the digestion of protein are carried out in the stomach. The enzyme pepsin works only in an acid medium; hence the presence of hydrochloric acid. The enzymes active in the intestine, on the other hand, will work only in an alkaline medium. This necessitates a separation of the two parts of the tract by the pyloric sphincter so that the two chemical processes will not interfere with one another.

Since collagenous and elastic fibers are protein, it is evident that this first

Figure 139   **The Digestive System** 163

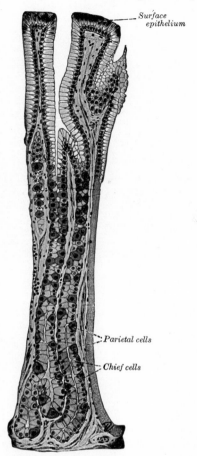

Surface epithelium

Parietal cells

Chief cells

Figure 139. Glands of the fundus of the stomach, showing chief and parietal cells.
  ×130. (After Braus.)

stage in digestion effectively attacks meat and causes it to disintegrate by destroying the connective tissue fibers. There is no enzyme in either stomach or intestine that digests cellulose, however; hence vegetable matter must be thoroughly ground up by the teeth.

PRACTICAL CONSIDERATIONS. The stomach is affected by many mild conditions which produce digestive upsets of various sorts and is further subject to two great disorders, cancer and ulcer. Cancer begins insidiously and, since it cannot be seen or felt, may go for a long time unrecognized. The only adequate treatment to date is operative, and this, to be effective, should be done as early as possible. The affected portion of the stomach is removed, and the part which remains attached to the esophagus is joined to, or, as it is technically called, anastomosed with, the small intestine.

Ulcers of the stomach, or gastric ulcers, are relatively common. They extend for varying distances through the stomach wall; in the severer cases they some-

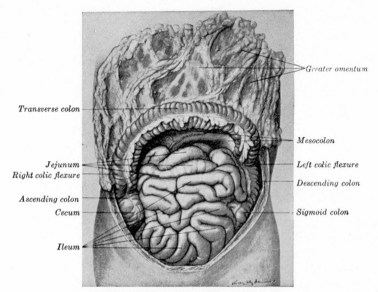

Labels on figure:
- Greater omentum
- Transverse colon
- Mesocolon
- Jejunum
- Left colic flexure
- Right colic flexure
- Descending colon
- Ascending colon
- Cecum
- Sigmoid colon
- Ileum

Figure 140. The lower abdominal organs. The great omentum has been reflected upward (Callander.)

times pass through all four layers and produce a perforation. A perforation is a serious condition, for the gastric contents then empty into the abdominal cavity and set up inflammation of the peritoneum, or peritonitis. Milder degrees of ulcer may yield to dietary measures, but under certain conditions operative treatment is necessary.

The Small Intestine. The small intestine[12] is a thin-walled muscular tube about 1 inch in diameter and approximately 20 feet in length. It is arbitrarily divided into three parts, the duodenum, the jejunum, and the ileum.

The *duodenum*[13] (Figs. 136, 144, 151), the shortest of the three parts, is about 10 inches in length. It is attached to the posterior abdominal wall in the form of a horseshoe with its convex margin pointing to the right. It is subdivided into three parts known as the first, second and third portions. The first part lies in the horizontal position, the second part is vertical, and the third is horizontal again. The head of the pancreas lies in the concavity of the horseshoe; the ducts of the liver and pancreas open into the duodenum in its second part.

---

[12] Intestine, from L. *intus,* within.

[13] Duodenum, from L. *duodeni,* twelve; so called because its length is approximately twelve fingerbreadths.

[14] Jejunum, from L., empty. It was thought to be empty after death.

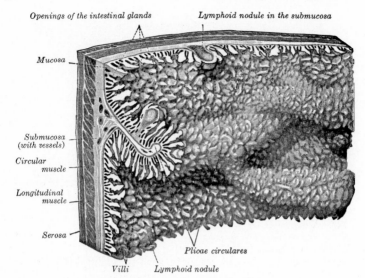

Openings of the intestinal glands   Lymphoid nodule in the submucosa

Mucosa

Submucosa
(with vessels)

Circular
muscle

Longitudinal
muscle

Serosa

Plicae circulares

Villi   Lymphoid nodule

Figure 141. The wall of the small intestine. ✕ 17. (After Braus.)

The *jejunum*[14] and *ileum*[15] (Figs. 127, 140) are not sharply delimited from each other and cannot be separately distinguished on their external surface. The jejunum occupies about the first two-fifths of the total length of the remainder of the small intestine, or about 8 feet, while the ileum takes up the remaining three-fifths. Together they form the prominent coils of small intestine already noted in the superficial inspection of the abdominal contents. They are attached to the posterior abdominal wall by a fan-shaped membrane called the *mesentery,* which runs the full length of the jejunum and ileum on its long margin, but is only 6 or 7 inches long on its abdominal attachment (Fig. 144).

Externally, the wall of the small intestine is smooth and is covered for the most part by peritoneum. Its internal surface has a soft and velvety appearance due to the presence of large numbers of tiny elevations called *villi*[16] (Fig. 141). Inside the duodenum and jejunum and extending more or less completely around the lumen are numerous transverse folds called *plicae circulares.* On the internal surface of the ileum are a number of round or oval elevations composed of lymphoid tissue and known as *patches of Peyer*[17] (Fig. 142).

[15] Ileum, from G. *ileos,* which comes from a verb meaning to roll up, or from *ill, ileum, ilium,* the flank. Note the difference in spelling between this word and *ilium,* part of the hip bone.

[16] *Villi,* plural of *villus,* L., shaggy hair, a tuft of hair.

[17] Peyer: from Johann Konrad Peyer, Swiss anatomist (1653–1712).

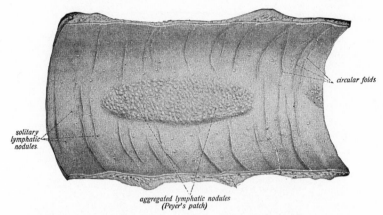

circular folds

*solitary
lymphatic
nodules*

*aggregated lymphatic nodules
(Peyer's patch)*

Figure 142.   A portion of the lower loop of the ileum, cut open along the line of the
attachment of the mesentery, showing Peyer's patches. (Sobotta and McMurrich.)

MICROSCOPIC.   In the microscopic section (Fig. 143) the same
four layers seen in the stomach are present. The mucosa is characterized by the presence of both glands and villi. The glands,
called *intestinal glands* or the *crypts of Lieberkühn*,[18] are of the
tubular type and are lined with columnar epithelium. Some of
their cells are modified by the secretion they contain to form the
goblet cells previously described. The *villi* are finger-like processes
which project into the lumen of the intestine. They are covered
with the same type of epithelium as that lining the glands. Under
the epithelium is a core consisting of connective tissue, blood vessels and a number of tiny vessels called *lacteals*.[19] The lacteals belong to the lymphatic system to be described later. (See p. 257).

The submucosa contains chiefly connective tissue. It has no
glands, except in the duodenum where the *glands of Brunner*[20] are
found. A variable amount of lymphoid tissue is found throughout
in the form of isolated nodules. Groups of nodules in the ileum
form the *patches of Peyer.*

The muscularis consists of well defined circular and longitudinal
layers.

ACTIVITIES OF THE SMALL INTESTINE.   In the small intestine the mass received
from the stomach, now called chyme, receives the digestive juices produced in
the crypts of Lieberkühn and the glands of Brunner and the secretions of the
liver and pancreas. Digestion of proteins is completed, resulting in compounds
called amino acids which are readily absorbed and later built up into new pro-

[18] Johann Nathaniel Lieberkühn, physician and anatomist in Berlin (1711–
1756).

[19] Lacteals, from L. *lacteus,* milky. The fluid within the lacteals is milky in
appearance.

[20] Johann Konrad Brunner (1653–1727), professor of medicine at Heidelberg.

Figure 143   *The Digestive System* 167

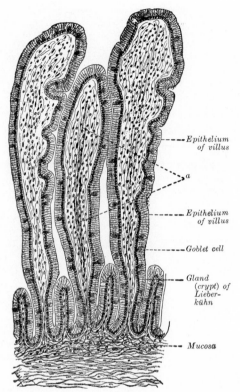

Epithelium
of villus

a

Epithelium
of villus

Goblet cell

Gland
(crypt) of
Lieber-
kühn

Mucosa

Figure 143. Section through mucous membrane of human small intestine. × 88. At *a* is a collapsed lacteal in the axis of the villus. (Bohm, Davidoff and Huber.)

teins by the body or used as fuel. Fats are broken down into fatty acids and glycerol, both of which are soluble. Carbohydrates, that is, starches and complex sugars, are reduced to simple sugar (glucose), which is the only form in which carbohydrate is regularly absorbed.

The muscles act upon the contents of the intestine in two ways. First, there are peristaltic movements produced by the wave-like contractions, which move the mass along. Second, there are movements of segmentation. These are rings of contraction produced by the circular fibers, which break up the intestinal contents into small masses. They serve the double function of bringing the material into closer contact with the glands and their juices for better digestion, and of bringing it into relation with the intestinal villi for absorption.

Absorption takes place through the intestinal epithelium. (There is little or no absorption in the stomach.) Beneath the epithelium, in the lamina propria, there are two channels, the lacteals and the blood vessels. The lacteals absorb the fats, which have been resynthesized, and carry them eventually to a duct, the thoracic duct, which opens into the general blood stream. The smallest blood vessels, the capillaries, absorb the amino acids and carbohydrates, and transport them to the liver. The course of these vessels will be described later.

PRACTICAL CONSIDERATIONS. Of the numerous conditions affecting the intes-

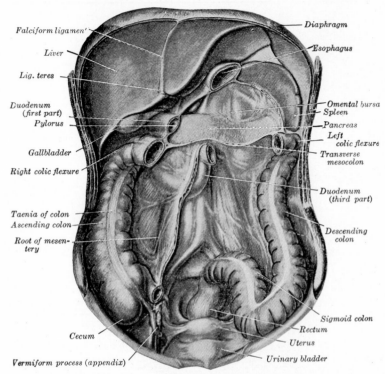

Falciform ligamen'
Liver
Lig. teres
Duodenum (first part)
Pylorus
Gallbladder
Right colic flexure
Taenia of colon
Ascending colon
Root of mesentery
Cecum
Vermiform process (appendix)

Diaphragm
Esophagus
Omental bursa
Spleen
Pancreas
Left colic flexure
Transverse mesocolon
Duodenum (third part)
Descending colon
Sigmoid colon
Rectum
Uterus
Urinary bladder

Figure 144. Abdomen, anterior view, female, with the stomach, transverse colon and most of the small intestine removed. (Reduced from Warren: Handbook of Anatomy, Harvard University Press.)

tine we shall name only a few. Ulcer, which we have already described as affecting the stomach, involves also the duodenum, particularly its first part. The patches of Peyer are often severely involved in typhoid fever. Intussusception is a peculiar mechanical disorder of the tract occurring chiefly in children. In this, the upper part of the intestine telescopes into the lower part or into the colon and sometimes continues so far that it appears at the anus.

The Large Intestine. The large intestine or colon (Figs. 127, 140, 144) is easily distinguished from the small intestine by its greater width, by the fact that its walls are thrown into sacculations, and by its definite course within the abdominal cavity. It is subdivided into several parts named partly from their position and partly from their shape. They are the cecum and appendix, the ascending, transverse, descending, iliac and pelvic colons, and the rectum.

The union of the small intestine does not appear in the adult as a direct end-to-end union, for the ileum enters the colon in the form of a letter **T** lying on its side (Fig. 144). The entry takes place in the lower right quadrant of the abdomen, the small intestine forming the stem of the **T** as it enters from the left. The cross part of the **T** below the stem is the cecum; the part above it is the ascending colon.

The *cecum*[21] is a round or elongated sac from the lower portion of which projects the *appendix*. Inside its cavity are two folds, one lying above, the other below, the entrance of the ileum. Together they form the *valvuli coli* or the *ileocecal valve* (O.T.), which functions to prevent the contents of the colon from passing backward into the ileum.

The *vermiform*[22] *process* or *appendix* is about 3½ inches long and somewhat thinner than a lead pencil. Its proximal end is attached to the cecum. Its distal end most commonly points downward and medially toward the brim of the pelvis, but it may point elsewhere. It occasionally points, for example, upward behind the cecum, when it is said to be in the "retrocecal" position. It has a small mesentery, the *meso-appendix*, by which it is attached to the mesentery of the small intestine. In the meso-appendix runs an artery, the artery to the appendix.

The *ascending colon* ascends on the right side of the posterior abdominal wall from the cecum inferiorly to the under surface of the liver superiorly. It is covered with peritoneum anteriorly and at the sides, while posteriorly it is bound to the abdominal wall. It has no mesentery.

The *transverse colon* sweeps across the abdominal cavity from right to left below the liver and the stomach and above the coils of small intestine. It has a mesentery, the *mesocolon*, which attaches it to the posterior abdominal wall. The places where the ascending colon bends to form the transverse colon, and where the transverse colon bends to form the descending colon are called flexures. The first lies under the liver and is called the *right colic flexure;* the second occurs in close relation to the spleen and is known as the *left colic flexure.*

The *descending colon* descends on the left side of the posterior abdominal wall from the left colic flexure to the iliac crest, where it becomes the iliac colon. Like the ascending colon, it is adherent to the posterior abdominal wall and has no mesentery.

The *iliac colon* passes from the iliac crest to the pelvic brim, and has no mesentery. The *pelvic colon* passes from the pelvic brim to the third piece of the sacrum. It courses in the form of a loop and is attached to the body wall by a well-defined mesentery. The iliac and pelvic colons together are called the *sigmoid colon.*

The striking features of the gross structure of the large intestine

---

[21] *Cecum* (or *caecum*): L., blind. The cecum is a blind end.
[22] Vermiform: L., worm-like.

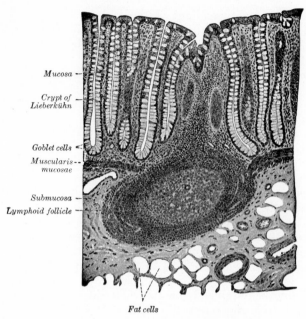

Mucosa

Crypt of
Lieberkühn

Goblet cells

Muscularis
mucosae

Submucosa
Lymphoid follicle

Fat cells

Figure 145. Mucosa of the large intestine. × 70. (After Braus.)

are, first, its great transverse diameter, which ranges from 1½ to
2½ inches, and second, the series of sacculations, called *haustra,*
into which its walls are thrown. The circular muscles form a continuous layer, but the external longitudinal muscle does not completely surround the gut as it does in the small intestine. Instead
it is confined to three narrow strips, called *taeniae,*[23] placed at
equal distances from each other. It is the relative shortness of these
taeniae in relation to the other coats which pulls the walls into
sacculations. The mucosa of the large intestine is smooth.

MICROSCOPIC.   In microscopic section (Fig. 145) the mucosa of
the large intestine can be seen to contain large numbers of glands
or crypts of Lieberkühn similar to those in the small intestine. In
these glands goblet cells are numerous. There are no villi. Large
amounts of lymphoid tissue are present in the submucosa.

ACTIVITIES OF THE LARGE INTESTINE.   In the large intestine probably no new
digestive juices are formed to be added to the contents, for the secretions of the
glands are largely mucus. The function of the colon is to absorb water from
the intestinal contents, together with some remaining nutritive material. In this
manner the solid feces[24] are formed. Bacteria are also incubated here which can
synthesize significant amounts of nutritional factors, such as certain vitamins.

---

[23] *Taeniae* (singular *taenia*): L., ribbon, tapeworm.
[24] Feces: from L. *faex,* dregs.

Figure 146   **The Digestive System**   171

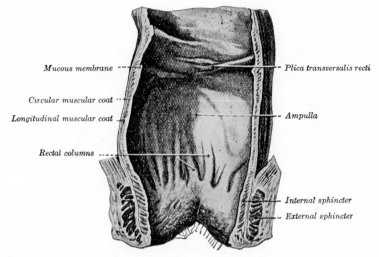

Mucous membrane

Circular muscular coat

Longitudinal muscular coat

Rectal columns

Plica transversalis recti

Ampulla

Internal sphincter

External sphincter

Figure 146.   Interior of the anal canal. (Cunningham's Textbook of Anatomy.)

Feces contain less residue of the food than is usually supposed. The proportion will vary chiefly with the amount of cellulose present. A large part of the fecal material consists of bacteria, the remains of bacteria and substances produced by the intestine. A considerable amount of feces is produced during starvation.

The movements of the colon are similar to those of the small intestine, but slower and less vigorous.

PRACTICAL CONSIDERATIONS.   The best known affection of this portion of the gastrointestinal tract is inflammation of the appendix, or appendicitis. In a simple case removal of the appendix is neither difficult nor particularly serious; in the more severe conditions when, for instance, an abscess has ruptured, the condition is most grave. In this case general peritonitis not infrequently sets in, and, until recent developments in chemotherapy, the mortality was high.

Cancer occasionally attacks the large intestine and may so block its cavity as to produce intestinal obstruction. Another cause of intestinal obstruction is a twisting of the loop of pelvic colon; strangulation of a herniated piece of intestine is a third. The condition is a surgical emergency and requires prompt treatment.

The Rectum.   The rectum[25] (Fig. 144) is the continuation of the gastro-intestinal tract from the pelvic colon to the anal orifice. It passes downward in front of the lower part of the sacrum and coccyx, and then bends directly backward to its termination. The terminal portion, which passes through the pelvic floor, is called the *anal canal.* Its opening on the surface is the *anus* or the *anal orifice.* The dilated portion of the rectum immediately above the anal canal is called the *ampulla.*

The mucosa of the rectum (Fig. 146) contains three or more

---

[25] *Rectum:* L., straight. It is not straight in man, but is so in the animals in which it was first described.

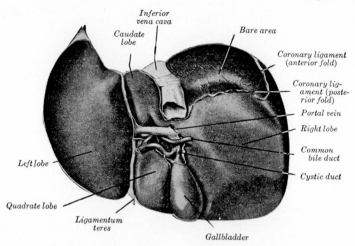

Figure 147. Liver, posterior and inferior surfaces. (Sobotta and McMurrich.)

large valve-like folds separated at some distance from each other. They are called *transverse rectal folds* or the *plicae transversales recti*. In the anal canal are large numbers of vertical folds called *rectal columns*. Each contains an artery and a vein, the latter being surgically the more important.

The muscular wall of the rectum contains the usual inner circular and outer longitudinal layers. The circular muscle is particularly well developed in the anal canal where it forms the *internal sphincter*. The *external sphincter* is a separate striated muscle encircling the lower end of the rectum (Figs. 146, 170, 178).

FUNCTION OF THE RECTUM.   The rectum has nothing to do with digestion and acts solely as an excretory canal. The longitudinal muscle acts during defecation; the sphincter keeps the tract closed at other times.

PRACTICAL CONSIDERATIONS.   The veins of the anal canal are subject to enlargement, a condition known as hemorrhoids or piles. Internal hemorrhoids are enlargements of the veins inside the canal itself; external hemorrhoids lie just outside the orifice. Cancer has a definite predilection for the rectum.

The Liver.   The liver (Figs. 144, 147) is an accessory gland of the gastro-intestinal tract and is the largest gland in the body. It lies directly beneath the diaphragm and fills a large part of the upper right quadrant of the abdomen. Its shape is roughly that of an irregular four-sided pyramid; it lies with its apex directed to the left and its base to the right. The shape of the anterior surface is that of a right-angled triangle, with its longest side running diagonally across the abdominal cavity, just below the costal margin.

The surfaces of the liver are marked off by ligaments and fissures into a number of subdivisions or lobes. The two main *lobes* are the *right* and *left,* the right being the larger of the two. Two smaller divisions, the *quadrate* lobe on the under surface, and the *caudate*[26] lobe on the posterior surface, are really separated portions of the right lobe. This division into lobes has no special functional significance; they are all alike in their internal structure and in their function.

The ligaments which bind the liver to the diaphragm and to the anterior abdominal wall are mainly reflections of peritoneum which pass from the liver to its supporting structures. The two passing to the anterior abdominal wall, the falciform ligament and the ligamentum teres hepatis, are easily identified.

The *falciform*[27] *ligament* (Fig. 144) forms the line of separation of the right and left lobes on the anterior surface of the liver. It passes to the midline of the anterior abdominal wall from the diaphragm to the umbilicus.

The *ligamentum teres hepatis*[28] (O.T., round ligament) (Figs. 144, 147) is found in the lower free border of the falciform ligament, and passes to the under surface of the liver between the right and left lobes. It is the remains of what was once a large vein in the fetus (the left umbilical vein).

The ligaments on the superior and posterior surfaces of the liver attaching the organ to the diaphragm are more complicated (Fig. 147). On the left is the *left triangular ligament.* On the right is the *coronary* ligament with widely separated anterior and posterior folds. These folds converge on the extreme right to form the *right triangular ligament.*

The liver is almost entirely covered with peritoneum. Between the two folds of the coronary ligament it has, however, no such covering and is directly adherent to the diaphragm. This region is called the *bare area* of the liver.

On the under surface of the liver, between the quadrate and the caudate lobes, is a transverse fissure called the *porta hepatis.* From this fissure a fold of peritoneum, the lesser omentum, passes to the lesser curvature of the stomach. In it run three important structures: the bile ducts, the hepatic artery and the portal vein (Fig. 147).

The bile ducts leaving the liver are two in number and are called the *right* and *left hepatic ducts.* These soon unite to form one vessel, the *common hepatic duct* (Fig. 151). The common hepatic duct joins the duct from the gallbladder, the *cystic duct,* and from this union the *common bile duct* is formed. The common bile duct opens into the second part of the duodenum on a small elevation

---

[26] Caudate: L., tail-like.

[27] Falciform: L., sickle-shaped.

[28] Hepatis, from G. *hepar,* the liver. Cf. hepatic duct.

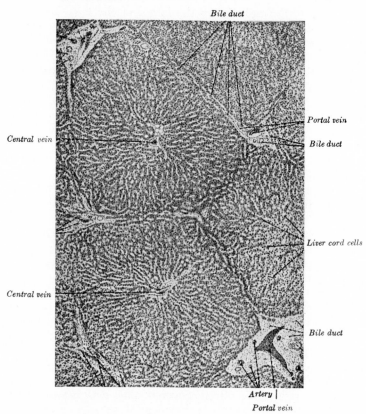

Figure 148.   Section of liver, showing two complete lobules surrounded by other lobules. (After Sobotta and McMurrich.)

known as the *duodenal papilla*. The main duct of the pancreas opens along with it.

The *gallbladder* (Figs. 136, 144, 147) is a thin-walled sac which lies on the under surface of the liver between the right and the quadrate lobes. Its apex projects forward beyond the anterior and inferior margins of the liver. Its duct, the cystic duct, has already been noted. It serves as a reservoir for bile.

The blood vessels carrying blood to the liver are the *hepatic* artery and the *portal vein*. They have already been seen entering the porta hepatis. The vein is the larger of the two. The vessels leaving the organ, the *hepatic veins,* are not easily seen, for they are embedded in the posterior portion of the liver substance. They open directly into the great vein of the abdomen, the *inferior vena cava* (Fig. 147), which lies on the posterior surface of the liver between the right and caudate lobes.

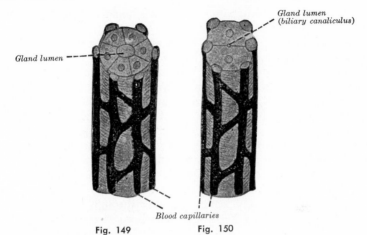

Fig. 149   Fig. 150

Figure 149. Diagram illustrating relation of cells to lumen and to blood capillaries in an ordinary tubular gland.
Figure 150. Relation of cells to lumen (biliary canaliculus) and to blood capillaries (biliary sinusoids) in liver. (Stöhr.)

MICROSCOPIC. The liver was earlier described as a gland, but its histologic structure is so different from that of the other glands we have seen so far that to the uninitiated it is hardly recognizable as such. This is because its blood supply is so great that the most easily recognized units are vascular rather than glandular.

The vascular units, called *liver lobules* (Fig. 148) are more or less polyhedral in shape. Each lobule is tightly fitted in between its neighbors, and the liver as a whole is made up of large numbers of these interlocking units. As seen in cross section these lobules are more or less hexagonal, and in their center lies a vein, the *central vein.* The liver cells which make up the lobules radiate in a series of cords from the central vein to the periphery. Each *cord* is a single glandular unit, and consists of a double row of cells with a tiny canal in between, the *biliary canaliculus* or bile capillary (Figs. 149, 150). The cords may branch and anastomose, but their general direction is perpendicular to the central vein. The canaliculus is not seen in the ordinary microscopic section, but can be demonstrated by special methods. The liver secretion or bile is poured into it. Separating the individual cords from one another are relatively large blood channels called *sinusoids.*[29] They converge from the periphery to the center and open into the central vein.

The liver lobules are separated by small amounts of connective tissue. At the corners, where three or more lobules come together, a group of vessels may usually be found. These are terminal branches

[29] Sinusoid: L., like a sinus.

of the portal vein, hepatic artery and hepatic duct. Of the three the portal vein is the largest.

It can now be seen that there are two systems for the transmission of fluids within the liver: (1) the blood channels and (2) the bile or hepatic vessels. Within the liver lobules the flow in these two systems is in opposite directions. The blood enters each lobule at the periphery, via the terminal branches of both the hepatic artery and the portal vein, and passes through the sinusoids to the central vein. From here it is conducted to the main veins leaving the liver, the hepatic veins. The flow of bile is in the reverse direction. It is secreted into the biliary canaliculi and passes toward the periphery of the lobule to enter the terminal branches of the hepatic ducts. From these it passes to larger and larger vessels and eventually leaves the liver through the right and left hepatic ducts. Its further course has been already studied.

THE FUNCTIONS OF THE LIVER. The functions of the liver are many. In the first place, it produces *bile,* which passes into the intestine and acts as an important digestive juice. Bile contains no enzymes, but aids in producing the alkaline condition necessary for the enzymes in the intestine, and it helps to emulsify the fats, thus acceleratig their digestion.

Second, it plays an important role in the metabolism of carbohydrates and proteins. The circulatory system is so arranged that all blood from the digestive tract below the esophagus flows to the liver through the portal vein and thence through the biliary sinusoids. This permits the liver cells to take out of the blood the glucose absorbed from the gut and store it as a complex carbohydrate, glycogen, until it is needed. As it is needed to maintain the normal, closely regulated concentration in the blood, it is reconverted into glucose and set free. Excess amino acids are also taken out of the blood. Their molecules may be split; part is stored as glycogen, and the remaining, nitrogenous fraction is combined with carbon dioxide to form urea, which is sent by way of the blood stream to the kidneys for elimination.

The liver also contains a substance necessary for the full development of red blood cells, as shown by its effectiveness in the treatment of pernicious anemia. Still other functions have been attributed to the liver, but these cannot be discussed here.

PRACTICAL CONSIDERATION. One of the best known conditions associated with the gallbladder is the formation of gallstones. Gallstones may be formed singly or in large numbers, and are of various types, shapes and sizes. Small stones may pass through the cystic and common bile ducts and then are eliminated by the gastrointestinal tract; large ones sometimes obstruct the ducts on the way down and cause the severe pain characteristic of the condition. For treatment the gallbladder may be opened and the stones removed, or the gallbladder may be taken out entirely. Obstructions to the hepatic or common bile ducts by gallstones, inflammatory conditions or tumors cause a backing up of the bile within the liver and its eventual absorption into the blood. The presence of bile pigments in the blood is responsible for the peculiar color of jaundice.

The Pancreas. The pancreas[30] (Figs. 144, 151), the remaining accessory gland of the gastro-intestinal tract, lies on the posterior

[30] *Pancreas:* G., all flesh.

Figure 151   ***The Digestive System*** 177

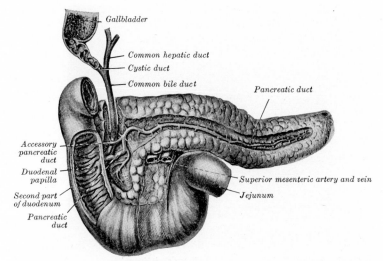

Gallbladder

Common hepatic duct

Cystic duct

Common bile duct

Pancreatic duct

Accessory
pancreatic
duct

Duodenal
papilla

Second part
of duodenum

Pancreatic
duct

Superior mesenteric artery and vein

Jejunum

Figure 151. Duodenum and pancreas, anterior view. Part of the anterior wall of the duodenum has been cut away, showing the duodenal papilla; a channel has been cut in the pancreas exposing the pancreatic duct. (Reduced from Warren: Handbook of Anatomy, Harvard University Press.)

abdominal wall behind the stomach. It is a long and slender organ with a head, neck, body and tail. The *head* is recurved upon itself and gives the gland the shape of a letter **J** lying on its side. The head and *neck* lie in the cavity formed by the horseshoe-like curve of the duodenum. The *body* stretches across the posterior abdominal wall and crosses the great blood vessels and the left kidney. The *tail* comes in contact with the spleen.

The main duct of the pancreas, the *pancreatic duct,* runs the length of the gland and opens into the duodenum along with the common bile duct. An accessory duct is occasionally present.

MICROSCOPIC. The pancreas is a compound tubulo-alveolar gland. It is similar to a salivary gland (particularly the parotid), and in microscopic sections (Fig. 152) many ducts and tubules are seen cut across at various angles. The gland as a whole is divided into lobes and lobules by connective tissue septa. Scattered throughout are small clusters of cells, somewhat paler than the others, which go by the name of *islands of Langerhans.*[31] They do not pour their secretions into the ducts of the pancreas, but pass them directly into the blood stream. Such a secretion is known as an *internal secretion,* and glands that produce it are glands of internal secretion or endocrine glands. The pancreas as a whole is, therefore, a mixed gland, producing an internal secretion from the islands

---

[31] Paul Langerhans (1847–1888), German physician and anatomist.

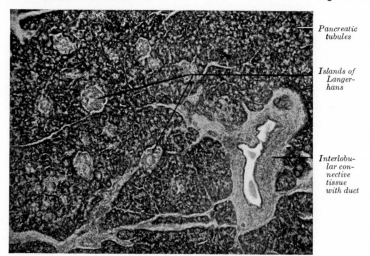

Pancreatic
tubules

Islands of
Langer-
hans

Interlobu-
lar con-
nective
tissue
with duct

Figure 152.   Section of the pancreas. (Maximow and Bloom.)

of Langerhans and an external secretion from the rest of the secreting epithelium.

THE PANCREATIC SECRETIONS.   The external secretion of the pancreas, called pancreatic juice, acts with the other digestive juices on the intestinal contents. The internal secretion, called insulin, is concerned with the metabolism of sugar. When insulin is diminished in amount, sugar is inadequately metabolized and appears in excess in the blood and urine. Insulin deficiency is one of the factors producing diabetes.

The Peritoneum.   The peritoneum is the thin, glistening serous membrane (p. 143) which lines the abdominal cavity and is reflected over the abdominal viscera. That portion of it on the abdominal wall is called the *parietal peritoneum;* that covering the viscera is called the *visceral peritoneum.* It is a complicated structure, and only its main features will be pointed out here.

The peritoneum can be most easily understood by studying a section of the abdomen made in the sagittal plane (Fig. 153). On the anterior abdominal wall it is regular and uninterrupted, but several reflections to the viscera take place from the posterior wall and the diaphragm. From the diaphragm two peritoneal folds pass to the anterior and posterior aspects of the liver to form its supporting ligaments. They pass around and envelop the organ and then pass downward to the stomach as the *lesser omentum.* They cover both aspects of the stomach and then continue downward as the anterior folds of the *greater omentum.* At the lower limits of this structure they fold backward on themselves and ascend as the posterior folds of the greater omentum to the transverse colon. The

Figure 153

The Digestive System 179

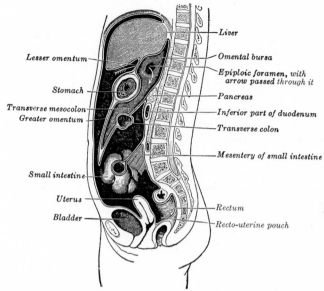

Figure 153. Diagrammatic median section of female body to show the peritoneum on vertical tracing. The great sac of the peritoneum is black and is represented as being much larger than in nature; the bursa omentalis is darkly shaded; the peritoneum on section is shown as a white line; and a white arrow is passed through the epiploic foramen from the great sac into the omental bursa. (Cunningham's Textbook of Anatomy.)

transverse colon is covered, and the folds then pass backward to the posterior abdominal wall as the *mesocolon*.

From the line of attachment of the mesocolon to the posterior abdominal wall, the peritoneum can be traced in two directions. Part of it passes upward to the under aspect of the diaphragm, where it was encountered first. Another part passes downward a short distance and is reflected over the small intestines as their mesentery. Continuing downward on the posterior wall, it passes forward over the pelvic organs and then courses upward on the anterior abdominal wall to the diaphragm, where it was first seen.

It should be noted that the omentum, mesocolon and mesentery are membranes formed of two layers of peritoneum. Both surfaces of such membranes are, therefore, covered with mesothelium. These membranes support the organs in the abdominal cavity and provide a pathway by which blood and lymph vessels and nerves can reach the organs.

If the peritoneum be now studied as a whole, it will be seen that two cavities of unequal size have been marked out. The smaller cavity lies behind the stomach and is called the *omental bursa.* The larger cavity is called the *greater peritoneal cavity.* The two communicate through an opening, the *epiploic*[32] *foramen* (Figs. 153, 136), which lies to the right of the midline on a level with the lesser omentum. The organs which lie on the posterior abdominal wall behind the peritoneum, such as the kidneys and pancreas, are said to be *retroperitoneal.*

The peritoneal cavity does not contain large empty spaces such as are shown in Figure 153. On the contrary, the various parts of the peritoneum are everywhere in contact with one another, so that the cavity, extensive as it is, contains only the thin layer of moisture that allows the organs to move easily over one another.

---

[32] Epiploic: from epiploön, the omentum, from the Greek, meaning to sail or float on. The epiploön floats on the small intestine.

CHAPTER 8

THE RESPIRATORY SYSTEM

Every living cell must have a constant supply of oxygen and must have the carbon dioxide it continuously produces removed promptly. This is accomplished by the blood, which brings oxygen to the tissues and carries away the carbon dioxide. The *respiratory system* is the mechanism that supplies the oxygen to the blood and takes from it the carbon dioxide. This system consists of an organ that makes possible rapid diffusion of oxygen from air to blood and of carbon dioxide from blood to air, and of passages for transmitting air to and from this organ. It includes the nasal cavity, the nasal and oral portions of the pharynx, the trachea, the bronchi and the lungs.

The Nasal Cavity. The bony structures forming the lateral walls, septum, floor and roof of the nasal cavity, together with the paranasal or accessory air sinuses, have been described in a previous chapter. Here we need make only a few additions.

The openings of the nasal cavity and the recesses in its lateral walls have been given special names. The anterior openings are called the *nares* or nostrils; the posterior, opening into the nasopharynx, are called the *choanae*[1] (O.T., posterior nares) (Fig. 155). The recesses beneath the superior, middle and inferior conchae are known as the *superior, middle* and *inferior meatuses*[2] respectively (Figs. 154, 32). The space between the superior meatus and the roof of the nasal cavity is called the *sphenoethmoidal recess*. The region of the nasal cavity lying just inside the nostrils is called the *vestibule*.

PRACTICAL CONSIDERATIONS. The common cold, technically called rhinitis, is an inflammation of the lining membrane of the nasal cavity. Hypertrophic rhinitis is a condition in which the mucous membrane over the inferior concha is enlarged and thickened. The excess tissue is sometimes removed by a cautery.

Most of the spontaneous hemorrhages from the nose occur from a group of vessels on the lower and anterior part of the nasal septum.

Inflammation of the paranasal sinuses has already been discussed.

[1] Choanae, plural of *choana,* G., a funnel.
[2] Meatuses, plural of meatus, a passage; from the L. *meare,* to go.

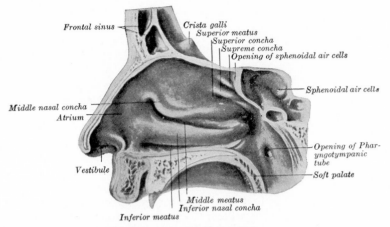

Frontal sinus

Crista galli
Superior meatus
Superior concha
Supreme concha
Opening of sphenoidal air cells

Sphenoidal air cells

Middle nasal concha
Atrium

Opening of Pharyngotympanic tube
Soft palate

Vestibule

Middle meatus
Inferior nasal concha
Inferior meatus

Figure 154. Lateral wall of right nasal cavity. (Callander.)

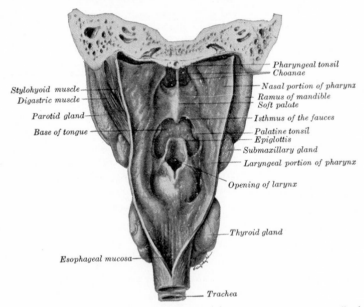

Stylohyoid muscle
Digastric muscle
Parotid gland
Base of tongue

Pharyngeal tonsil
Choanae
Nasal portion of pharynx
Ramus of mandible
Soft palate
Isthmus of the fauces
Palatine tonsil
Epiglottis
Submaxillary gland
Laryngeal portion of pharynx
Opening of larynx

Thyroid gland

Esophageal mucosa

Trachea

Figure 155. Posterior view of the pharynx and esophagus. The posterior wall of the pharynx is opened. (Callander.)

The Nasopharynx. The nasopharynx (Figs. 154, 155, 134) is that portion of the pharynx lying directly behind the nasal cavity. Superiorly it rests against the bones of the skull; posteriorly it rests against the upper cervical vertebrae; inferiorly it continues into the oral part of the pharynx. In each lateral wall is the opening of

Figure 156

The Respiratory System   183

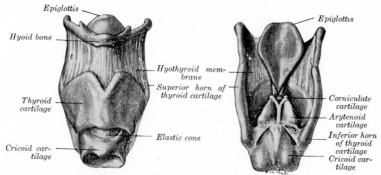

Epiglottis

Hyoid bone

Thyroid cartilage

Cricoid cartilage

Hyothyroid membrane

Superior horn of thyroid cartilage

Elastic cone

Epiglottis

Corniculate cartilage

Arytenoid cartilage

Inferior horn of thyroid cartilage

Cricoid cartilage

Figure 156.   Anterior and posterior views of the laryngeal cartilages, the hyoid, and some of the connecting membranes and ligaments. (Callander.)

the *pharyngotympanic tube* (auditory tube, eustachian[3] tube), which leads into the cavity of the middle ear. Attached to the posterior wall and roof are small accumulations of lymphoid tissue which form the *pharyngeal tonsil.*

PRACTICAL CONSIDERATIONS.   Enlargements of the pharyngeal tonsil are commonly known as "adenoids." When they are large enough to form a serious obstruction to air, the patient, usually a child, becomes a mouth breather, and has a characteristic appearance and expression which has been called the "adenoid facies."

The pharyngotympanic tube admits air to the cavity of the middle ear and thus equalizes the pressure on both sides of the tympanic membrane. It may also serve as a pathway for infection of the middle ear from a cold in the head.

The Oral Part of the Pharynx.   The air passes from the nasopharynx through the oral portion of the pharynx to the larynx. During chewing or sucking, the soft palate and the tongue close the passage from mouth to pharynx so that these operations can go on without interfering with respiration. Respiration is, of course, momentarily interrupted during swallowing.

The Larynx.   The larynx or organ of voice (Figs. 155, 156) lies in the midline of the neck, where it may easily be felt beneath the skin. It is a cylindrical structure which contains as its important element a pair of vocal ligaments or cords which may be set in vibration by the air expired from the lungs.

The outer framework of the larynx consists of the thyroid cartilage, the cricoid cartilage and the hyothyroid membrane. The *thyroid*[4] *cartilage* (Fig. 156) consists of two more or less rectangular plates or *lamina* which meet anteriorly at an angle of about 90 degrees in adult males and 120 degrees in females. In

---

[3] From Bartholommeo Eustachii (1510–1574), professor of anatomy in Rome and one of the founders of the science of human anatomy.

[4] Thyroid: G., shield-shaped.

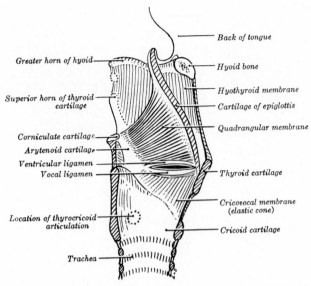

Greater horn of hyoid

Superior horn of thyroid cartilage

Corniculate cartilage
Arytenoid cartilage
Ventricular ligamen
Vocal ligamen

Location of thyrocricoid articulation

Trachea

Back of tongue

Hyoid bone

Hyothyroid membrane

Cartilage of epiglottis

Quadrangular membrane

Thyroid cartilage

Cricovocal membrane (elastic cone)

Cricoid cartilage

Figure 157. Internal view of the cartilages and membranes of the left half of the larynx.

the male the angle is prominent and forms the "Adam's apple." The posterior border of each lamina is prolonged into a *superior* and an *inferior horn.* The superior horn extends toward the end of the greater horn of the hyoid, to which it is attached by a ligament containing a nodule of cartilage. The ligament is the posterior edge of the *hyothyroid membrane,* which attaches the thyroid cartilage to the body and greater horns of the hyoid (Figs. 156, 157).

The *cricoid*[5] *cartilage* is shaped like a signet ring. It lies below the thyroid cartilage in front, while posteriorly its wide "signet" part projects upward between the two lamina. It is the only complete ring of cartilage in the respiratory tract.

The postero-inferior corner of each lamina of the thyroid cartilage articulates by a small synovial joint with the cricoid. This permits the thyroid to rotate up and down like the visor of a helmet.

Wrapped around the outside of the outer framework of the larynx is the *inferior constrictor muscle* shown in Figure 106.

The inner framework of the larynx consists of the arytenoid cartilages, the cartilage of the epiglottis, the quadrangular membrane and the cricovocal membrane. The *arytenoid*[3] *cartilages,* shaped somewhat like small pyramids, but concave on two sides, rest on the posterior part of the cricoid, one on each side of the midline.

---

[5] Cricoid: G., ring-shaped.
[6] Arytenoid: G., like a ladle.

Figure 158   **The Respiratory System** 185

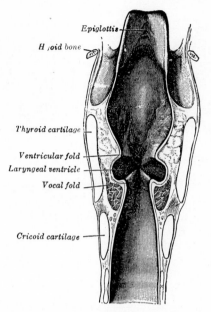

Figure 158. Frontal section through the larynx to show its compartments. (Cunningham's Textbook of Anatomy.)

The unpaired *cartilage of the epiglottis* is shaped like a narrow leaf with its apex directed upward and its stalk attached inferiorly in the angle of the thyroid cartilage (Figs. 156, 157).

From each side of the cartilage of the epiglottis a *quadrangular membrane* extends back to the arytenoid. Its superior edge forms the side of the opening of the larynx (Fig. 155). Its inferior edge is a poorly defined ligament, the *ventricular ligament.*

Extending from the superior edge of the cricoid cartilage into the angle of the thyroid in front, attaching near the stalk of the epiglottis, and to the arytenoid cartilages behind, is the *cricovocal membrane* or *elastic cone* (Figs. 156, 157). Its superior borders, stretching from the angle of the thyroid to the arytenoid on each side, are free, and each consists of a well-defined ligament of yellow elastic fibers. These are the two *vocal ligaments.*

Between the inner and outer framework are the complex intrinsic muscles of the larynx. Mucous membrane lines the inner framework and is continuous above with the pharynx and below with the trachea. The epithelium is stratified over the upper half of the epiglottis, the rim of the opening of the larynx and the vocal ligaments. The rest is ciliated. The *vocal cord* or *vocal fold* consists of the vocal ligament and the closely adherent stratified epithelium.

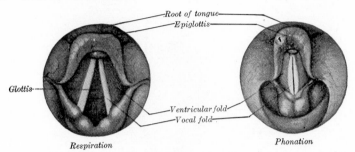

Root of tongue

Epiglottis

Glottis

Ventricular fold

Vocal fold

Respiration

Phonation

Figure 159. The position of the vocal cords during respiration and phonation, as seen from above. (Callander.)

The ventricular ligament and the fold of epithelium over it form the *ventricular fold* or so-called false vocal cord. The mucosa extends laterally between the ventricular and vocal ligaments, where the inner framework is deficient, to form a pouch, the *laryngeal ventricle* (Fig. 158).

MECHANISM OF THE LARYNX.   The changes in the position and tension of the vocal folds are brought about largely by intrinsic muscles which move the arytenoid cartilages. By rotating the arytenoids they hold the vocal folds about 5 mm. apart during normal breathing (Fig. 159) and even farther apart during forced breathing. In speaking and singing, the vocal cords are brought close together so that they vibrate as the air is forced out between them, and they are tensed by swinging the thyroid cartilage down. Fine adjustments are made by muscles parallel to the cords (Fig. 158).

The pitch of the voice is determined by the relative length and tension of the vocal cords. A high note is produced when the cords are short and tense; a low note occurs when they are long and lax. Women as a general rule, have shorter vocal cords than men and have, therefore, voices of higher pitch. The character and quality of the voice depends upon the size and shape of the various resonating chambers in the head, including the pharynx, nose, mouth and accessory sinuses. This is again analogous to a musical instrument in which the quality of tone depends not only on the vibrating mechanism, but also upon the character of the resonance chamber and the sounding boards of the frame.

The larynx produces voice, but not speech. Speech, by which is meant the articulation of vowels and consonants, is dependent upon several mechanisms. Thus the enunciation of the different vowels depends chiefly upon the shape given to the mouth and throat; the various consonants are produced by specific movements and positions of the lips, tongue and other parts.

During the act of swallowing, the larynx is acted upon in two ways: (1) it is elevated as a whole, and (2) its orifice is closed by the approximation of the arytenoid cartilages to the epiglottis. The first is performed by the contraction of some of the muscles of the hyoid bone, the second by the intrinsic muscles of the larynx itself.

PRACTICAL CONSIDERATIONS.   Laryngitis is an inflammation of the mucosa of the larynx. It produces a swelling of the vocal folds, and the voice as a result becomes hoarse. Croup is a condition of spasm of the muscles of the vocal folds. It temporarily closes the glottis and seriously interferes with respiration.

Figure 160   The Respiratory System   187

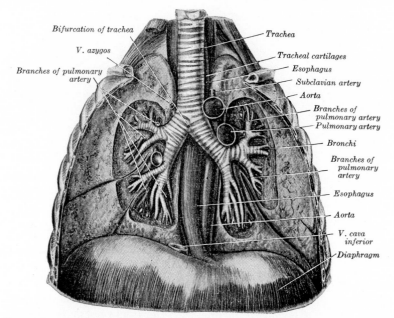

Figure 160. The trachea, bronchi and lungs. Parts of the lungs have been cut away. (Reduced from Warren: Handbook of Anatomy, Harvard University Press.)

The Trachea.   The trachea[7] (Fig. 160) is a tube beginning at the lower end of the larynx and passing into the thorax. It terminates by dividing into right and left primary bronchi. In its walls are a series of cartilaginous rings which keep its cavity open, thus contrasting with the esophagus, which is flattened. The rings are incomplete posteriorly; hence in a cross section of the larynx they appear in the form of a letter **C**.

The mucosa of the trachea contains ciliated epithelium. The cilia beat upward toward the nose and mouth and waft particles of dust entangled in mucus in that direction.

PRACTICAL CONSIDERATIONS.   Tracheotomy, the operation of opening the trachea, is sometimes necessary when obstructions in the throat (from, for example, diphtheria or cancer) prevent air from passing in and out of the lungs by the natural channel. A small tube is inserted into the artificial opening made, and the patient breathes through this until the obstruction has been removed.

The Primary Bronchi.   The primary bronchi (Fig. 160) are two

---

[7] Trachea: G., rough (artery). The term "artery" was originally used for the windpipe or trachea. Later Aristotle included in the term the blood vessels that we now call arteries. The windpipe was then distinguished as the rough artery, the trachea or *arteria aspera;* the blood vessels were called the smooth arteries (Hyrtl).

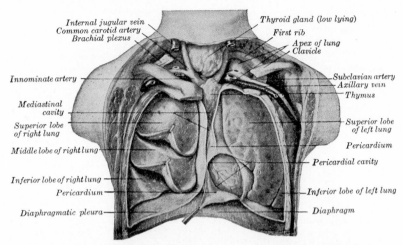

Internal jugular vein
Common carotid artery
Brachial plexus

Thyroid gland (low lying)
First rib
Apex of lung
Clavicle

Innominate artery

Subclavian artery
Axillary vein
Thymus

Mediastinal cavity

Superior lobe of right lung

Superior lobe of left lung

Middle lobe of right lung

Pericardium
Pericardial cavity

Inferior lobe of right lung
Pericardium
Diaphragmatic pleura

Inferior lobe of left lung

Diaphragm

Figure 161. Lungs and their relations to the pleurae and mediastinum. (Callander.)

large tubes which begin at the lower end of the trachea and pass into the lungs. The right bronchus is larger than the left and passes down more nearly in line with the trachea. For this reason objects taken into the lungs by children, such as safety pins, coins and buttons, usually find their way into the right side. The further course of the bronchi will be described later.

The Thoracic Cavity as a Whole.   The thoracic cavity is divided into two lateral chambers by a thick median septum, the *mediastinal septum* or *mediastinum*.[8] The lateral chambers contain the lungs. The mediastinum contains the heart, the great blood vessels, the esophagus, the terminal portion of the trachea, the beginnings of the primary bronchi, and the like. The *mediastinal cavity* (Figs. 161, 162, 163) is not a cavity like the pleural cavities; it is the space occupied by organs and connective tissue.

The Lungs.   The lungs (Figs. 160, 161) are cone-shaped organs which entirely fill the pleural cavities in which they lie. They rest with their bases on the diaphragm and their apices projecting a short distance above the level of the clavicles. Their anterior, lateral and posterior surfaces are convex and lie against the inner surface of the thoracic wall. Their mesial surfaces are concave and are indented by the structures of the mediastinum, particularly the heart. Since the heart extends more to the left than to the right, the left lung is the more indented.

Each lung has two borders, one anterior, the other posterior. The posterior border is rounded and ill defined; the anterior border is

---

[8] Mediastinum: Medieval Latin, medial, intermediate.

thin and sharp. *In situ* the anterior borders of the two lungs almost reach the midline from the second to the fourth costal cartilages. Lower down they diverge to the right and left to make room for the heart. The notch so formed is greater on the left.

The lungs are subdivided by deep fissures into a number of lobes. Of these, two are on the left and three are on the right. In the left lung the *interlobar fissure* arises on the posterior surface a short distance below the apex, and passes downward and forward to terminate near the junction of the base with the anterior margin. Above it lies the *superior lobe;* below it, the *inferior lobe.* The superior lobe fills up most of the anterior aspect of the lung; the inferior lobe the posterior (Figs. 161, 164).

In the right lung are two interlobar fissures: an oblique fissure similar to that just described for the left lung, and a horizontal fissure running across the anterior surface at about the level of the fourth rib. In this lung, therefore, there are three lobes: superior, middle and inferior. The middle lobe is the smallest of the three.

The larger bronchi and the main vessels enter and leave the lung on its medial surface. They are bound together with connective tissue and form a mass known as the *root of the lung.* Each root contains one primary bronchus, one pulmonary artery and two pulmonary veins.

The surface of the lung is covered by a serous membrane known as the *pleura.* It encloses the root of the lung and is reflected onto the lateral aspect of the mediastinum, the diaphragm and the thoracic wall. The portion on the lung itself is known as the *pulmonary pleura;* the remainder is called the *parietal pleura.* Since the lung fills the cavity in which it lies, the two portions of the pleura are in contact with each other. The potential space between them is called the *pleural cavity.*

The lungs contain a good deal of elastic tissue and, if permitted to do so, will contract to a size much smaller than the thoracic cavity they occupy. They fill the thoracic cavity only because the pleural cavity contains no air and is closed. If air is admitted by puncture of the thoracic wall, a condition called *pneumothorax,* the lung immediately contracts and enlargement of the thorax no longer draws air into the lung. If this happens on both sides at once, it is, of course, fatal. In tuberculosis one lung is sometimes collapsed in this way by the surgeon. The inactive lung heals faster. The air is gradually resorbed by the pleura and function of the lung re-established.

TOPOGRAPHIC MARKINGS OF THE LUNGS AND PLEURA. The topographic or surface projections of the lungs and pleura on the external thoracic wall (Fig. 164) are often of great importance. The apices of the lungs lie at the level of the first rib posteriorily, or at a point on the anterior aspect of the body about 1½ inches

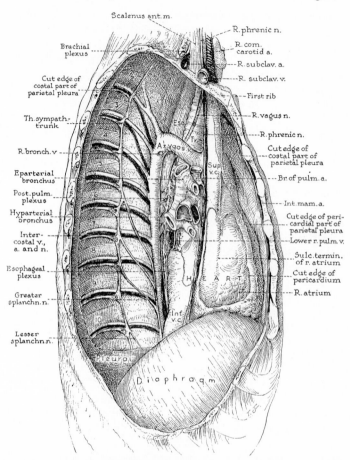

Scalenus ant. m.

Brachial plexus

Cut edge of costal part of parietal pleura

Th. sympath.- trunk

R. bronch. v.

Eparterial bronchus

Post. pulm. plexus

Hyparterial bronchus

Inter- costal v., a. and n.

Esophageal plexus

Greater splanchn. n.

Lesser splanchn. n.

R. phrenic n.

R. com. carotid a.

R. subclav. a.

R. subclav. v.

First rib

R. vagus n.

R. phrenic n.

Cut edge of costal part of parietal pleura

Br. of pulm. a.

Int. mam. a.

Cut edge of peri- cardial part of parietal pleura

Lower r. pulm. v.

Sulc. termin. of r. atrium

Cut edge of pericardium

R. atrium

Figure 162. The right thorax, showing mediastinal septum. The costal and mediastinal parts of the pleura have been removed and the pericardium partly dissected away, exposing the heart. (After Cunningham, Jones and Shepard: Manual of Surgical Anatomy.)

above the clavicle. The anterior borders of the lungs and pleurae, when traced downward, meet in the midline behind the sternum at the level of the second costal cartilage. They remain together as far as the fourth rib, where they diverge. The right continues more or less straight down as far as the sixth costal cartilage, while the left diverges laterally to make room for the heart.

The lower borders are marked by their position on vertical lines dropped from the midpoint of the clavicle (the midclavicular line), the midpoint of the axilla or armpit (the midaxillary line) and the spinous processes of the vertebrae. The pleura reaches the eighth rib in the midclavicular line, the tenth rib in the midaxillary line and the twelfth thoracic spine posteriorly. The lungs themselves do not extend so far downward and terminate about two ribs above the limits of the pleurae. The lowest portions of both lungs and pleurae are in the midaxillary

Figure 163 **The Respiratory System** 191

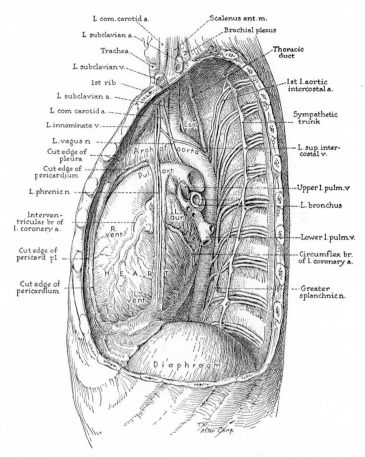

Figure 163. The left thorax, showing mediastinal septum. The costal and mediastinal parts of the pleura have been removed and the pericardium party dissected away, exposing the heart. (After Cunningham, Jones and Shepard: Manual of Surgical Anatomy.)

line, for on account of the obliquity of the ribs, the tenth rib in the midaxillary line is lower than the twelfth thoracic spine posteriorly.

The Internal Structure of the Lungs. The *primary bronchi* divide after entering the lung into a number of branches or *secondary bronchi* (Fig. 160). These in turn divide into smaller branches, the smaller ones divide again, and so on until a complicated bronchial tree is formed. The smaller branches are called *bronchioles;* the terminal ones, *respiratory bronchioles*.

The respiratory bronchioles give off a number of branches called *alveolar ducts* (Fig. 165), from which arise single *alveoli* and

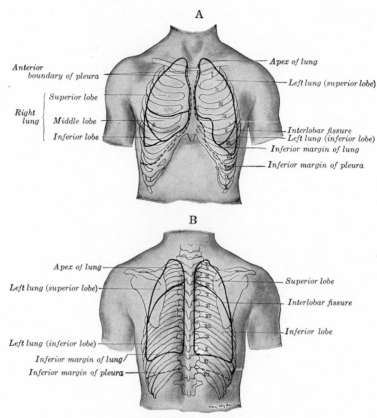

A

B

Figure 164. Borders of the pleurae and lungs in anterior and posterior views. (Callander.)

alveolar sacs containing several alveoli. An alveolus is a small pocket about 0.25 mm. in diameter. Its thin wall, through which the actual exchange of gases between air and blood takes place, consists of a fine network of small blood vessels (capillaries) supported by connective tissue. No typical epithelium lines it; at most there are thin non-nucleated plates whose nature and existence are still matters for debate. At any rate, the tissue through which oxygen and carbon dioxide must pass is reduced to a minimum. It has been estimated that the blood capillaries available for respiration have a total surface area of about 140 square meters (equal to a plot about 40 feet square). Only about 20 per cent of this is utilized under ordinary circumstances, so that there is a large margin available.

In a microscopic section of the lung (Fig. 165) an irregular meshwork formed by large numbers of alveolar ducts, alveolar sacs

Figure 165   *The Respiratory System*   193

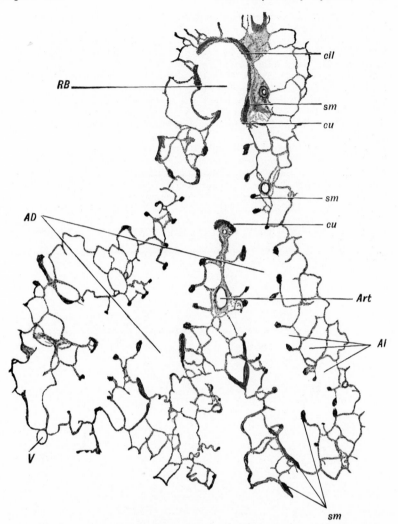

RB

AD

V

cil

sm

cu

sm

cu

Art

Al

sm

Figure 165. Section through a respiratory bronchiole (RB) and two alveolar ducts (AD) of a human lung, showing the smooth muscles, *sm* (in black), in the wall of the alveolar ducts; *cil*, ciliated epithelium; *cu*, cuboidal epithelium; *Art*, arteriole; *Al*, alveolar sacs; V, vein. (From Maximow and Bloom, redrawn and slightly modified after Baltisberger.)

and alveoli is seen. Scattered throughout are the thicker-walled bronchi and bronchioles, and the branches of the pulmonary arteries and veins. The capillaries are not readily seen in the ordinary preparations, but by special technics they can be easily demonstrated.

RESPIRATION.   In the act of respiration a transference of gases takes place between the blood in the pulmonary capillaries and the air inside the alveoli. The air and blood are separated by only the two thin membranes which form the walls of their respective containers. Oxygen passes from the air to the blood, and carbon dioxide passes in the reverse direction.

PRACTICAL CONSIDERATIONS.   Pneumonia is an inflammation of the alveoli of the lung. The inflammatory products fill up these terminal chambers so that the portion of the lung involved becomes practically solid. In lobar pneumonia a whole lobe is involved; in bronchopneumonia the disease is diffusely scattered throughout both lungs. Bronchitis is an inflammation of the lining mucosa of the bronchi.

In pulmonary tuberculosis the disease process may affect the alveoli, the bronchi or both. Large numbers of small round masses or tubercles are produced which give the disease its name. The tubercles increase in number, coalesce, and often break down in the center, forming large cavities. A severe hemorrhage from the lung is due to the disease process invading and opening up a large vessel.

Pleurisy is an inflammation of the pleural membranes. Two types are recognized, known popularly as the dry and the wet varieties. In the wet type a variable amount of watery fluid is secreted into the pleural cavity which presses on and interferes with the expansion of the lung. Empyema is a pleurisy associated with the formation of pus.

CHAPTER 9

THE URINARY SYSTEM

THE URINARY system has two functions to perform: (1) to excrete wastes, (2) to help regulate the composition of the blood.

Carbon dioxide, one of the chief products of metabolism, is volatile and passes out of the body by way of the lungs. Other waste products, mostly compounds containing nitrogen, such as urea, uric acid and creatinine, are not volatile and must be carried out of the body in solution. This the urinary system does.

The composition of the blood cannot be allowed to vary beyond narrow limits lest the conditions within the tissues necessary for the life of the cells be lost. Regulation of the composition of the blood involves not only the removal of harmful waste products, but the conservation or excretion, as conditions demand, of such normal constituents as water, sugar and salts. In this the kidney plays an important part.

The urinary system (Fig. 166) consists of (1) two large glands, called the *kidneys,* which excrete urine; (2) the ducts leading from them, the *ureters;* (3) a large urinary reservoir, the *bladder;* and (4) the tube leading from it to the surface of the body, the *urethra.* The parts are essentially the same in both sexes with the exception of the urethra.

The Kidney. The kidney[1] (Fig. 167) lies on the posterior abdominal wall opposite the last thoracic and the first three lumbar vertebrae and behind the peritoneum. Its shape, that of an elongated oval with a notch taken out of one side, is so well known as to give rise to a descriptive term, "kidney-shaped." The region of the notch is called the *hilum,*[2] and here the ureter and blood vessels enter and leave the organ. The surface of the kidney is relatively

---

[1] Kidney, renal. Kidney is an English term of uncertain origin. The Latin term for kidney is *ren,* from which the adjective renal, pertaining to the kidneys, is derived.

[2] Hilum or hilus: L., a little thing, a trifle; used originally to designate the mark or scar on the concave edge of a bean; later applied to similar regions in the kidney, spleen and lymph nodes.

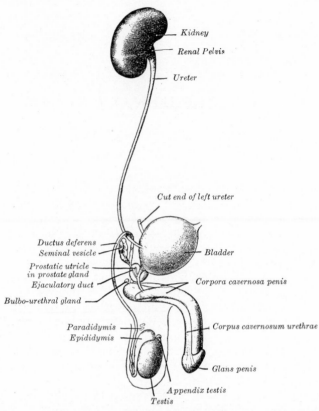

Figure 166. Diagram of the urinary and reproductive systems of the male. The right kidney and ureter only are shown. (Sobotta and McMurrich.)

smooth and is covered with a thin membrane of connective tissue called the *capsule.* In position the hilus faces medially, and the whole organ is surrounded and kept in place by a certain amount of *perirenal fat.*

If a kidney is sectioned longitudinally (Fig. 167) and the ureter followed inward, it will be found to open up into a large cavity called the *renal pelvis.* From the pelvis a number of large branches called *calices* are given off which project still further into the kidney substance. Into their ends project a number of cone-like elevations or *papillae.*

The solid substance of the kidney can be differentiated into two portions, an outer, more or less homogeneous layer, the *cortex,*[3] and an inner portion, the *medulla.* The medulla is made up of a number

---

[3] *Cortex:* L., bark.

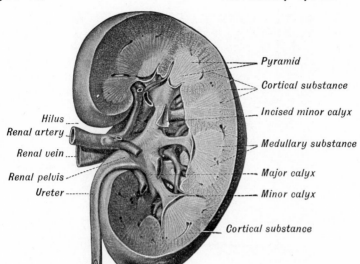

Figure 167. The interior of the kidney, seen from behind after removal of a part of the organ. (After Braus.)

of *pyramids,* perhaps twelve or fifteen, the bases of which are directed toward the cortex, while the apices form the papillae which project into the renal calices as already noted. In the pyramids a large number of fine lines may sometimes be seen radiating from the apex to the base. They represent the larger tubules of the gland.

MICROSCOPIC. In a microscopic section of the kidney (Fig. 168) there are three main elements: (1) tubules, (2) blood vessels, and (3) renal corpuscles. The tubules make up the greater part of the solid substance of the gland and run for the most part parallel to one another along lines drawn from the apices of the pyramids to the periphery of the organ. The blood vessels lie scattered between the tubules. The *renal corpuscles* are small round bodies which lie scattered throughout the cortex. Each consists of the expanded upper end of a renal tubule into which is invaginated a little ball of capillary blood vessels. The ball of vessels is called the *glomerulus,*[4] the surrounding part of the tubule, the *glomerular capsule* (Fig. 169).

Each *renal* or *uriniferous tubule* takes a complicated course throughout the kidney (Fig. 169). On leaving the renal corpuscle it becomes constricted into a neck and then widens out into a larger duct which takes several turns near its origin (the *proximal con-*

---

[4] Glomerulus: L., a little ball.

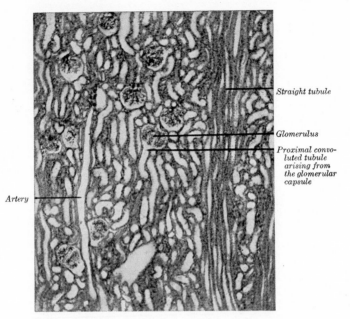

Straight tubule

Glomerulus

Proximal convo-
luted tubule
arising from
the glomerular
capsule

Artery

Figure 168.   Section of the cortex of the kidney. X 50. (Maximow and Bloom.)

voluted portion) and then descends toward the apex of the pyra- · mid (the *descending limb of Henle*[5]). Before reaching the apex, however, it turns sharply and retraces its way toward the cortex again (the *ascending limb of Henle*). Once more it goes through a number of turns or convolutions (*distal convoluted portion*), and it then opens along with a number of other tubules into a larger duct called the *collecting tubule.* This last pursues a more or less straight course toward the apex of the pyramid again. On the way down, several collecting tubules coalesce until finally a relatively small number of still larger ducts open into the renal calices. The ever-present connective tissue forms the supporting substance of the kidney.

The capillary blood vessels that constitute a glomerulus are supplied by a small artery (arteriole) (Fig. 169). A small vein conveys the blood away from the glomerulus to the capillaries that surround the renal tubule throughout its length. From these capillaries the blood is carried away by a second small vein.

The functional unit of the kidney consists of a renal corpuscle and a renal tubule. There are nearly a million of these units in each human kidney.

---

[5] After Friedrich Gustav Jakob Henle (1809–1885), one of the best known of the nineteenth century German histologists.

Figure 169   **The Urinary System**   199

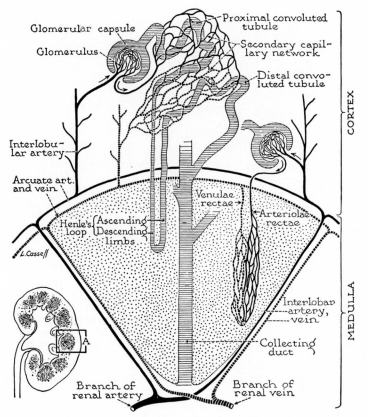

Figure 169. Diagram of a renal tubule and its blood circulation. Inset A indicates the location of the region shown. The arteriolae rectae supply the collecting ducts and the loops of Henle. (From Millard and King: Human Anatomy and Physiology. 3rd edition.)

MECHANISM OF THE KIDNEY.   Because of the small size of the corpuscles and tubules and their inaccessibility within the substance of the kidney, it has been difficult to work out the details of their physiology. It is now well established, however, that they operate as follows: The blood in the glomerulus is under high pressure, and the renal corpuscle acts as a filter. Some of the fluid part of the blood, with its dissolved substances, passes through the wall of the blood capillary and the epithelium of the capsule into the lumen of the latter. Unable to penetrate the filter and therefore held back in the blood are the blood cells, droplets of fat and large molecules such as protein. The filtrate in the lumen of the capsule contains all the other constituents of the blood in about the same concentration as they were before filtration. As the filtrate passes down the renal tubule, epithelial cells of the tubules take certain substances out of the urine and put them back into the blood. The result is that nearly all the waste substances are removed from the blood, while the useful and necessary constituents are adjusted to their optimum concentrations. Thus, if the concentration of sugar in the blood is too high (usually due to malfunction of the islands of Langerhans

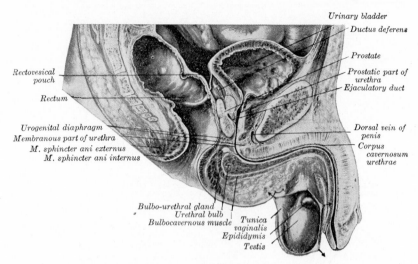

Figure 170. Sagittal section through the male pelvis, perineum and external genitalia.
(After Wesson.)

in the pancreas), some will be excreted, though normally it is all put back into the blood and none appears in the urine. Again, if there is too much water in the blood, less than usual is put back and the urine is more copious and less concentrated. The energy for filtration is supplied by the heart, which maintains the necessary pressure. The energy for concentrating the urine and for pulling substances out of it is doubtless developed by the epithelium of the tubules. The mechanism here is not understood, but the kidney uses oxygen at a high rate to accomplish its work.

The final product, urine, is poured into the renal pelvis, from which it is passed to the ureter and bladder.

PRACTICAL CONSIDERATIONS. Inflammation of the substance of the kidney is known as nephritis or Bright's disease. The corpuscles and tubules may be chiefly affected (parenchymatous nephritis), or the supporting tissue may receive the main damage (interstitial nephritis). Nephritis is a serious condition, for it interferes with the excretion of the poisonous waste products of the body. Tuberculosis of the kidney is not infrequent. If only one kidney is involved, it may be removed, but if both are attacked, little can be done.

Inflammation of the renal pelvis is called pyelitis. Stones may form in this cavity as they do in the gallbladder and cause severe pain. A "movable kidney" is one which has lost its firm attachment to the posterior abdominal wall.

The Ureter. The ureter (Fig. 203) is a tube of small diameter which leads from the renal pelvis to the urinary bladder, a distance of about 10 inches. It descends on the posterior abdominal wall and then crosses the floor of the pelvis to its termination. Like the kidney, it lies in the connective tissue behind the peritoneum. Its walls contain nonstriated muscle and a lining of epithelium.

The Urinary Bladder. The urinary bladder (Fig. 170) is a large muscular bag which lies in the pelvis behind the pubic bones. It has three openings, all on the floor of the organ: one anteriorly for the urethra, two posteriorly and laterally for the ureters. The triangular area marked out by the three orifices is called the *trigone*.

The interior of the bladder is lined with a membrane which is smooth when the organ is full and distended, and thrown into folds when it is empty and collapsed. Its external surface is covered with peritoneum on its superior aspect only. Elsewhere it is bound to the neighboring structures by connective tissue. The bladder capacity of the adult varies normally from about 8 fluid ounces to over a quart.

Microscopically, the mucosa of the bladder (and also of the ureter and renal pelvis) is composed of a special type of epithelium known as *transitional epithelium*. It is remarkable for its elasticity. In the contracted state several layers of polygonal cells are found; in the state of extreme distention the number of layers is reduced and the individual cells are seen to be stretched laterally and flattened from above downward.

The muscularis of the bladder is composed of smooth muscle and is quite strong. It consists of three not distinctly separate layers: an outer and inner longitudinal layer and a circular or spiral middle layer.

MECHANISM OF THE BLADDER. The muscularis relaxes as the bladder fills, maintaining a constant slight pressure until a certain point is reached, when the stretching of the muscle fibers acts as a stimulus and rhythmic contractions begin, accompanied by painful sensations. When the sphincters of the urethra, which are under voluntary control, are relaxed and the bladder is emptied, the muscle contracts to reduce the size of the organ. The ability to maintain constant tension over long periods and at different lengths is characteristic of smooth muscle.

The Urethra. The urethra is a tube passing from the anterior and inferior aspects of the urinary bladder to the external surface of the body. It is different in character in the two sexes.

The urethra of the female (Fig. 181) is from 1 to $1\frac{1}{2}$ inches in length. It lies behind the symphysis pubis and in front of the vagina. Close to its entrance into the bladder the circular muscle in its wall forms an *internal sphincter,* while at a lower level the surrounding muscle forms an *external sphincter.*

The urethra of the male (Fig. 170) is about 8 inches long, and consists of three portions called the prostatic, the membranous and the cavernous urethras. The *prostatic urethra* lies next to the bladder and is about 1 inch in length. It is surrounded by a small organ, the prostate, from which it receives its name. Two small ducts belonging to the generative system, the ejaculatory ducts, open into it on its posterior aspect. Between these openings is a small elevation or crest, the *urethral crest,* which contains a tiny recess, the *prostatic utricle,* which receives the ducts from the prostate gland. The utricle is the homologue of the uterus of the female. An *internal sphincter* is found in this part of the urethra.

The *membranous urethra,* the second part of the tube, is about ½ inch in length and is the narrowest part of the whole urethra. It lies between two fibrous sheets, the superior and inferior layers of the *urogenital diaphragm,* which stretch across the triangular space between the descending pubic rami. The *external sphincter* surrounds the urethra here.

The *cavernous urethra* is the longest of the three parts, and takes its name from the fact that it lies in that part of the penis known as the corpus cavernosum. Opening into it are a number of glands, the largest of which are the two *bulbo-urethral glands.* They lie between the two layers of the urogenital diaphragm and open into the cavernous urethra near its origin.

The urethral canal as a whole passes first downward, then forward, and finally, in the flaccid state of the penis, downward again.

CHAPTER 10

THE REPRODUCTIVE
SYSTEM OF THE MALE

THE REPRODUCTIVE system of the male (Fig. 166) consists of the following: (1) two glands called the testes, which produce the spermatozoa and a hormone (p. 366); (2) a system of ducts which convey the spermatozoa to the urethra; (3) a number of accessory glands which secrete fluid; and (4) an organ of copulation, the penis.

The Testis and Epididymis. Each testis[1] (Figs. 166, 170, 171) is an oval body, about 1½ inches in length, which lies suspended from the under surface of the body in the scrotum. It lies with its long axis directed vertically and its flattened sides facing laterally. Attached to it and differentiated from it by a groove is the *epididymis*.[2] The epididymis has a large upper pole or head which lies on the upper border of the testis, and a smaller body and tail which descend on its posterior border. A thick-walled tube, the *ductus deferens*[3] (O.T., vas deferens) (Fig. 171), leaves the lower pole of the epididymis to ascend in the scrotum to the inguinal canal.

There is a cavity in each half of the scrotum which is a detached portion of the peritoneal cavity, as will be explained later. It is lined with a serous membrane, the *tunica vaginalis*, which is reflected onto the testis and epididymis along their posterior borders. Here the arteries enter and the veins leave the organ. The arteries are small and few; the veins, on the other hand, are large and tortuous and form a thick plexus, the *pampiniform*[4] *plexus* (Fig. 171), which passes upward with the ductus deferens into the inguinal canal.

If a testis be cut open (Fig. 172), it will be found to contain, under the tunica vaginalis, a tough fibrous coat called the *tunica*

---

[1] *Testis,* plural *testes,* L.

[2] *Epididymis:* G., upon the testis.

[3] *Deferens:* L., carrying or conducting away.

[4] Pampiniform: L., tendril-like.

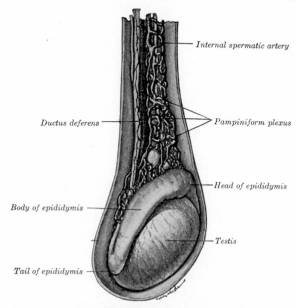

Internal spermatic artery

Ductus deferens

Pampiniform plexus

Head of epididymis

Body of epididymis

Testis

Tail of epididymis

Figure 171. Lateral view of right spermatic cord and testicle. (Callander.)

albuginea.[5] In addition, a number of connective tissue septa divide the organ into a number of compartments. Each compartment contains a small convoluted tubule less than 0.25 mm. in diameter, the *seminiferous tubule,* which passes backward toward the posterior aspect of the testis. The tubules unite to form a plexus, from the upper end of which a number of ducts are given off to enter the head of the epididymis. These ducts in turn unite to form the single duct of the epididymis, which, after much coiling, eventually reaches the lower pole of the organ and becomes the ductus deferens. The duct of the epididymis is so tortuous that when unravelled it has the length of 18 to 20 feet.

MICROSCOPIC.   The epithelium of the seminiferous tubules (Fig. 173) contains two chief types of cells: germinal cells and sustentacular cells.

The *germinal* or *spermatogenic cells* are arranged around the tubule several layers deep. In the outermost layer, which lies against the periphery of the tubule, are large round cells called *spermatogonia.* All the others are derived from them by a method of modified mitosis. The intermediate cells are formed directly from those on the periphery, the more centrally placed cells are derived from the intermediate group, and so on. The final product,

---

[5] Albuginea: L., from *albus,* white.

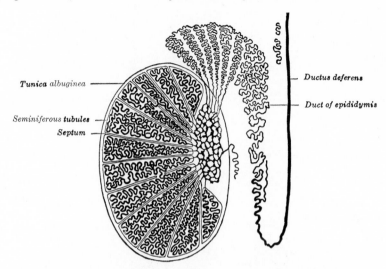

Tunica *albuginea* ⸺

Seminiferous *tubules* ⸺
Septum ⸺

⸺ *Ductus deferens*

⸺ *Duct of epididymis*

Figure 172.   Diagram of the arrangement of the seminiferous tubules and the excretory ducts in the testis and epididymis. (Maximow and Bloom.)

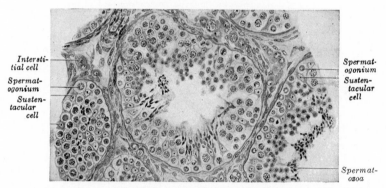

Intersti-
tial cell

Spermat-
ogonium

Susten-
tacular
cell

Spermat-
ogonium

Susten-
tacular
cell

Spermat-
ozoa

Figure 173.   Seminiferous tubules in cross section. × 170. (Maximow and Bloom.)

which lies most internally, is the mature sperm[6] cell, the *spermatozoon*[7] (Fig. 174, *F*). The shape of this cell is highly characteristic: it has a head, a middle piece and a tail. The *head* is oval as seen from the top or bottom and flattened as seen from the side. It consists almost entirely of the nucleus. The *middle piece* is slender and contains a spiral filament. The *tail* is long and whip-like. By its lashing back and forth the spermatozoon swims about. The head is 4 to 5 microns in length, and the tail about 52 microns.

---

[6] Sperm: G., seed.

[7] Spermatozoon: G., seed, plus living thing, animal.

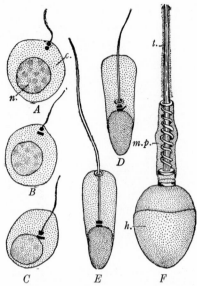

Figure 174. Diagram showing several stages in the development of the spermatozoon. c, Cytoplasm; h, head; m.p., middle piece; n, nucleus; t, tail. (After Meves in Lewis and Stohr.)

The *sustentacular cells* (or the cells of Sertoli[8]) (Fig. 173) are tall, pillar-like elements of irregular shape which rest against the periphery of the tubule. They give support to the more centrally placed spermatogenic cells.

A small amount of connective tissue, the *interstitial tissue*, lies between the seminiferous tubules. It contains the interstitial cells (Fig. 173) which probably produce the hormone that the testis secretes into the blood.

The Ductus Deferens and the Spermatic Cord. The *ductus deferens* (O.T., vas deferens) (Figs. 166, 171, 176) is a long narrow tube which begins as the continuation of the duct of the epididymis. It ascends in the posterior part of the scrotum to the groin and then passes through the inguinal canal (p. 119). It enters the abdominal cavity and, after passing to the under surface of the bladder, ends by uniting with the duct of the seminal vesicle to form the ejaculatory duct. In its wall is a thick layer of muscle.

The *spermatic cord* (Figs. 95, 171) consists of the ductus deferens and all the arteries, veins and nerves which pass along with it from the abdominal wall to the testis and epididymis. Surrounding it are three thin coverings: two membranes and one muscular layer.

---

[8] Enrico Sertoli (1842–1910), Italian physiologist.

Figure 175   **The Reproductive System of the Male**   207

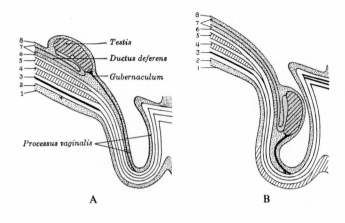

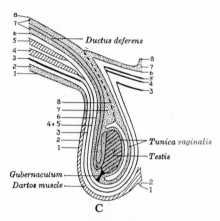

Figure 175. Diagrams illustrating the descent of the testis and the origin of the tunica vaginalis and the other layers of the scrotum and of the sheaths of the spermatic cord. Blood vessels and nerves of the spermatic cord have been omitted.

Layers of the Abdominal Wall	Layers of the Scrotal Wall
1. Skin	1. Skin
2. Superficial fascia	2. Dartos muscle
3. Aponeurosis of external oblique muscle	3. External spermatic fascia
4. Internal oblique muscle	4 & 5. Cremasteric muscle
5. Transversus muscle	
6. Fascia transversalis	6. Internal spermatic fascia
7. Extra-peritoneal tissue	7. Loose connective tissue
8. Peritoneum	8. Tunica vaginalis

(In part from Grant: Method of Anatomy.)

In order to understand the structure of the scrotum and its cavities and the sheaths of the spermatic cords, it is necessary to follow the development of these parts (Fig. 175). In the fetus an outpocketing of the peritoneum, called the *processus vaginalis,* pushes obliquely through the abdominal wall on each side of the midline, just superior to the inguinal ligament. In so doing it carries the various layers of the abdominal wall before it. The opening it makes through the abdominal wall is the inguinal canal.

The testis, meanwhile, has developed in the tissue outside the peritoneum on the posterior wall of the abdominal cavity. From it the *gubernaculum,* a long strand of fibrous tissue with some smooth muscle, extends down to the bottom of the scrotum. Now the testis begins to descend, moving through the connective tissue beneath the peritoneum, apparently guided, and perhaps pulled, by the gubernaculum. It moves across the wall of the pelvis and through the inguinal canal *beside* the processus vaginalis and finally lodges in the bottom of the scrotum. In descending, it has dragged after it its duct, blood vessels and nerves. These now form the spermatic cord. The gubernaculum atrophies.

The proximal part of the processus vaginalis now closes, shutting off the cavity in the scrotum from the peritoneal cavity in the abdomen. (In some lower mammals this passage remains open throughout life.) The peritoneum lining the cavity in the scrotum is the tunica vaginalis mentioned earlier. Sometimes a fibrous strand can be found in the spermatic cord which is the obliterated part of the processus vaginalis.

The external oblique is aponeurotic at the inguinal canal, and its aponeurosis is represented in the sheath of the spermatic cord and in the scrotum as the external spermatic fascia. Internal to this is the *cremasteric*[9] *muscle* (Fig. 95), a thin, incomplete layer, partly fascial, representing the internal oblique and the transversus. Under certain physiologic conditions, such as cold, or in response to stimuli on the skin, the cremasteric pulls up the testis. On the inner side of the muscle is the internal spermatic fascia, an extension of the fascia transversalis. This fascia surrounds the loose connective tissue in which the spermatic cord lies.

The skin and superficial fascia form an unpaired sac, the scrotum, within which lie the two testes and the two cavities. In the superficial fascia there appear smooth muscle fibers forming the *dartos muscle,* which wrinkles the skin and helps support the testes.

PRACTICAL CONSIDERATIONS. The inguinal canal is of considerable importance because it is frequently the site of hernia. A hernia is the protrusion of some part of the abdominal viscera, usually the intestine, into some abnormal region. The intestine may pass through the inguinal canal and into the scrotum, in which

---

[9] Cremasteric, from a Greek verb meaning to hang.

Figure 176   **The Reproductive System of the Male   209**

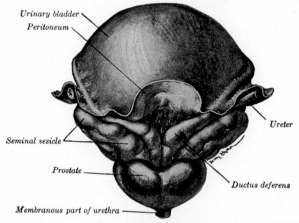

Urinary bladder
Peritoneum

Ureter

Seminal vesicle

Prostate

Ductus deferens

Membranous part of urethra

Figure 176. Posterior view of the bladder and male pelvic genitalia. (Callander.)

case it is known as an oblique inguinal hernia; or it may protrude directly forward above the medial part of the inguinal ligament without passing through the canal, when it is known as direct inguinal hernia. Other sites of hernia are in the thigh just below the inguinal ligament (femoral hernia), or between the rectus abdominis muscles in the region of the umbilicus (umbilical hernia).

The Seminal Vesicles and the Ejaculatory Ducts. The *seminal vesicles* (Figs. 166, 176) are two elongated, sac-like structures lying on the posterior and inferior aspects of the bladder. Internally, each consists of a tortuously bent tube from the sides of which project several small branches or diverticula. Its lower end forms a duct which unites with the ductus deferns to form the ejaculatory duct.

FUNCTION. The function of the seminal vesicles is to secrete a fluid which is added to the material coming from the testis and epididymis during ejaculation. They are probably not reservoirs for semen as was once thought.

The *ejaculatory ducts* (Figs. 166, 170), two in number, are short tubes which arise from the union of the ductus deferens and the duct of the seminal vesicle. They traverse the prostate and open into the floor of the urethra by the side of the urethral crest.

The Prostate and the Bulbo-urethral Glands. The *prostate*[10] (Figs. 170, 176) is a glandular organ, about 1 by ¾ inch in size, which surrounds the first part of the urethra. It has a base which lies in contact with the under surface of the bladder, and an apex which points downward toward the superior layer of the urogenital diaphragm. It is enclosed in a fibrous capsule and is traversed by the two ejaculatory ducts on their way to the urethra.

---

[10] Prostate, from G., one who stands before. The prostate lies in front of the seminal vesicles.

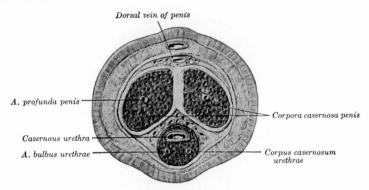

Dorsal vein of penis

A. profunda penis

Corpora cavernosa penis

Cavernous urethra

A. bulbus urethrae

Corpus cavernosum urethrae

Figure 177. Cross section of penis. (Callander.)

Microscopically, the prostate contains a number of small branched glands, a large amount of connective tissue, and some smooth muscle. The glands open into the floor of the prostatic urethra.

The *bulbo-urethral glands* are two small glands about the size of peas. They lie between the two layers of the urogenital diaphragm and open into the cavernous urethra near its origin.

The Penis. The penis consists of three long cylindrical masses (Figs. 170, 177) composed of a special kind of tissue called erectile tissue. Two of the masses, called the *corpora cavernosa penis,*[11] lie on the dorsal or upper part of the organ. The third, the *corpus cavernosum urethrae,* lies below the other two and is traversed by the urethra. The three are bound together with connective tissue and are covered with skin.

Each corpus cavernosum penis is prolonged backward to be attached to the descending ramus of the pubis. The corpus cavernosum urethrae is prolonged backward on the inferior layer of the urogenital diaphragm to the place where the urethra pierces it. The backward extension is known as the *urethral bulb* or *bulb of the penis* (Fig. 170). The anterior end is expanded into the smooth, cone-like tip of the organ, the *glans penis.* The fold of skin lying over the glans is called the *prepuce.*

Covering each of the three backward extensions of the penis is a small muscle (Fig. 178). The *bulbocavernosus muscle* lies over the urethral bulb; the *ischiocavernosus muscles* lie over the other two parts. The first by its contraction expels the urine and seminal fluid from the urethra; the second prevents the return of the blood from the veins of the penis, and thereby assists in making the organ erect and turgid during sexual excitement.

---

[11] *Corpora,* plural of *corpus:* L., body. Corpora cavernosa penis: the cavernous bodies of the penis.

Figure 178   **The Reproductive System of the Male**   211

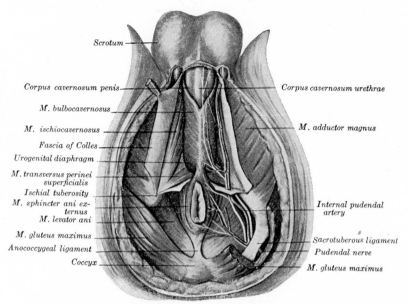

Scrotum

Corpus cavernosum penis

M. bulbocavernosus

M. ischiocavernosus

Fascia of Colles

Urogenital diaphragm

M. transversus perinei
superficialis

Ischial tuberosity

M. sphincter ani ex-
ternus

M. levator ani

M. gluteus maximus

Anococcygeal ligament

Coccyx

Corpus cavernosum urethrae

M. adductor magnus

Internal pudendal
artery

Sacrotuberous ligament

Pudendal nerve

M. gluteus maximus

Figure 178.   Superficial structures of the male perineum. (Callander.)

Microscopically, the erectile tissue of the penis is sponge-like and contains numerous spaces of varying size and shape. These spaces, called *cavernous spaces,* are directly connected with the blood vessels of the organ. In the flaccid state of the penis the spaces are collapsed and contain little blood; in the erect state they are enlarged and filled.

THE MECHANISM OF THE MALE GENERATIVE SYSTEM.   We can now review the mechanism of the male reproductive system as a whole. The spermatozoa are formed in the testes and make their way through its tubules into the duct of the epididymis. During sexual excitement the penis is erected, enlarged and made firm by an accumulation of blood within its cavernous spaces. This is brought about partly by an active dilatation of the arteries which brings more blood to the organ, and partly by a mechanism which slows down the return of the blood through the veins. Two factors go to produce this last: (1) a constriction of the ischiocavernous and bulbocavernous muscles, and (2) a peculiar valve-like arrangement in the veins which permits the blood to pass through them only in small amounts. Ejaculation is produced by rhythmic contraction of the muscles of the ductus deferens and the bulbocavernosus muscle. The fluid secretions of the seminal vesicles and prostate are added to the mass of sperm cells as they pass along. The alkaline secretions of the prostate and the bulbo-urethral glands serve to neutralize any slight acidity in the urethra or vagina which might be harmful to the spermatozoa. Each ejaculate has been estimated to contain 300 to 500 million spermatozoa.

PRACTICAL CONSIDERATIONS.   Two well known disorders of the male reproductive system are gonorrhea, an infectious bacterial disease, and enlargement of the prostate. Gonorrhea begins as an inflammation of the urethra and often spreads backward to involve the prostate, the seminal vesicles and the epididymis. Enlargement of the prostate occurs in older men. If the prostate becomes large enough to obstruct the urethra and make urination difficult, surgical intervention becomes necessary.

CHAPTER 11

THE REPRODUCTIVE
SYSTEM OF THE FEMALE

THE REPRODUCTIVE system of the female consists of a pair of ovaries which produce ova and hormones, a system of tubes, the uterine tubes, the uterus, the vagina, which lead to the outside, and a group of external structures surrounding the opening of the vagina. The mammary glands, anatomically a part of the skin, are usually described with the reproductive system because their activity is largely controlled by it. The external organs will be described first.

THE EXTERNAL GENITAL ORGANS

The external genital organs of the female (Fig. 179) are called collectively the *pudendum*[1] or the *vulva*.[2] The most superficial of the group are the mons pubis and the labia majora. The *mons pubis* is the rounded fatty eminence in front of the symphysis pubis. It is covered with hair after puberty. The *labia majora*[3] are two large folds which meet in the midline of the body below the pubic arch. Internal to and covered by these large folds are two smaller ones, the *labia minora*.[4] The two labia minora meet anteriorly and enclose a small organ, the *clitoris*,[5] which is the homologue of the penis of the male. Behind the clitoris and between the smaller folds are two orifices. Anteriorly is the small opening of the urethra; posteriorly is the larger entrance to the *vagina*. The vaginal orifice is partly closed in the virgin by a thin membrane, the *hymen*.[6] Between the vaginal orifice and the labia minora are the openings of

---

[1] *Pudendum:* L., that which one ought to be ashamed of.
[2] Vulva, from L. *volvere,* to roll.
[3] *Labia majora* (singular, *labium majus*): L., major lip.
[4] *Labia minora* (singular, *labium minus*): L., minor lip.
[5] Clitoris: from Greek verb, to close. It is covered by the labia minora.
[6] Hymen: G., originally a skin or membrane.

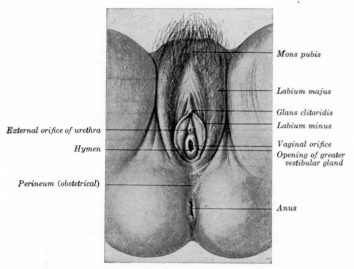

Mons pubis

Labium majus

Glans clitoridis
Labium minus

External orifice of urethra

Vaginal orifice
Opening of greater
vestibular gland

Hymen

Perineum (obstetrical)

Anus

Figure 179. The external genital organs of the female. (Callander.)

the two *greater vestibular glands* (O.T., glands of Bartholin[7]), which correspond to the bulbo-urethral glands in the male.

A deep dissection of the external generative organs (Fig. 180) shows the clitoris to be composed in the main of two masses, the *corpora cavernosa of the clitoris,* which correspond to the corpora cavernosa penis of the male. Posteriorly, they are attached to the pubic rami. The *bulb of the vestibule,* a large mass of erectile tissue on either side of the vaginal orifice, corresponds to the urethral bulb of the male. It is prolonged forward in a poorly developed structure, the *pars intermedia,* which corresponds to the male corpus cavernosum urethrae. Forming the tip of the clitoris is the *glans clitoridis.*

In sexual excitement the clitoris becomes enlarged and erected by the same mechanisms that operate in the male. The greater vestibular glands secrete a lubricating fluid.

The Perineum. The perineum,[8] the region of the outlet of the pelvis, contains all those structures found between the pubic symphysis and the coccyx. The *obstetrical perineum* is the region between the vaginal and anal orifices. It is the part of the pelvic floor most likely to be torn in childbirth.

---

[7] From Caspar Bartholin (1655–1738). He was first professor of philosophy, then of natural science and medicine, and finally Advocate General and Deputy of Finances in Copenhagen.

[8] Perineum. The adjective derived from this word is perineal. It must be distinguished from peroneal, relating to the lateral aspect of the leg.

Figure 180   **The Reproductive System of the Female**   215

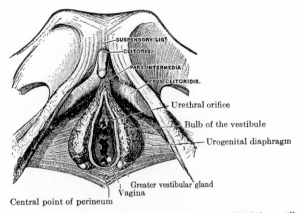

Central point of perineum

Figure 180. Dissection of female perineum to show the clitoris, the bulb of the vestibule and the greater vestibular glands. (Cunningham's Textbook of Anatomy.)

THE INTERNAL REPRODUCTIVE ORGANS

The internal reproductive organs consist of the vagina, the uterus, the uterine tubes, the ovaries and their supporting structures.

The Vagina. The vagina[9] (Fig. 181) is a tube about 3 inches long which passes upward and backward from the orifice between the labia minora. In front of it lies the bladder; behind it is the rectum. At its upper end the lowest portion of the uterus, the cervix, projects into it. Around the cervix is a circular recess which is arbitrarily divided into four parts called *anterior, posterior* and *lateral fornices.*[10] The posterior fornix is the deepest of the four. The cavity of the vagina is flattened anteroposteriorly. In the mucosa of its walls are numerous transverse folds or *rugae.*

Microscopically, the vagina contains a mucosa, a muscular layer and an outer fibrous coat.

The Uterus and Its Ligaments. The uterus (Figs. 181, 182), commonly called the *womb,* is a pear-shaped organ about 3 inches in length. It is flattened anteroposteriorly. The larger, upper portion is called the *body;* the smaller, lower portion, the *cervix.*[11] The body lies above and behind the bladder; the lower end of the cervix projects into the upper end of the vagina, as already noted. In its normal position the uterus as a whole lies tilted forward at an angle of about 90 degrees with the vagina; in addition, the body of the uterus is bent forward to a smaller degree in relation to the cervix.

The walls of the uterus are surprisingly thick, and the central cavity, triangular in shape, is small. It has three openings, two in

---

[9] *Vagina:* L., a sheath or scabbard.

[10] *Fornices:* plural of *fornix,* L., an arch or vault.

[11] *Cervix:* L., neck.

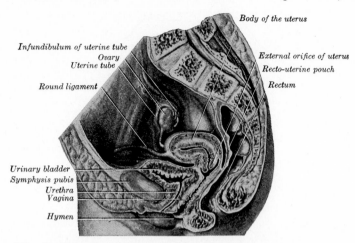

Figure 181.   Sagittal section of the female pelvis. (Callander.)

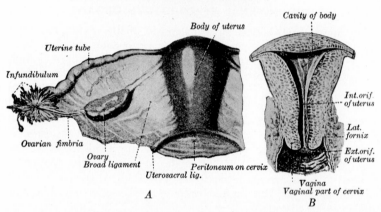

Figure 182.   A, The posterior aspect of the uterus and broad ligament (the broad ligament
has been spread out); B, diagrammatic representation of the uterine cavity opened up
from its anterior aspect. (Cunningham's Textbook of Anatomy.)

the upper lateral corners of the body for the uterine tubes, and one
passing through the cervix to open into the vagina, the *cervical
canal.* The cervical canal is fusiform in shape and is constricted at
both ends. Its lower opening into the vagina is called the *external
orifice of the uterus;* its upper opening into the cavity of the body
of the uterus is called the *internal orifice of the uterus.*

The uterus is fixed in position by several bands or ligaments, the
most important of which are the broad and the round ligaments.

The *broad ligaments,* two in number, are wide peritoneal folds
extending from the lateral aspects of the uterus to the side walls of
the pelvis. Each has two surfaces, an *anterior surface,* which looks

downward as well as forward, and a *posterior surface,* looking upward and backward. On the posterior surfaces rest the ovaries; in the anterior free borders run the uterine or fallopian tubes.

The *round ligaments,* two in number, arise from the upper and lateral angles of the uterus and pass outward and forward in the anterior folds of the broad ligaments. They enter the inguinal canals and terminate in the connective tissue of the labia majora. The round ligament, plus the ligament of the ovary that lies in the broad ligament and stretches from the ovary to the uterus (Fig. 182), is the homologue of the gubernaculum of the male, and the labia majora are the homologue of the scrotum. Both ligaments contain smooth muscle fibers. Like the testis, the ovary descends along the abdominal wall, but stops in the pelvis. In some cases a vestigial processus vaginalis is present; and the ovary has been known to descend during development into the labium majus.

MICROSCOPIC. The walls of the uterus are made up of three chief layers: an inner mucosa, a middle muscular layer and an outer serous coat. The mucosa, called the *endometrium*[12] (Fig. 183), is thick and contains many glands. The muscular layer makes up the bulk of the uterine wall and consists of smooth muscle fibers running in many directions. In it may be found the ramifications of many large blood vessels. The serous coat contains the usual layer of flat cells bound to the deeper structures by connective tissue.

During menstruation (Fig. 183) and pregnancy striking changes take place in the histologic picture of the uterus. In menstruation the mucosa becomes swollen and engorged with blood. Hemorrhages occur within it, and the superficial parts are completely sloughed off. After the bleeding has ceased the lining is slowly renewed. The new epithelium arises from the lower parts of the uterine glands that remain. In pregnancy, changes take place in the mucosa and also in the muscular layer. The individual muscle fibers become enormously large, many of them increasing as much as ten times in length and two and a half times in width. The blood channels at the same time become huge sinuses.

The Uterine Tubes. The uterine tubes (O.T., fallopian[13] tubes) (Figs. 181, 182) are attached to the upper and lateral angles of the uterus. They run laterally in the anterior free borders of the broad ligaments to the side walls of the pelvis. They are about 4 inches in length. At their outer ends they arch upward and backward over the ovary where each tube widens out to form a funnel-shaped *infundibulum.*[14] Projecting from the infundibulum are a number of

---

[12] Endometrium: G., within the uterus.

[13] From Gabriello Fallopio (1523–1562), an Italian anatomist and one of the greatest of his time.

[14] *Infundibulum:* L., a funnel; from *infundere,* to put in or into.

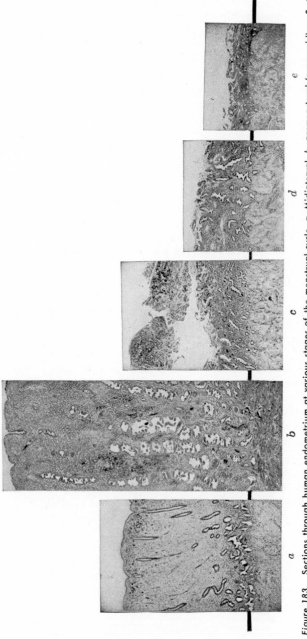

Figure 183. Sections through human endometrium at various stages of the menstrual cycle. *a*, Midinterval; *b*, premenstrual (progravid); *c*, first day of menstruation; *d*, second day of menstruation; *e*, fourth day of menstruation. The black line indicates the boundary between endometrium and muscularis. × 14. (Maximow and Bloom, courtesy of G. W. Bartelmez.)

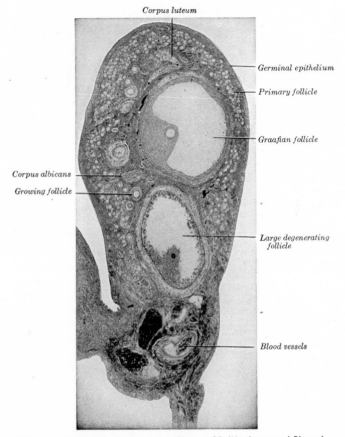

Corpus luteum

Germinal epithelium

Primary follicle

Graafian follicle

Corpus albicans

Growing follicle

Large degenerating follicle

Blood vessels

Figure 184. A section of the ovary of a monkey. $\times$ 25. (Maximow and Bloom.)

finger-like processes or *fimbriae*,[15] one or more of which are directed toward, and sometimes attached directly to the ovary. Within the fimbriae is a small opening through which the eggs enter the uterine tubes.

The mucosa of the uterine tubes is thrown up into a large number of longitudinally running folds. Microscopically, it contains ciliated epithelium. Surrounding the mucosa is a muscular layer.

The Ovary. Each ovary[16] (Figs. 181, 182) is a flattened, oval body about 1 inch in length. It lies vertically against the side wall of the pelvis in contact with the posterior surface of the broad ligament. The fold of peritoneum which supports it from above is

---

[15] *Fimbriae,* plural of *fimbria,* L., a fiber, fringe.

[16] Ovary: L., an egg holder; from *ovum,* egg.

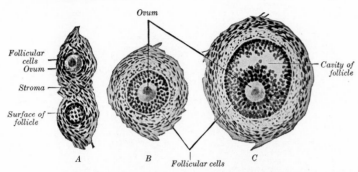

Figure 185. Growth and transformation of a human primary follicle into a vesicular follicle. A, Primary follicles in sectional and surface views. B, Enlarged primary follicle. C, Young vesicular follicle with fluid-filled cavity. (Bumm.)

called the *suspensory ligament of the ovary;* the fold binding its anterior border to the broad ligament is called the *mesovarium.*

MICROSCOPIC.   Microscopically, three main elements can be identified in the ovary (Fig. 184): (1) a connective tissue ground substance or stroma[17]; (2) a superficial germinal epithelium; and (3) a varying number of ovarian follicles. The *stroma* contains the usual collagenous and elastic fibers along with numerous elongated spindle-shaped cells. The *germinal epithelium* consists of a single layer of columnar or cuboidal cells. It is called germinal because it gives rise to the egg cells or ova which become embedded in the stroma.

The *ovarian follicles*[18] (Figs. 184, 185) are of two types: (1) primary follicles, and (2) vesicular or graafian follicles. The *primary follicles* are the greatest numerically. Each consists of a single egg cell or *ovum* surrounded by a number of small epithelial cells called *follicular cells.* Many follicles never advance beyond this state; others become active and develop into vesicular follicles.

Activity is indicated by an increase in the size of the follicle. The increase is brought about partly because of the multiplication of the follicular cells. Soon clefts filled with a clear fluid, the *liquor folliculi,* appear between the cells. The liquor increases in amount, greatly enlarging the follicle, and the clefts coalesce to form a single cavity. The cavity continues to increase in size, and the ovum is pushed to one side of the follicle. This is the stage of the *vesicular* or *graafian*[19] *follicle.*

The graafian follicle becomes progressively larger and produces

---

[17] *Stroma:* G., bed covering or bedding.
[18] Follicle: L., a small bag, husk, pod.
[19] From Regner de Graaf (1641–1673), a celebrated Dutch anatomist and physician.

Figure 186   *The Reproductive System of the Female*   221

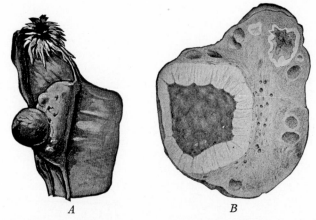

A   *B*

Figure 186. Human ovary and follicles. A, Uterine tube and ovary with a nearly mature graafian follicle. (Ribemont-Dessaignes.) B, Sectioned ovary with a corpus luteum at left and corpora albicantia of different ages at upper right. (Arey.)

an elevation on the surface of the ovary (Fig. 186). Eventually it ruptures, with the result that the ovum and liquor folliculi are discharged into the abdominal cavity. The process of rupture is known as *ovulation*. The mature ovum is about 120 microns in diameter.

After ovulation the walls of the follicle crumple up and changes take place in the follicular cells. They enlarge and acquire a certain amount of yellowish pigment, so that they have been given the name of *lutein cells*. The mass itself is called a *corpus luteum* or yellow body (Figs. 184, 186). The lutein cells and the central cavity are later replaced by connective tissue, and the final result is a white scar, the *corpus albicans* (Fig. 184). The rate at which these changes take place depends upon the fate of the discharged ovum. If the ovum is not fertilized, the corpus luteum never becomes very large, and reaches its maximal development in about two weeks. After that it begins to disappear. If, on the other hand, the ovum is fertilized and pregnancy ensues, the corpus luteum continues to develop for five or six months and becomes much larger in size. The rate of its retrogression is also proportionately slower.

The number of follicles in the ovary varies with the age of the person. Estimates of the number in the two ovaries at birth range from 40,000 to 400,000. Accounts vary as to what happens after birth. Some investigators claim that no new follicles are developed; others, that all those present at birth degenerate and the follicles that become graafian follicles during sexual maturity arise from the germinal epithelium after birth. It is agreed, however, that there is a decrease in numbers by a process called involution or *atresia*.

As a rule, only one ovum matures each month during the thirty years or so of reproductive life, but after the climacteric (*menopause* or change of life) no follicles can be found in the ovary.

The ovary as an organ of internal secretion will be discussed on page 366.

The Pelvic Peritoneum. The peritoneum covering the pelvic viscera (Figs. 153, 181) is a continuation of the peritoneum lining the general abdominal cavity. Traced from the posterior abdominal wall downward and forward, it passes down over the rectum and is reflected on to the posterior aspect of the uterus. It covers this organ and forms the folds of the broad ligament. Anteriorly it passes over the bladder and is reflected from it on to the anterior abdominal wall. In its course it forms two pockets or pouches: one between the bladder and uterus, the other between the uterus and rectum. The second, the *recto-uterine pouch,* is the deeper of the two. Its importance lies in the fact that it is the lowest region of the peritoneal cavity, and abnormal fluids formed within the pelvis tend to gravitate into it.

PRACTICAL CONSIDERATIONS. Inflammation of the various parts of the reproductive system may be caused by gonorrhea or other infective agents. Inflammation of the cervix is called cervicitis; of the mucosa of the uterus, endometritis; of the uterine tubes, salpingitis; of the ovaries, oophoritis or ovaritis. Infections of the ovaries and tubes readily spread to the peritoneum and set up a general or, more commonly, a local peritonitis. In the latter case a large part of the pelvic contents become firmly glued together to form what is often called a pelvic tangle. Pus may be formed, which will tend to drain into the recto-uterine pouch, as already noted.

Tumors of the reproductive organs are not uncommon. The uterus is frequently attacked by cancer or by a hard, fibrous tumor known as a fibroid. In the ovary cysts sometimes occur from failure of the graafian follicles to rupture, and from other causes.

THE MECHANISM OF THE FEMALE REPRODUCTIVE SYSTEM. We have already traced the development of the ovum up to the time of its discharge from the ovary. After ovulation it enters the uterine tube and passes down to the uterus. The factors which bring about its entrance into the tube are not entirely clear. It has been suggested that the fimbriae grasp the ovum as it is discharged, and that the beating cilia in the tube set up currents which draw it in. Cases have been reported in which pregnancy has occurred after the removal of one ovary and the opposite uterine tube. In these the ovum from the intact ovary must have crossed the pelvic cavity to reach the tube of the other side.

After entering the uterine tube the ovum passes into the uterus and is usually discharged through the vagina. If it becomes fertilized by the sperm (which usually takes place in the uterine tube), it becomes imbedded in some part of the uterine wall and further developmental changes occur. These changes will be discussed in a later chapter. The date of discharge of the ovum from the ovary is not coincident with the onset of menstruation, as was once thought, but occurs from ten to twenty days later, probably about the fifteenth day.

Figure 187   **The Reproductive System of the Female**   223

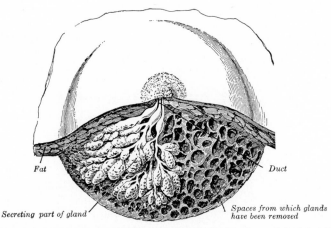

Fat

Duct

Secreting part of gland

Spaces from which glands have been removed

Figure 187.   Dissection of the lower half of the mamma during the period of lactation. (Luschka.)

THE FEMALE BREASTS

The breasts, *mammae*, or *mammary glands* (Fig. 187) would properly be considered with the skin because they are integumentary glands, developing from the epidermis and lying in the superficial fascia. Since their function is related to, and controlled by, the reproductive system, however, they are described here.

Each breast consists of fifteen to twenty compound alveolar glands supported in a stroma of connective tissue and fat. The individual glands radiate like the spokes of a wheel from the centrally placed nipple. The extent of development of the terminal alveoli of the glands varies with the physiologic state of the person. In pregnancy and lactation they are large and numerous; at other times they are small and few.

The *nipple* contains the openings of the ducts of the glands, along with a certain amount of smooth muscle and connective tissue. The skin of the nipple and the surrounding *areola* contains pigment.

CHAPTER 12

THE CIRCULATORY SYSTEM

IT IS THE FUNCTION of the circulatory system to transport materials quickly from one part of the body to another—food from the intestine, where it has been absorbed, to the tissues that need or can store it; oxygen from the lungs; wastes to the kidneys; and so forth. The transporting medium that picks up, carries and discharges these materials is the blood, a tissue that is unique in being fluid, but which resembles in many respects connective tissues and is often classified with them. The blood makes its way to all parts of the body in a closed system of tubes, the blood vessels, through which it is driven by a pump or, rather, a pair of pumps, the heart. A second system of tubes, the lymphatic system, is also a part of the circulatory system. Its role will be discussed later.

THE BLOOD

The blood has been mentioned as a variety of connective tissue in which the intercellular substance is liquid. The liquid is called *blood plasma;* the cells suspended in it, *blood cells.*

The blood cells are of two main types: red cells or *erythrocytes,* and white cells or *leukocytes.* The red cells far outnumber the whites, there being approximately 5,000,000 red cells and 7500 white cells per cubic millimeter of blood.

The **red cells** or **erythrocytes** (Figs. 188, 189) are small round disks as seen from the top or bottom, and biconcave as seen from the side. Single cells have a yellowish tint; in large numbers they appear reddish. No nuclei are present in the specimens normally seen in the blood. In size, the erythrocytes average 7.74 microns in diameter and 1.9 microns in thickness at the edge.

The **white cells** or **leukocytes** (Fig. 189) are larger than the red cells, and in addition each has a nucleus. By the ordinary blood stains the nucleus appears relatively dark, and the cytoplasm a pale blue. The leukocytes are divided into two main groups: (1) cells having a nongranular cytoplasm and a more or less regular nucleus; (2) cells having a granular cytoplasm and a highly irregular or

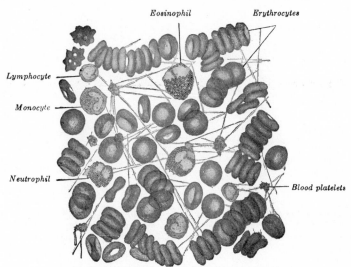

Figure 188. Fresh preparation of human blood. Note the strands of fibrin which indicate that clotting has begun. High magnification. (Maximow and Bloom.)

polymorphous nucleus. The subdivisions of these two groups with the percentage of cells in each are as follows:

A. Nongranular or lymphoid leukocytes:
    Lymphocytes........................ 20–25 per cent
    Large monocytes..................... 3–8   per cent
B. Granular leukocytes or granulocytes:
    Acidophil or eosinophil cells.............. 2–4   per cent
    Basophil cells........................ 0.5   per cent
    Neutrophil cells...................... 65–75 per cent

The *lymphocytes* are the smallest of the white cells. They have a nucleus which is more or less spherical and almost fills the cell. The small amount of surrounding cytoplasm contains no granules.

The *large monocytes* are larger cells. They have a nucleus shaped like a kidney or a horseshoe and a large amount of nongranular cytoplasm.

The *acidophil* or *eosinophil cells* have a nucleus which is divided into two or more lobes. The cytoplasm contains a number of heavy granules which stain intensively with acid dyes. These granules appear red by the ordinary stains.

The *basophil cells* are similar to the acidophil cells except that their granules stain with basic dyes. With the usual stains these granules are purple.

The *neutrophil cells* have a nucleus which is more irregular than that of any of the preceding types, and for that reason the cells are often called *polymorphonuclear cells* or "polymorps." The cyto-

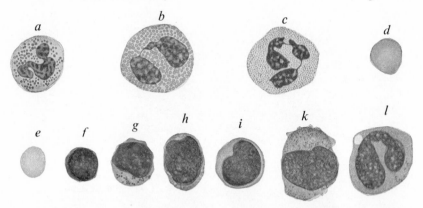

Figure 189. Blood cells of various types as they appear in stained preparations. *a*, Basophil leukocyte; *b*, eosinophil leukocyte; *c*, neutrophil leukocyte; *d, e*, erythrocytes (different stains); *f, g, h, i*, lymphocytes; *k, l*, large monocytes. (Maximow and Bloom.)

plasm contains a large number of fine granules which may appear either slightly reddish or slightly purple when stained.

Blood platelets (Fig. 188) are small granular bodies found normally in the blood. They are flat plates of various shape; they often appear pear-like or stellate. As stained by the usual methods they can be seen to contain a number of purple granules.

Blood plasma is the fluid intercellular substance in which the cells and platelets lie. It is about 90 per cent water. A number of proteins, constituting about 7 per cent of the plasma, are in colloidal solution. There are also to be found inorganic salts, enzymes, antibodies and other substances, some of them not yet identified. In addition to all these, the plasma carries its load of sugar, amino acids, fats, hormones and gases that it is transporting from point to point within the body.

One of the proteins of the plasma is called *fibrinogen*. In the clotting process the soluble fibrinogen is converted into the insoluble *fibrin*. The fibrin is precipitated in the form of a network (Fig. 188) in the meshes of which the blood corpuscles are caught to form the clot. When the clot is removed, the remaining fluid portion of the plasma is called *blood serum*.

The total amount of blood in the body, a figure difficult to determine accurately, is probably about 7 per cent of the weight of the body. Blood cells and platelets make up 40 to 50 per cent of the volume of the blood, and the plasma, 50 to 60 per cent.

FUNCTIONS OF THE VARIOUS BLOOD ELEMENTS. The erythrocytes are important because of the hemoglobin which they contain. Hemoglobin is an iron-containing protein which has the dual capacity of combining with oxygen in the lungs, where the concentration of oxygen is high, and setting it free in the tissues, where the concentration is low, and of taking carbon dioxide from the tissues and setting it free in the lungs. Under certain conditions it can be precipitated in a crystalline form. The crystals are characteristic in shape for the different animal groups; hence they are sometimes used in medicolegal cases to determine whether a given specimen of blood is human or animal.

The neutrophil leukocytes and, to a certain extent, the monocytes are able to engulf bacteria and other foreign elements. They congregate in large numbers in regions of injury or disease, and attempt to ingest the offending organisms. If they are successful, the inflammation subsides; if not, they may themselves be destroyed. Pus contains large numbers of dead and dying neutrophils. The eosinophils are increased in number in certain parasitic diseases, and they accumulate in the respiratory mucous membrane in asthama.

The functions of the basophil cells and of the lymphocytes are not clearly known. The latter tend to increase in number and accumulate in regions of chronic rather than acute inflammation. The blood platelets appear to be concerned in the clotting process.

The blood plasma transports food material for absorption and waste material for excretion.

THE HEART

Since oxygen must be supplied to all the tissues all the time and in abundance, the circulatory system is so arranged that the entire blood stream flows through the lungs before it is pumped to other parts of the body. In order to avoid the high pressure and inefficiency such an arrangement might entail, there are two pumps combined in a single organ, the heart. One drives the blood through the vessels of the lungs. The second receives the blood from the lungs and drives it through the other organs of the body. On returning from the organs it flows into the first pump again, and the process is repeated. The circulation from the heart through the lungs and back to the heart is called the *pulmonary circulation,* and the circulation from the heart through the remainder of the body and back is called the *systemic circulation.*

The heart (Figs. 190, 191) is a cone-shaped organ a little larger than the fist, which lies in the thorax mostly to the left of the midline. Its apex points downward and to the left; its base is directed upward and to the right and has attached to it several large vessels.

The heart is divided into four chambers called the right and left atria and the right and left ventricles (Fig. 192). The ventricles together form the larger part of the heart and make up most of the organ as seen from the front. The atria form the superior and posterior portions. The right atrium receives the blood from the systemic circulation and transmits it to the right ventricle, which in turn sends it to the lungs. The left atrium receives the blood from the lungs and sends it to the left ventricle. From the left ventricle it passes once more into the systemic circulation.

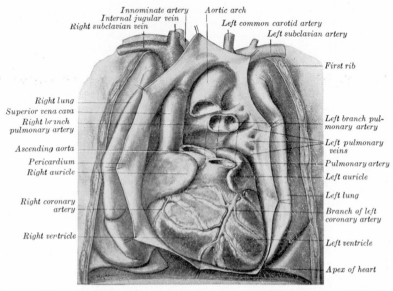

Innominate artery · Aortic arch
Internal jugular vein · Left common carotid artery
Right subclavian vein · Left subclavian artery

First rib

Right lung
Superior vena cava
Right branch pulmonary artery
Ascending aorta
Pericardium
Right auricle
Right coronary artery
Right ventricle

Left branch pulmonary artery
Left pulmonary veins
Pulmonary artery
Left auricle
Left lung
Branch of left coronary artery
Left ventricle
Apex of heart

Figure 190.   Heart and the great vessels from the front, showing the reflections of the pericardium. (Callander.)

The *right atrium*[1] (O.T., auricle) is a thin-walled chamber lying in the base of the heart and forming its right border. Only a small portion of it, the *auricle* (O.T., auricular appendix) is usually seen from the front (Figs. 190, 191). It contains three large openings (Figs. 192, 193): (1) the opening for the superior vena cava, (2) the opening for the inferior vena cava, and (3) the atrioventricular orifice. The superior vena cava is a large vein which enters the posterior wall superiorly; the inferior vena cava enters the same wall inferiorly; the *atrioventricular orifice* lies in the floor and leads into the right ventricle. Between the opening for the inferior vena cava and the atrioventricular orifice is a small opening for the *coronary sinus* (Fig. 193), the vein that drains most of the heart wall. There are also in the wall of the right atrium a number of small apertures where small veins from the wall of the atrium empty. On the left or interatrial wall is an oval depression, the *fossa ovalis*. The lining of the atrium is partly smooth, and partly raised into muscular ridges, called *musculi pectinati*.[2]

The *left atrium* (Figs. 190, 191) lies in the base of the heart on the left side. Its *auricle* projects forward and, as in the right atrium, is the only part that can be seen from the front. On its posterior wall (Fig. 192) are four openings for the four pulmonary veins.

---

[1] *Atrium* (plural *atria*): L., a room or hall.
[2] Pectinati: from L. *pecten*, a crest or comb.

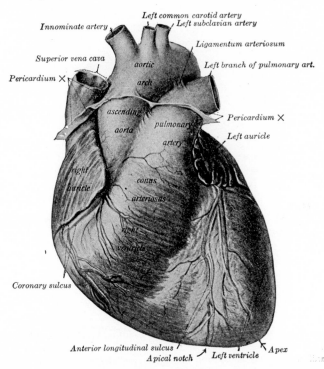

Figure 191.   The heart seen from in front, with its great vessels attached. (Sobotta and McMurrich.)

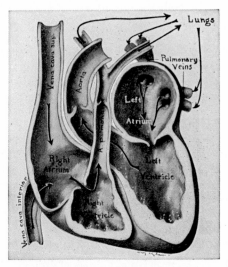

Figure 192.   Diagram of the chambers, valves and vessels of the heart, and the direction of blood flow. (Callander, after Page and Butler.)

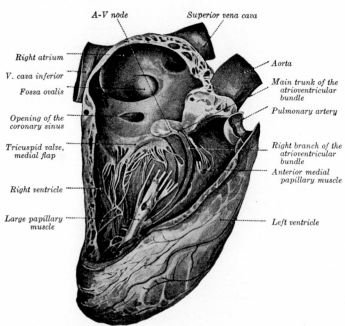

Figure 193. The interior of the right atrium and ventricle, showing the atrioventricular bundle. The atrioventricular node and bundle have been exposed by removal of the endocardium and of the muscle layer covering it. (Spalteholz.)

In the floor is the left *atrioventricular orifice.* The lining is smooth except in the auricle, where musculi pectinati are present.

The *right ventricle* (Figs. 191, 193) has a much thicker wall than either atrium. It has two orifices, one deeply placed and connecting with the right atrium, the atrioventricular orifice; the other placed more superficially and leading into the pulmonary artery, the *pulmonary orifice.* Both are guarded by valves. In the atrioventricular orifice is the *right atrioventricular* or *tricuspid valve;* in the pulmonary orifice, the *pulmonary valve.* The interior of the ventricular wall (Fig. 193) contains many irregular muscular ridges and bands known as *trabeculae carneae.*[3]

The *left ventricle* (Fig. 192) has a thicker wall than the right because it has heavier work to perform: it must drive the blood through the whole systemic circulation, while the right ventricle has only to drive it through the pulmonary circulation. Otherwise it is similar in pattern to the right ventricle. Its two openings are the *left atrioventricular* and the *aortic orifices.* The valves are the *left atrioventricular* or *mitral valve,* and the *aortic valve.*

---

[3] *Trabeculae carneae:* L., small beams or bands of flesh.

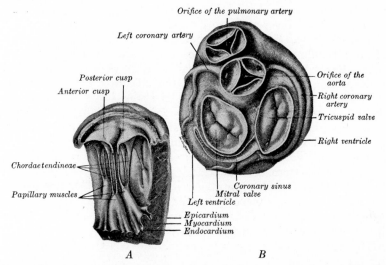

Orifice of the pulmonary artery

Left coronary artery

Posterior cusp
Anterior cusp

Orifice of the aorta
Right coronary artery
Tricuspid valve
Right ventricle

Chordae tendineae
Papillary muscles

Coronary sinus
Mitral valve
Left ventricle

Epicardium
Myocardium
Endocardium

A   B

Figure 194. A, Longitudinal section through the mitral valve to show its mechanism. *B,* Pulmonary, aortic, bicuspid and tricuspid valves seen from above after the atria have been removed. (Callander.)

The four valves of the heart (Fig. 194) are of two types. The right and left atrioventricular valves are essentially similar and form one pattern; the aortic and pulmonary valves form the other.

The *right atrioventricular* or *tricuspid valve* contains three triangular flaps or cusps. One border of each cusp is attached to the atrioventricular orifice; the others project into the ventricle. Numerous small cords, called *chordae tendineae,* extend from the free margins and insert into the *papillary muscles,* small muscular elevations from the ventricular walls. This arrangement of cusps and cords permits the blood to flow from the atrium to the ventricle, but prevents it from flowing in the reverse direction. It cannot pass backward into the atrium because the valves float up and close the orifice. The chordae tendinae are the proper length to insure that the cusps will fit tightly; were they too long or too short, the valve would leak.

The *left atrioventricular, bicuspid* or *mitral valve* is similar to the tricuspid valve except that it has only two flaps or cusps. The name "mitral" comes from its fancied resemblance to an ecclesiastical headdress, the bishop's miter.

The *pulmonary valve* lies in the beginning of the pulmonary artery, and consists of three small cusps which form the pockets around the inside of the vessel. The pockets open away from the heart and, therefore, do not interfere with the outward flow of blood; they intercept, however, all that passes in the reverse direction. Each cusp is shaped like a half moon, so that the name "semilunar" has been given to the valve.

The *aortic valve* lies in the beginning of the aorta. It consists of three semilunar cusps similar to those in the pulmonary valve.

The Heart Wall. The heart wall consists of three layers: the endocardium, the myocardium and the epicardium. The *endocardium* is a thin membrane which lines the heart chambers. It consists of endothelium (simple squamous epithelium) and a layer of fibrous tissue. The cusps of the valves are folds of endocardium strengthened with a little extra connective tissue.

The *myocardium,* or the muscle of the heart, is organized in a complicated pattern of whorls and spirals. A band of specialized fibers is called the *atrioventricular bundle* (Fig. 193). It arises in the right atrium at a place called the *atrioventricular* or A-V *node.* After passing a short distance it divides into two main branches which pass into the ventricles to be distributed to their walls.

The *epicardium* is a serous membrane covering the external surface of the heart.

The Pericardium. The *pericardium* (Figs. 161, 190) is a sac which surrounds and encloses the heart. It is attached superiorly to the great blood vessels above the heart; inferiorly it reaches the diaphragm. It is a serous membrane which is reflected onto the heart as the epicardium. The opposed surfaces of epicardium and pericardium are kept smooth and slippery, like all serous membranes, by the secretion of a small amount of lubricating fluid.

HEART ACTION. The circulation of the blood is kept going by the alternate contraction and relaxation of the atria and the ventricles. The atria contract together while the ventricles dilate; when the ventricles contract, the atria dilate. The phase of contraction is called *systole;* the phase of dilatation, *diastole.* Each atrium during its diastolic period is filled with blood from the veins; during its systolic period it pumps the blood into the ventricle. The ventricles receive blood from the atria during their diastole and force it into the main arteries during systole. The action of the valves in preventing the blood from passing in the wrong direction has already been noted.

The mechanism for coordinating the contractions of the four chambers is an interesting one. The heart beat starts in the right atrium at a spot, difficult to identify structurally, called the *sino-atrial node,* which lies near the entrance of the superior vena cava. It spreads over the atria and quickly reaches the atrioventricular node previously mentioned. From here it is conducted to the ventricles by way of specialized muscle fibers that conduct more rapidly than do ordinary cardiac muscle fibers. The fibers leave the atrioventricular node as a bundle (atrioventricular bundle) about the size of a match. This bundle soon divides, one branch running down each side of the interventricular septum. The fibers then spread out beneath the endocardium to all parts of the ventricular walls. The rate of conduction along these fibers is just the proper speed to bring the ventricles into action at an appropriate interval after the atria have contracted.

The heart beat is not a simple in-and-out motion like the squeezing of a rubber ball, but, because of the arrangement of the muscle fibers in whorls and

Figure 195   *The Circulatory System* 233

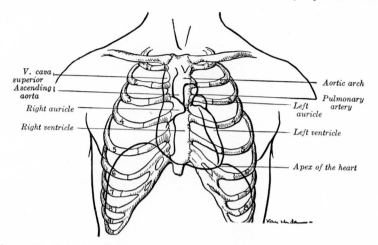

V. cava, superior
Ascending aorta
Right auricle
Right ventricle

Aortic arch
Pulmonary artery
Left auricle
Left ventricle
Apex of the heart

Figure 195. Projection of heart and great vessels on the thorax. (Callander, after Butler.)

spirals, the heart undergoes a twisting, wringing motion. This twisting causes the apex of the heart to pound against the chest wall during ventricular systole.

PRACTICAL CONSIDERATIONS. Valvular heart disease is a relatively common condition. Two types of defect are found. In one the scar (the end result of an inflammatory process) produces irregularities in the cusps and shortens the chordae tendineae. The valve no longer fits tightly, so that a leak, or technically a regurgitation, is produced. In the second type fusions take place between the edges of the cusps, and a funnel-shaped opening is produced. This condition, called stenosis, reduces the size of the orifice so that an adequate amount of blood can pass through it only with difficulty. The heart in either case is much less efficient than before; in an attempt to compensate for its deficiency it often becomes enlarged or hypertrophied.

Heart failure occurs when the heart muscle becomes unduly weakened. It may be due to any of several causes, such as inflammation of the heart muscle (myocarditis); overwork from forcing blood through a leaky or narrowed valve; or from malnutrition of the heart muscle because of disease of the arteries which supply it with blood.

Endocarditis is an inflammation of the lining membrane of the heart. Pericarditis is an inflammation of the pericardium. In the latter a certain amount of excess fluid is sometimes produced in the pericardial cavity. If it interferes with the free action of the heart, it must be drained off.

Medically, the surface markings of the heart are important (Fig. 195). Its upper border lies just below the second rib; its lower border lies below the fifth rib. The left margin curves from a point 1 inch (2.5 cm.) to the left of the sternum on the upper border to one 3½ inches (8.75 cm.) to the left of the midline on the lower. The right margin extends about 1 inch (2.5 cm.) to the right of the sternum.

If one listens to the beating of the heart through an instrument made for the purpose, called a stethoscope, two sounds may be heard for each beat. They can best be phonetically transcribed as "lupp-dupp." The first sound is produced by the contracting ventricular muscle, the second by the vibration of the semilunar valves as they shut.

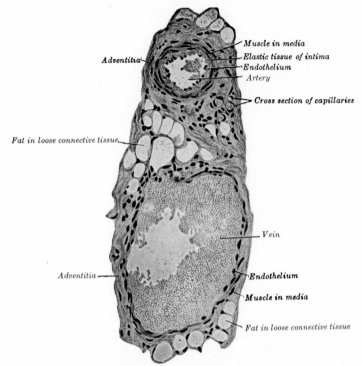

Adventitia
Muscle in media
Elastic tissue of intima
Endothelium
Artery

Cross section of capillaries

Fat in loose connective tissue

Vein

Adventitia

Endothelium

Muscle in media

Fat in loose connective tissue

Figure 196. Cross section through a small artery and its accompanying vein from the submucosa of a human intestine. Only the nuclei of the endothelial cells can be seen. × 140. (Maximow and Bloom.)

THE BLOOD VESSELS

The *arteries*[4] carry the blood away from the heart to the tissues; the *veins*[5] return the blood from the tissues to the heart. The large arteries nearest the heart divide into smaller divisions, these in turn divide into still smaller ones, and so on. The smallest arteries are known as *arterioles*. They lead into vessels of narrow caliber invisible to the naked eye, called *capillaries*.[6] The capillaries branch and form a network throughout the area supplied by the artery. It is through the walls of the capillaries that the exchange of materials between blood and tissue fluid takes place. The blood

---

[4] Artery, from Greek, containing air. The term was originally used for the windpipe, or trachea, and was later applied to what we now call arteries. (See p. 187.) The arteries were thought to be air tubes, for they were usually found empty after death.

[5] Veins, from L. *vena;* originally used for arteries and other tubes, as well as what are now called veins. Thus the *vena alba* was the ureter.

[6] Capillary, from L. *capillus,* a hair.

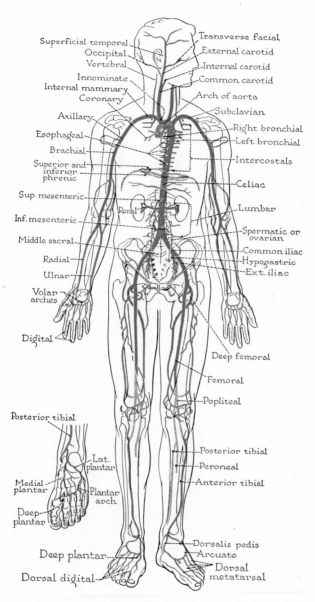

Figure 197. Diagram of the arterial system. (Millard and King: Human Anatomy and Physiology. 3rd edition.)

after passing through the network is collected into the smallest veins or *venules*. The venules unite to form small veins, these combine to form larger vessels, until eventually the great veins which open into the heart are reached. Because of the direction of the flow of blood through the vessels, the arteries are said to give off branches, while the veins are said to receive tributaries. The veins are equipped at intervals with valves which prevent the blood from flowing in the reverse direction. The arteries have no valves.

MICROSCOPIC. A typical artery in cross section (Fig. 196) consists of three layers, which, named from within outward, are the intima, the media and the adventitia. The *intima* consists of a lining membrane of flat cells, the *endothelium,* surrounded by a small amount of elastic tissue. The *media* contains a variable amount of nonstriated muscle which runs circularly around the vessel. In the large arteries it also contains elastic tissue. The *adventitia* is composed of loose connective tissue.

The *veins* (Fig. 196) have the same three layers as the arteries, but differ from them in having much thinner walls. They have little elastic tissue or muscle.

THE PULMONARY CIRCULATION

The pulmonary circulation (Fig. 192) carries the blood from the heart to the lungs and back to the heart again. It leaves by way of the large pulmonary artery, and returns through the pulmonary veins.

The *pulmonary artery* (Figs. 190, 191) is a large vessel taking origin in the right ventricle. It passes upward and backward for a short distance, and then divides into right and left branches which enter the roots of the lungs. Within the lung each trunk breaks up into small branches which follow more or less closely the subdivisions of the bronchi (Fig. 160). The terminal arterioles open into the capillary networks which course over the alveolar air sacs (p. 192).

The *pulmonary veins* entering the left atrium are four in number, two coming from each lung. Their smallest tributaries arise as venules from the capillary networks just described. These venules, after uniting with others, form larger and larger vessels, until eventually the four large pulmonary veins which enter the heart are reached.

THE SYSTEMIC ARTERIES

The systemic circulation leaves the left ventricle of the heart by way of the great artery called the aorta. After being distributed

Figure 198   **The Circulatory System   237**

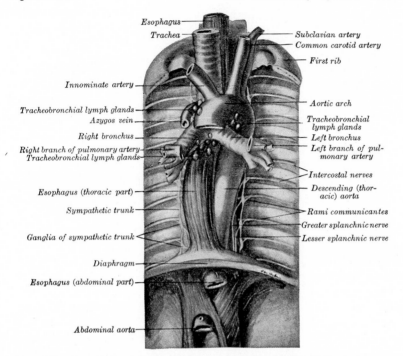

Esophagus
Trachea
Subclavian artery
Common carotid artery
First rib
Innominate artery
Tracheobronchial lymph glands
Azygos vein
Right bronchus
Right branch of pulmonary artery
Tracheobronchial lymph glands
Aortic arch
Tracheobronchial lymph glands
Left bronchus
Left branch of pulmonary artery
Intercostal nerves
Esophagus (thoracic part)
Descending (thoracic) aorta
Sympathetic trunk
Rami communicantes
Greater splanchnic nerve
Ganglia of sympathetic trunk
Lesser splanchnic nerve
Diaphragm
Esophagus (abdominal part)
Abdominal aorta

Figure 198. Topography of the trachea, aortic arch and esophagus. (Callander.)

to practically all parts of the body, it returns to the right atrium through two veins, the superior and inferior venae cavae.

The *aorta*[7] is the largest artery in the body. It arises from the left ventricle and ascends behind the pulmonary artery (Figs. 190, 191). It then arches to the left and passes backward toward the fourth thoracic vertebra (Fig. 198), from where it descends on the posterior thoracic and abdominal walls to the fourth lumbar vertebra. It ends by dividing into right and left common iliac arteries (Fig. 203). It is divided for convenience of description into three parts: the ascending aorta, the aortic arch and the descending aorta. The descending aorta is further subdivided into thoracic and abdominal portions.

The different parts of the aorta have many important relations with other structures, of which we can mention only a few. The lower limit of the aortic arch is demarcated on the surface of the body by the sternal angle. Beneath the arch lie the bifurcation of the pulmonary artery and the root of the left lung (Fig. 198). In

---

[7] Aorta, from G. verb meaning to hold up, lift up; originally used for the large bronchi which uphold the lungs; later transferred to the great vessel from which the heart appears to be hung (Hyrtl).

front of the descending aorta is the esophagus; to the right of it is the inferior vena cava; the thoracic duct crosses from right to left behind it (Fig. 218).

The chief branches of the aorta are the following:

From the ascending aorta:
1. The coronary arteries
From the aortic arch:
2. The innominate artery
3. The left common carotid artery
4. The left subclavian artery
From the descending thoracic aorta:
5. The intercostal arteries (also small arteries to esophagus, bronchi, mediastinum, pericardium and diaphragm).
From the abdominal aorta:
6. The lumbar arteries
7. The celiac artery
8. The superior mesenteric artery
9. The renal arteries
10. The internal spermatic arteries (male) or the ovarian arteries (female)
11. The inferior mesenteric artery
12. The common iliac arteries (terminal branches of the aorta).

The Branches of the Ascending Aorta and the Aortic Arch.   The *coronary*[8] *arteries* (Figs. 190, 194), two in number, arise from the ascending aorta just above the aortic valve. They divide into a number of branches which supply the heart itself.

PRACTICAL CONSIDERATIONS.   To the layman it sometimes seems surprising that the heart needs to be supplied with arteries since its cavities are constantly filled with blood. Actually, however, the coronary arteries are vitally necessary for the nourishment of the heart muscle; if they are suddenly obstructed, heart failure sets in rapidly.

The walls of large blood vessels are also provided with small blood vessels (*vasa vasorum*) to insure their nourishment.

The *innominate*[9] *artery* (Figs. 191, 198) arises from the aortic arch just to the right of the midline of the body. After a short course upward and to the right it divides into two branches: the *right common carotid*[10] *artery* and the *right subclavian artery* (Fig. 199).

The *left common carotid artery* (Figs. 191, 198) arises from the aortic arch to the left of the innominate artery.

The *left subclavian artery* (Figs. 191, 198) arises from the aortic arch to the left of the left common carotid artery.

---

[8] Coronary, from L. *corona,* crown; so called because the vessels encirlce the heart like a crown.

[9] Innominate: L., unnamed. The vessel was unnamed by the earlier anatomists. A commentator of Galen called the vessel, unnamed by him, the innominate artery. Cf. the innominate bone.

[10] Carotid, from G., deep sleep. Pressure on the carotid arteries produces anemia of the brain, with resulting unconsciousness.

Figure 199   **The Circulatory System** **239**

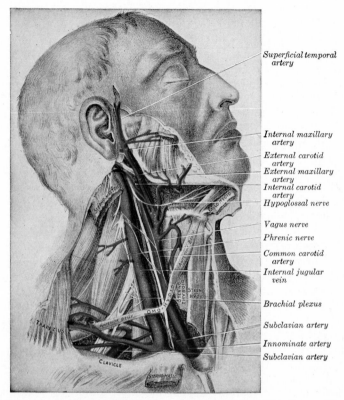

Superficial temporal artery

Internal maxillary artery
External carotid artery
External maxillary artery
Internal carotid artery
Hypoglossal nerve

Vagus nerve
Phrenic nerve
Common carotid artery
Internal jugular vein

Brachial plexus

Subclavian artery

Innominate artery
Subclavian artery

Figure 199. Superficial dissection of the right side of the neck, showing the carotid and subclavian arteries. (After Maclise.)

The Arteries of the Head and Neck. The two *common carotid arteries* (Figs. 199, 211) pass upward in the neck under cover of the anterior borders of the sternocleidomastoid muscles. Each ends opposite the upper border of the thyroid cartilage of the larynx by dividing into two branches: (1) the external carotid artery, and (2) the internal carotid artery.

1. The *external carotid artery* (Fig. 199) passes upward in the neck to end in the substance of the parotid gland by dividing into terminal branches. It gives many branches to the neck, face and scalp. One of these, the *external maxillary artery* (O.T., facial), crosses the mandible and runs obliquely across the face to the side of the nose. Another, the *internal maxillary artery*, passes under cover of the mandible to supply the tissues beneath it. A third, the *superficial temporal artery*, passes up the side of the head in front of the ear and sends branches to the temple and scalp.

2. The *internal carotid artery* (Fig. 199) ascends in the neck on a deeper plane than the external carotid artery and eventually enters the cranial cavity through the carotid canal (Fig. 27). Within the cranium it gives off the *ophthalmic artery*, which passes into the orbit to supply the eye. Terminally, it divides into *anterior cerebral* and *middle cerebral arteries*, which supply the brain (Fig. 200).

The *carotid sinus* is a slight enlargment of the terminal part of each common carotid artery and the adjacent part of the internal carotid. The walls of this sinus are more elastic than adjoining parts of the arterial walls and contain many microscopic sensory organs. These are supplied by the glossopharyngeal nerve. Distention of the sinus sets up nerve impulses that play an important part in the regulation of blood pressure by slowing the heart, relaxing certain blood vessels, and the like.

The *subclavian arteries* (Figs. 199, 211), right and left, arise as noted before, differently on the two sides of the body. Each vessel arches in the neck a short distance above the clavicle and then passes into the armpit, where it changes its name to the axillary artery. Its most important branch, the *vertebral artery*, passes upward through the transverse foramina in the transverse processes of the upper six cervical vertebrae. Emerging from the transverse foramen of the atlas, it passes posteriorly and medially, superior to the posterior arch and posterior to the mass that articulates with the occipital condyle of the skull. The groove in which it runs is clearly shown in Figure 15. It then passes anteriorly and enters the foramen magnum along its antero-lateral edge. In the cranial cavity it gives off a pair of arteries to the cerebellum (Fig. 200) and then unites with its fellow to form the basilar artery.

The *basilar artery*, after giving off two more pairs of branches to the cerebellum, divides into the two *posterior cerebral arteries*. Each posterior cerebral artery sends a communicating branch to the internal carotid artery. These vessels with the branches of the internal carotid form a circle of arteries on the base of the brain known as the *circulus arteriosus* or *circle of Willis*[11] (Fig. 200, unlabelled).

PRACTICAL CONSIDERATIONS. The blood supply of the brain comes largely from the internal carotid and to a lesser extent from the vertebral arteries. Occlusion of the terminal branches of these vessels will produce anemia and loss of function in the area of the brain it supplies. Hemorrhage within the brain is particularly serious. One small vessel situated at the base of the brain is particularly susceptible to rupture in elderly people, and has been called the "artery of

---

[11] From Thomas Willis (1621–1675), professor of natural science at Oxford, and afterward physician in London.

Figure 200   **The Circulatory System**   241

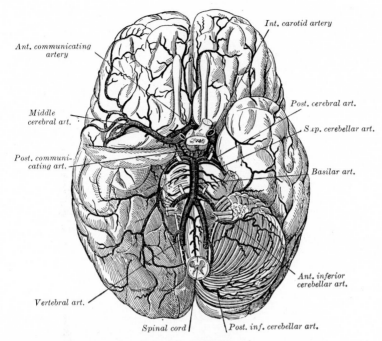

Figure 200.   The arteries of the base of the brain. (Spear.)

cerebral hemorrhage." A sudden hemorrhage from this vessel leads to a paralysis of the opposite side of the body, an occurrence known popularly as apoplexy or stroke.

The Arteries of the Upper Extremity.   The *axillary artery* begins as a continuation of the subclavian artery. It courses through the axilla until it reaches the side of the upper arm, where it becomes the brachial artery. Its branches are not sufficiently important to enumerate.

The *brachial artery* (Fig. 201) passes down the medial and anterior aspects of the upper arm and ends opposite the head of the radius by dividing into radial and ulnar arteries.

The *radial artery* (Fig. 201) passes down the radial side of the front of the forearm. At the wrist it lies to the lateral side of the tendon of the flexor carpi radialis muscle, where it may easily be palpated to take the pulse. It winds around the base of the thumb to the first metacarpal space, through which it passes to enter the palm.

The *ulnar artery* (Fig. 201) passes down the ulnar side of the front of the forearm. It may be felt at the wrist, though not as

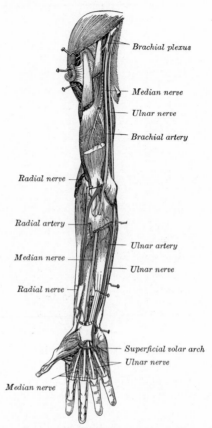

Brachial plexus

Median nerve

Ulnar nerve

Brachial artery

Radial nerve

Radial artery

Median nerve

Radial nerve

Ulnar artery

Ulnar nerve

Superficial volar arch

Ulnar nerve

Median nerve

Figure 201. The arteries and nerves of the upper extremity. (After Gerrish.)

easily as the radial artery, and hence is rarely used in taking the pulse. From the wrist it continues into the palm.

The terminal branches of the radial and ulnar arteries anastomose to form two arterial arches in the palm. One, the *superficial volar arch* (Fig. 202), lies superficial to the long flexor tendons; the other, the *deep volar arch,* lies beneath them. The branches of these arches supply the fingers and hand.

PRACTICAL CONSIDERATIONS. Bleeding from the palm of the hand may be difficult to control because of the many anastomosing vessels. If one artery is ligated, the blood may continue to pour in from another direction.

The Arteries of the Thorax and Abdomen. The *intercostal arteries* arise in pairs from the descending thoracic aorta. They pass around the thoracic walls, one under each rib. (See p. 120 and Fig. 97.)

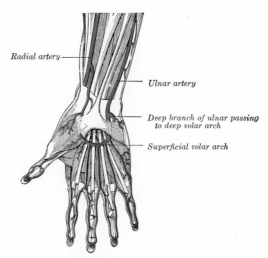

Radial artery

Ulnar artery

Deep branch of ulnar passing
to deep volar arch

Superficial volar arch

Figure 202.   The superficial volar arch. (After Gerrish.)

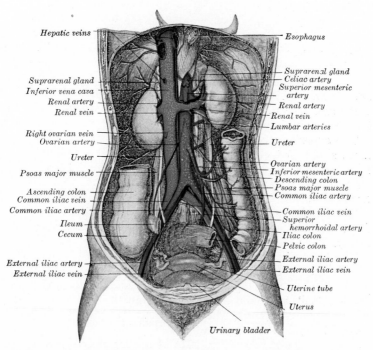

Hepatic veins

Esophagus

Suprarenal gland
Celiac artery
Superior mesenteric
artery
Renal artery
Renal vein
Lumbar arteries

Suprarenal gland
Inferior vena cava
Renal artery
Renal vein

Right ovarian vein
Ovarian artery

Ureter

Ovarian artery
Inferior mesenteric artery
Descending colon
Psoas major muscle
Common iliac artery

Ureter

Psoas major muscle

Ascending colon
Common iliac vein
Common iliac artery

Common iliac vein
Superior
hemorrhoidal artery
Iliac colon
Pelvic colon

Ileum
Cecum

External iliac artery
External iliac vein

External iliac artery
External iliac vein

Uterine tube

Uterus

Urinary bladder

Figure 203.   The abdominal aorta and the inferior vena cava. (Cunningham's Textbook of
Anatomy.)

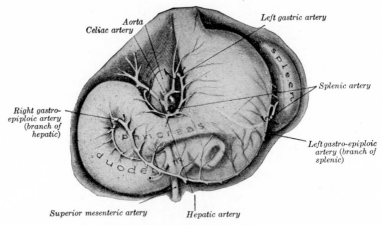

Figure 204. The celiac artery and its branches. (Babcock.)

The *lumbar arteries* arise from the abdominal aorta and pass around the abdominal wall parallel to the intercostal vessels.

The *celiac*[12] *artery* (O.T., celiac axis) (Figs. 203, 204) arises from the anterior aspect of the abdominal aorta just below the diaphragm. After a course of about ½ inch it divides into three branches, the *hepatic,* the *left gastric* (O.T., coronary) and the *splenic arteries.* They supply the liver, stomach, duodenum, pancreas and spleen. The vessels supplying the stomach run along its greater and lesser curvatures.

The *superior mesenteric artery* (Figs. 203, 205) arises from the aorta about ½ inch below the celiac artery. It supplies the small intestine, the ascending colon, and part of the transverse colon. Its primary branches anastomose to form loops from which the terminal vessels to the gut are derived.

The *renal arteries* (Fig. 203) are two short, wide vessels arising from the abdominal aorta just below the superior mesenteric artery. They pass laterally to supply the kidneys.

The *internal spermatic arteries* of the male are two long slender vessels arising from the abdominal aorta a little below the renal arteries. They pass down the posterior abdominal wall, through the inguinal canal, and end by supplying the testes, forming part of the spermatic cord. They arise here because the testes were near this level in the embryo.

The *ovarian arteries* (Fig. 203) of the female correspond to the

---

[12] Celiac (or coeliac), from G., belly, hollow.

Figure 205   **The Circulatory System   245**

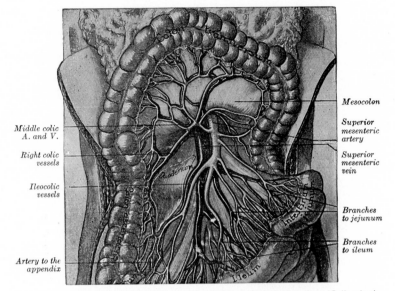

Figure 205.   The superior mesenteric artery and vein and their branches. (Callander.)

internal spermatic arteries of the male. They terminate by supplying the ovary.

The *inferior mesenteric artery* (Fig. 203) arises from the aorta about 1½ inches above its bifurcation. It supplies the remainder of the colon and the rectum.

The *common iliac arteries* (Figs. 203, 206), the terminal branches of the aorta, arise opposite the fourth lumbar vertebra. They course downward and laterally to end opposite the lumbosacral junction by dividing into hypogastric and external iliac arteries.

Each *hypogastric artery* (O.T., internal iliac) (Fig. 206) descends into the pelvis and gives off numerous branches. Some of these supply the pelvic viscera, including the bladder, rectum, prostate, uterus, vagina, and so forth; others pass backward to terminate in the gluteal and sacral regions.

The *external iliac artery* (Figs. 203, 206) courses forward along the pelvic brim. After passing under the midpoint of the inguinal ligament it becomes the femoral artery.

The Arteries of the Lower Extremity.   The *femoral artery* (Figs. 207, 79) passes down the front of the thigh and after winding around the mesial aspect of the lower part of the femur it comes to lie behind the knee. Here it changes its name to the popliteal artery.

The *popliteal artery* (Fig. 208) after a short course behind the knee divides into the anterior tibial and posterior tibial arteries.

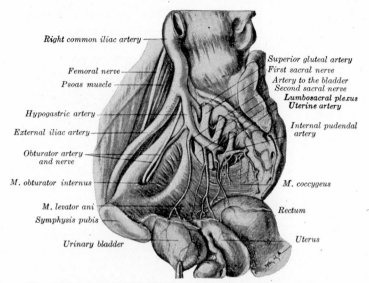

Right common iliac artery

Femoral nerve
Psoas muscle

Hypogastric artery
External iliac artery

Obturator artery
and nerve

M. obturator internus

M. levator ani
Symphysis pubis

Urinary bladder

Superior gluteal artery
First sacral nerve
Artery to the bladder
Second sacral nerve
Lumbosacral plexus
Uterine artery

Internal pudendal
artery

M. coccygeus

Rectum

Uterus

Figure 206. Medial view of the right half of the female pelvis to show the main arteries and nerves. The bladder, rectum and the pelvic genitalia are drawn downward to show their arterial supply. (Callander.)

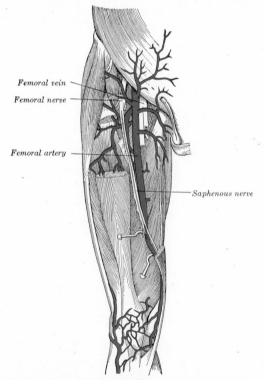

Femoral vein
Femoral nerve

Femoral artery

Saphenous nerve

Figure 207. The femoral artery. (After Gerrish.)

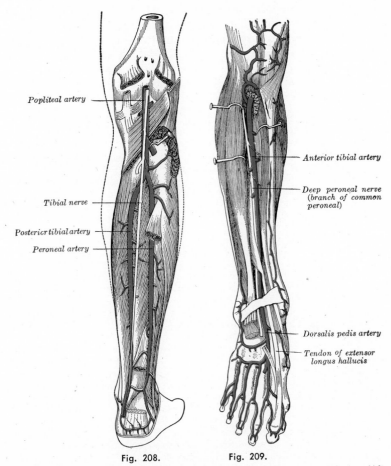

Popliteal artery

Tibial nerve

Posterior tibial artery

Peroneal artery

Anterior tibial artery

Deep peroneal nerve
(branch of common
peroneal)

Dorsalis pedis artery

Tendon of extensor
longus hallucis

Fig. 208.   Fig. 209.

Figure 208.   The popliteal, posterior tibial and peroneal arteries in the right leg. (After
Gerrish.)

Figure 209.   Anterior tibial and dorsalis pedis arteries. (After Gerrish.)

The *anterior tibial artery* (Figs. 209, 84) passes forward between
the upper ends of the tibia and fibula and then runs down the
front of the leg to the middle of the ankle. Here it becomes the
dorsalis pedis artery, which supplies the dorsal aspect of the foot
and toes.

The *posterior tibial artery* (Figs. 208, 84) passes down the back of the leg close to the tibia. High up it gives off the large *peroneal artery,* which passes down parallel to it behind the fibula. Terminally, and at a point on the inside of the ankle midway between the internal malleolus and the prominent part of the heel, the posterior tibial artery divides into two branches, the *lateral plantar* and the *medial plantar arteries,* which supply the sole of the foot.

A single *plantar arch* is formed on the sole by the union of the lateral plantar artery with a branch of the dorsalis pedis.

THE FUNCTION OF THE ARTERIES.   In the large arteries the elastic tissue is an important component of the wall. For a number of reasons a steady flow of blood through the capillaries is better than a pulsating one. To make this possible, the arteries stretch to accommodate the sudden outflow of blood when the ventricles of the heart contract and then, while the ventricles are relaxed and filling, the elastic walls of the arteries maintain a steady flow through the capillaries. This alternate expanding and contracting can be felt as a pulse.

In the smallest arteries the smooth muscle is important. There is not enough blood to fill all the capillaries of the body at the same time, and the various organs receive a supply in accordance with their needs from moment to moment. This regulation is largely accomplished by the small arteries, which are, of course, the inlets to the capillary beds. This mechanism is partly under nervous and partly under chemical control.

The endothelial lining contains a substance which prevents the blood from clotting; if it is injured, the blood may coagulate in the vessels.

PRACTICAL CONSIDERATIONS.   The most common disease of the arteries is arteriosclerosis, popularly called "hardening of the arteries." The affected vessels become hard and tortuous; microscopically, a deposit of calcium salts can be found in their walls. The disease has serious ill effects. The loss of elasticity in the walls of the arteries increases resistance to outflow from the heart. As a result, the heart must work harder and may, if too severely overtaxed, eventually fail. The arterial pressure at each systole becomes high, and the arteries, especially the smaller ones, become susceptible to rupture, so that a serious hemorrhage may result. The channels within the diseased vessels become progressively smaller, with the result that the areas they supply become inadequately nourished with blood.

Hemorrhage from a large blood vessel is a serious matter. To control the bleeding from an artery, it must be tied or compressed proximally to the wound, i.e., on the side of the wound nearest the heart. Bleeding veins, on the other hand, must be compressed on the distal side. Arterial bleeding is, as a rule, the more difficult to control because of the greater pressure with which the blood is forced out.

As an emergency measure to control severe arterial bleeding, the main artery supplying the region should be compressed against a bone (provided it crosses one in an accessible location). Thus the external maxillary artery can be compressed where it crosses the mandible, and the superficial temporal artery can be controlled over the temple. The brachial artery can be pressed laterally against the humerus, and the radial and ulnar arteries can be pressed against the bones behind them. The femoral artery is accessible at the groin, and the dorsalis pedis can be easily controlled at the ankle. These and other points, called "pressure points," should be familiar to all who hope to become proficient in first aid.

Figure 210   **The Circulatory System**   249

Figure 210. Capillary from the mesentery of a frog. The boundaries of the endothelial cells are stained black with silver nitrate. ✕ 350. (Maximow and Bloom, after Ranvier.)

CAPILLARIES

Substances can enter and leave the blood stream only through the walls of the capillaries. Diffusion through cells and tissue fluids is, at best, a slow process, and the capillary part of the circulatory system is designed to insure every cell adequate nourishment in spite of this. The following features facilitate exchange between blood and tissue: (1) The walls of the capillaries are extremely thin, consisting only of endothelium (Fig. 210). (2) The capillaries are very small, so that all blood must pass close to a capillary wall. They are about 8 microns in diameter, so small that red cells must pass through in single file. (3) The capillaries are numerous, their number varying in proportion to the maximum needs of the particular tissue they serve. In striated muscle, which has a high rate of metabolism when active, there is a capillary adjacent to nearly every muscle cell throughout its length. The capillaries form networks in the tissues, the meshes being a millimeter or less in length. (4) The great number of capillaries results in a large surface area through which diffusion may take place. (See estimate of capillary area in the lungs, p. 192.) (5) The blood moves through the capillaries slowly, less than 1 mm. per second, to allow time for diffusion. The rate in large arteries is about 250 mm. per second. Thus a blood corpuscle will travel from the heart to an organ in, say, two or three seconds and then spend an entire second traveling through a capillary a millimeter or less in length. The reason for this change of rate is as follows: The rate of flow through the system will be in inverse proportion to the total cross-section area at any level. Wherever an artery divides into two branches, each branch is smaller in diameter than the artery from which it arises, but its cross-section area is more than half as great, so that the total cross-section area of the blood channel is increased and the flow is decreased in proportion. For this reason the blood flows more and more slowly as it approaches the periphery of the arterial system. At the beginning of the capillaries the cross-section area increases suddenly because the capillaries, though small, are numerous, and the rate of flow drops abruptly. In the veins a similar situation, in the reverse direction, exists, so

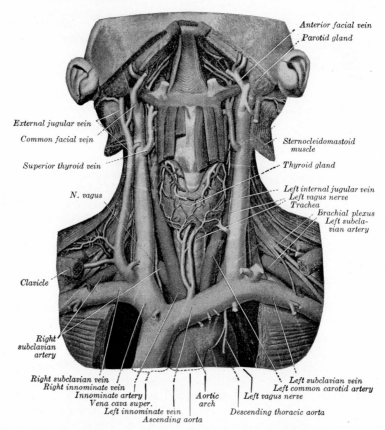

Figure 211. The arteries and veins of the neck. (Sobotta and McMurrich.)

that the blood flows faster and faster as it approaches the heart. It never equals the speed in the aorta, however, because the veins entering the heart have a total cross-section area greater than that of the aorta.

FUNCTION OF THE CAPILLARIES. Exchange of materials between cells and blood is not direct, but through the *tissue juice* or *tissue fluid*, small amounts of fluid surrounding and bathing the cells. A molecule diffuses through the capillary wall into the tissue fluid and from the tissue fluid into the cell, or in reverse direction, as the case may be. In addition to this diffusion, there is some filtration of the fluid part of the blood through the capillary walls, especially at the arterial end, where the blood pressure is high, so that the blood is continually contributing to the tissue fluid. This is similar to the more rapid filtration in the glomerulus of the kidney (p. 199). Part of the tissue fluid passes back into the blood capillaries at the venous end of the network or at any point where the pressure in the capillary happens to be low (assisted by osmosis). The remainder enters the lymphatic capillaries, which will be described later, and finds its way indirectly back into the blood by way of the thoracic ducts.

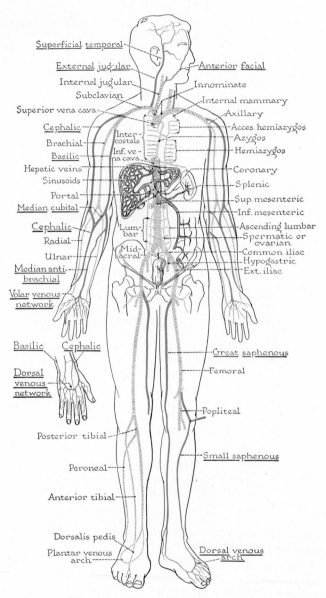

Figure 212. Diagram of the venous system. Deep veins are cut across, superficial veins are in solid blue. The labels of the superficial veins are underlined. Vessels of the portal system are in black. (Millard and King: Human Anatomy and Physiology. 3rd edition.)

THE SYSTEMIC VEINS

The blood from the systemic group of vessels returns to the heart through three main channels:

1. That from the wall of the heart returns through the coronary sinus.

2. That from the head, neck, upper extremity and part of the trunk returns through the superior vena cava.

3. That from the remainder of the trunk and the lower extremity returns through the inferior vena cava.

The Coronary Sinus. The coronary sinus receives most of the veins of the heart. It lies on the posterior aspect of the organ and terminates by emptying into the right atrium (Figs. 193, 194).

The Superior Vena Cava and Its Tributaries. The *superior vena cava* (Figs. 190, 211) is a short, wide vessel which runs from a point behind the first right costal cartilage downward to empty into the right atrium of the heart. It is formed above by the union of the right and left innominate veins, which drain the head, neck and upper extremities, and it receives as a tributary the azygos vein, which drains most of the blood from the thoracic and abdominal walls.

The *azygos*[13] *vein* (Fig. 218) is a long, slender unpaired vessel which passes upward on the right posterior abdominal and thoracic walls and receives the intercostal and lumbar veins. It terminates by entering the superior vena cava.

The right and left *innominate veins* (Fig. 211) are formed superiorly by the union of the internal jugular and subclavian veins. The right innominate vein is about 1 inch long and descends vertically behind the right clavicle to terminate in the superior vena cava. The left innominate vein passes obliquely from left to right across the upper end of the thorax behind the manubrium sterni.

The Veins of the Head and Neck. The two *internal jugular veins* (Figs. 211, 199) are the chief veins draining the head and neck. They are formed superiorly at the base of the skull as the continuations, through the jugular foramina (Figs. 27, 28), of the two large transverse sinuses which receive the blood from the brain. Inferiorly they unite with the subclavian veins to form the innominate veins. In the lower part of their course they run alongside and superficial to the common carotid arteries. They receive numerous tributaries from the face and neck (Fig. 213).

The *external jugular veins* (Figs. 211, 213) are smaller vessels which lie superficially in the lateral aspects of the neck. They

---

[13] Azygos: G., not yoked, not one of a pair, single.

Figure 213   **The Circulatory System** 253

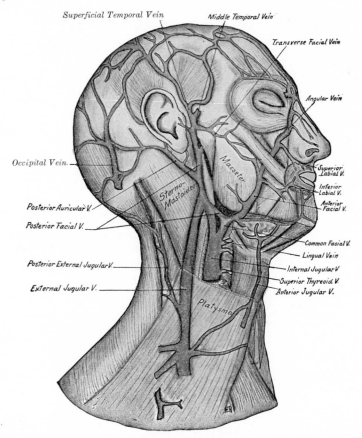

Figure 213. The veins of the right side of the head and neck. (Radasch.)

receive tributaries from the face and neck and empty into the subclavian veins.

The Veins of the Upper Extremity. The *subclavian veins* (Fig. 211), the chief veins draining the arm, accompany the subclavian arteries. Each is continuous peripherally with the *axillary vein,* which in turn receives the *brachial vein.* They follow the arteries of the same name.

The remaining veins of the arm are arranged in a superficial and a deep set. The deep set of veins follows the arteries. The superficial veins (Fig. 214) lie just beneath the skin and may easily be seen on the back of the hand and the front of the elbow.

PRACTICAL CONSIDERATIONS. The large superficial veins in front of the elbow are commonly used by surgeons when drawing blood from the body, or when injecting medicinal substances into the blood stream.

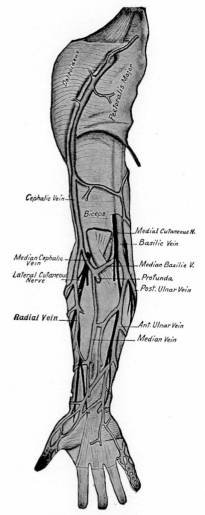

Figure 214. Superficial veins of the flexor aspect of the upper extremity. (Radasch.)

The Inferior Vena Cava and Its Tributaries. The *inferior vena cava* (Fig. 203) is a longer vessel than the superior vena cava. It begins at the level of the fifth lumbar vertebra by the union of the two common iliac veins, and passes upward on the posterior abdominal wall, through the diaphragm, to terminate in the right atrium of the heart. In its course it lies to the right of the aorta. Its largest tributaries are the hepatic and the renal veins.

The *hepatic veins* (Fig. 203) pass from the posterior aspect of

Figure 215   **The Circulatory System   255**

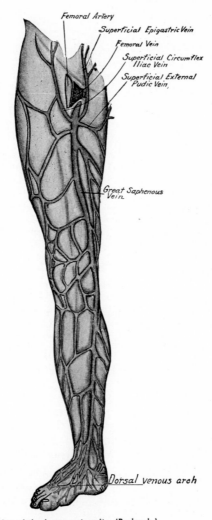

Femoral Artery

Superficial Epigastric Vein

Femoral Vein

Superficial Circumflex
   Iliac Vein

Superficial External
   Pudic Vein

Great Saphenous
  Vein

Dorsal venous arch

Figure 215.   The superficial veins of the lower extremity. (Radasch.)

the liver to the inferior vena cava. They receive the blood directly
from the liver and indirectly from the portal system.

The *renal veins* (Fig. 203) are two wide vessels which arise
in the kidneys and after a short course terminate in the inferior
vena cava.

The *common iliac veins* (Fig. 203) accompany the common iliac
arteries. Inferiorly they are formed by the union of the hypogastric
and external iliac veins; superiorly they unite to form the inferior
vena cava.

The *hypogastric veins* (O.T., internal iliac veins) receive the smaller veins of the pelvis.

The *external iliac veins* drain the legs.

The Veins of the Lower Extremity. The veins of the leg, like those of the arm, are arranged in a superficial and a deep group. The deep veins accompany the arteries and take their names, there being *femoral, popliteal, anterior tibial* and *posterior tibial veins.* The femoral vein passes into the external iliac vein.

The superficial veins of the leg (Fig. 215) lie directly beneath the skin. Many of them empty into the *great saphenous*[14] *vein,* a long vessel which begins on the foot, runs up the medial side of the leg, and enters the femoral vein just below the groin.

PRACTICAL CONSIDERATIONS. The great saphenous vein, because of its dependent and superficial position, is particularly vulnerable to the condition of varicosity ("varicose veins"). This condition is usually due to prolonged standing when the circulation in the leg is poor and the back pressure on the veins is high. This back pressure applied over a long period may make not only the saphenous vein but also its tributaries large and tortuous.

The Portal Circulation. The portal circulation (Fig. 216), a subdivision of the systemic circulation, consists of those vessels which drain the gastro-intestinal tract and spleen. It is formed as follows:

The veins draining the gastro-intestinal tract are the *superior mesenteric* and the *inferior mesenteric veins;* the vein draining the spleen is the *splenic vein.* The inferior mesenteric vein enters the splenic vein; the splenic vein unites with the superior mesenteric vein to form the *portal vein.* The portal vein is a large vessel which may easily be found in the lesser omentum passing alongside the hepatic artery and the bile ducts to the under surface of the liver. Inside the liver it breaks up into the large capillaries or sinusoids which we have already noted as being prominent in that organ. The blood from the sinusoids is drained into the *hepatic veins,* and is then passed on to the inferior vena cava.

The portal system is peculiar in that the blood it contains passes through two capillary networks during a single circuit. First, it is distributed through the celiac and mesenteric arteries to the capillaries of the gastro-intestinal tract and spleen. Second, after being collected in the portal vein, it is passed through the sinusoids of the liver. From the liver it is returned to the main systemic circulation.

---

[14] Saphenous: of Arabic origin and meaning the secret one; so called because it could not be easily identified on the surface of the body, and was of no use to the Arabs in letting blood (Hyrtl).

Figure 216   *The Circulatory System* **257**

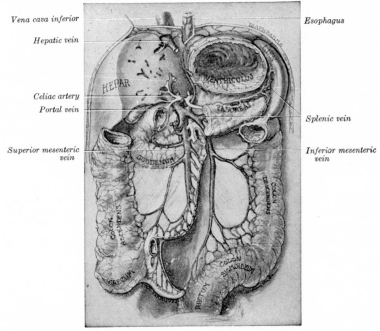

Figure 216. Veins of the portal system. Part of the liver (hepar) and stomach (ventriculus) have been cut away. (Callander.)

FUNCTION. The function of the portal circulation is to collect the blood from the gastro-intestinal tract, which after meals is rich in food materials, and to transmit it to the liver, where certain of these foodstuffs can be extracted and stored until needed. Toxic substances absorbed by the gut may be removed from the blood by the liver.

PRACTICAL CONSIDERATIONS. Obstruction to the flow of blood in the portal system occurs from various causes, such as cirrhosis (hardening) of the liver, cancer of the head of the pancreas, and so on. It leads to stasis of blood and hence to impairment of function in many of the organs of the abdominal cavity. If the portal vein is completely obstructed, the blood is slowly returned to the systemic circulation by a complicated round-about route.

THE LYMPHATIC SYSTEM

The lymphatic system consists of (1) a large number of lymphatic capillary vessels distributed widely through the tissues; (2) a system of collecting ducts which open into the blood stream; and (3) a number of lymph nodes or glands. The system as a whole differs from the blood vascular system in that it does not form a complete tubular circuit, for the lymphatic capillaries begin as blind ends. There is no part corresponding to the arteries.

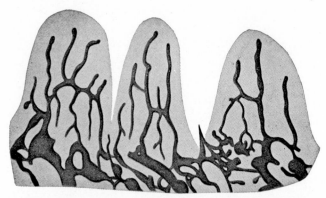

Figure 217. Lymphatic capillaries (lacteals) filled with Berlin blue in the villi of the intestine of a rat. (Maximow and Bloom, after Ranvier.)

The fluid within the lymphatic vessel is called *lymph*[15] from its watery appearance. It is derived from the tissue juices (p. 250) and is, on the whole, similar to, but not identical with, the blood plasma. The lymph within one group of lymphatic capillaries, namely, the *lacteals* of the intestinal villi, is called *chyle*. It contains a considerable amount of fat and is milky in appearance. The fat has been resynthesized and is present in the form of small droplets.

The **lymphatic capillaries** are structurally similar to blood capillaries, but they are somewhat larger in diameter and they have, as already stated, many blind ends. These blind ends are easily demonstrated in the lacteals (Fig. 217).

The lymphatic capillaries unite to form larger lymph vessels which are similar to small veins and, like them, are provided with valves. The larger vessels eventually open into two main ducts, the thoracic and right lymphatic ducts. The *thoracic duct* (Fig. 218) is the larger of the two. It begins on the posterior abdominal wall at the level of the second lumbar vertebra in a saccular dilatation called the *cisterna chyli*, passing upward behind the aorta. It drains the lower limbs, abdomen, including the digestive tract, and the left half of the thorax. It receives left jugular and subclavian branches and terminates by emptying into the junction of the left internal jugular and left subclavian veins. The *right lymphatic duct* is formed by the union of the right jugular, subclavian lymph and broncho-mediastinal trunks. It opens into the junction of the right internal jugular and right subclavian veins. (The left

---

[15] Lymph: L., water. The term is used by some anatomists to cover both the fluid within the lymphatic vessels and that free in the tissues; others restrict it to include the fluid in the vessels only. The second usage is adopted here.

Figure 218

The Circulatory System 259

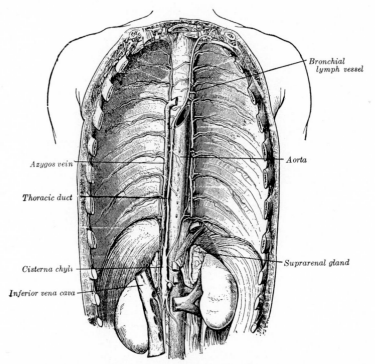

Bronchial
lymph vessel

Aorta

Azygos vein

Thoracic duct

Suprarenal gland

Cisterna chyli

Inferior vena cava

Figure 218. The thoracic duct and its tributaries. (Cunningham's Textbook of Anatomy.)

jugular and subclavian lymph trunks enter the thoracic duct near its termination.)

Movement of the lymph is due to the massaging action of muscles and organs that surround the vessels. Backflow is prevented by the valves. The slight negative pressure in the thorax during inspiration is also of importance in this connection, drawing lymph into the thoracic vessels.

The Lymph Nodes. The *lymph glands* or *lymph nodes* are flattened, ovoid or kidney-shaped bodies found at intervals along the lymph vessels. In size they range from 1 to 25 mm. Each gland has several lymph vessels entering it and a smaller number leaving it. The entering (or afferent) vessels are scattered over its external surface; those leaving it (the efferent vessels) pass out from an indented area called the *hilum.*

Microscopic. The lymph glands (Fig. 219) are composed largely of lymphoid tissue. *Lymphoid tissue* is not a primary tissue, but a collection of round cells called *lymphocytes* within the meshes of reticular tissue (Fig. 8). The cells may be evenly distributed throughout the whole mass (diffuse lymphoid tissue) or

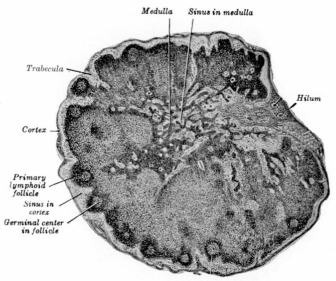

Figure 219. Section through a small lymph node of man. × 13. (Maximow and Bloom, after Sobotta.)

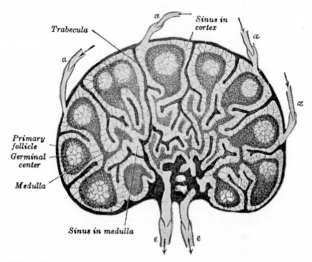

Figure 220. Diagram of a lymph node. *a*, Afferent and, *e*, efferent lymphatic vessels with valves; the arrows indicate the direction of lymph flow. (Maximow and Bloom.)

may be concentrated into spherical masses called primary *lymphoid follicles*. In the center of the follicle a less dense area is sometimes seen. It is sometimes called the *germinal center*, for here the lymphocytes are thought to be formed. Lymphoid tissue is found in many places throughout the body.

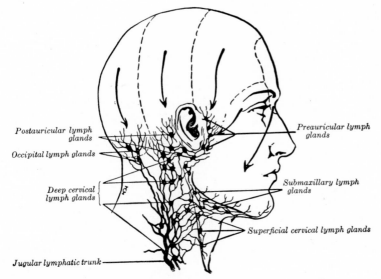

Postauricular lymph glands

Occipital lymph glands

Deep cervical lymph glands

Jugular lymphatic trunk

Preauricular lymph glands

Submaxillary lymph glands

Superficial cervical lymph glands

Figure 221. Regional lymph drainage from the scalp and face. (Callander.)

Each lymph gland consists of two easily differentiated parts: a superficial *cortex* and a deeply placed *medulla.* In the cortex are many lymphoid follicles; in the medulla the lymphoid tissue is solely of the diffuse type. Scattered throughout are many histiocytes. The organ as a whole is permeated by numerous large channels or *sinuses* (Fig. 220) which transmit the fluid lymph through the substance of the gland from the afferent to the efferent vessels. Many well-defined connective tissue *trabeculae* or septa are found within the gland.

FUNCTION OF THE LYMPH NODES. Lymph nodes have two main functions. One is the filtering out and destruction of foreign bodies, including bacteria. The other is the production of new lymphocytes.

Distribution of Lymph Nodes. The lymph nodes are found in various parts of the body and tend to be concentrated into groups. In the head and neck (Fig. 221) seven groups can be easily recognized:

1. The *submental*[16] *glands* lie beneath the chin.

2. The *submaxillary glands* lie under cover of the angle of the jaw.

3. The *preauricular glands* lie in front of the ear.

4. The *postauricular glands* lie behind the ear in close relation to the mastoid process.

---

[16] Submental: from L. *mentum,* chin. It is not to be confused with mental, pertaining to the mind!

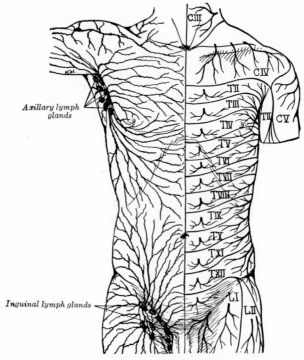

Figure 222. Lymph drainage (left) and nerve distribution (right) of the anterior body wall. (Callander.)

5. The *occipital glands* lie in the occipital region.

6. The *superficial cervical glands* lie in the neck over the sterno-cleidomastoid muscle.

7. The *deep cervical glands* lie deep in the neck in close relation to the carotid artery and the internal jugular vein.

These glands receive the lymph which comes from the regions of the head and neck directly above them. Thus the submental glands drain the lymph from the lower lip and the lower teeth; the submaxillary glands drain the lymph from the nose and part of the mouth; the preauricular glands drain the lymph from the head and face in front of the ear. The cervical glands receive lymph from the neck and in addition drain the glands above them.

In the upper extremity there are two chief groups of glands: the superficial cubital glands and the axillary glands.

1. The *superficial cubital*[17] *glands* lie near the medial epicondyle of the humerus. They drain the lymph from the forearm and hand.

---

[17] Cubital: L., pertaining to the elbow.

Figure 223   **The Circulatory System**   263

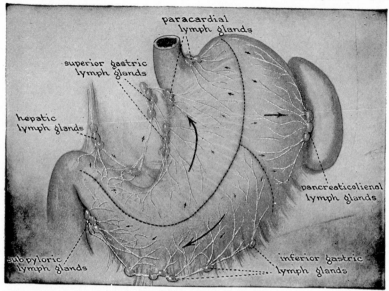

Figure 223. The lymphatic drainage of the stomach. (Babcock.)

2. The *axillary glands* (Fig. 222) lie alongside the axillary vessels. They receive the lymph from the arm and from the upper and lateral parts of the thoracic wall, including the breast.

In the lower extremity the most important glands are the *inguinal glands* (Fig. 222), which lie in the groin. They drain the lymph from the leg and the external genitalia.

In the thoracic and abdominal cavity there are numerous groups of glands. The following may be mentioned:

1. The *tracheobronchial glands* (Fig. 198) lie in close relation to the thoracic part of the trachea, the primary bronchi and their smaller branches within the lungs. They drain the lungs, heart and mediastinum.

2. The *gastric glands* (Fig. 223) lie along the lesser and greater curvatures of the stomach.

3. The *mesenteric glands* lie in the connective tissue of the mesentery. They receive the lymph from the intestine.

4. Numerous lymph glands lie alongside the aorta and the common iliac, external iliac and hypogastric vessels. They receive the lymph from the pelvic viscera and from the leg.

PRACTICAL CONSIDERATIONS. The lymph nodes are of importance in many infective diseases, for they are frequently involved in septic infections in the region which they drain. Thus the submaxillary glands are often infected from abscessed teeth, the inguinal glands become enlarged and tender in gonorrhea, and the superficial cubital and axillary glands may be involved in septic wounds

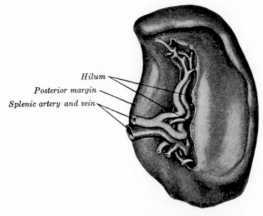

Hilum
Posterior margin
Splenic artery and vein

Figure 224. The spleen. (Callander.)

of the fingers and hand. In the latter case they are danger signs of spreading infection. Tuberculosis not infrequently invades the cervical and bronchial lymph glands.

In addition to their role in infective conditions, the lymph nodes are tremendously important in cancer. Cancer tends to spread along the lymphatic channels and to involve an increasing number of glands. In cancer of the breast the axillary glands are soon invaded, and in cancer of the stomach the gastric glands are rapidly involved. Hence to insure complete removal of a cancer, the associated lymph nodes must be removed also.

The Spleen.   The spleen[18] (Fig. 224) is an ovoid organ about 5 inches long which lies in the upper left quadrant of the abdominal cavity (Figs. 136, 204). Its lateral surface is convex and regular; its medial surface is irregular and is molded by neighboring structures. The *hilum,* where the blood vessels enter, lies in the center of the medial surface. The whole organ is covered with peritoneum, which is reflected from it in two folds, one passing forward and medially to the greater curvature of the stomach, the other backward to the kidney.

In histologic section (Fig. 225) the spleen appears to be a modified lymph node. It contains two kinds of tissue, a large amount of *red pulp* and a smaller amount of *white pulp.* The white pulp consists of a number of masses called *malpighian corpuscles* composed of lymphoid tissue and similar in structure to ordinary lymphoid follicles. The *red pulp* is found in cords or strands. It consists of lymphoid tissue with the addition of numerous cells of other types, including histiocytes and erythrocytes. The erythrocytes give it its characteristic red color. Between the cords of red pulp are wide *sinuses* filled with blood.

---

[18] Spleen: a Greek term; its equivalent in Latin is lien.

Figure 225   The Circulatory System 265

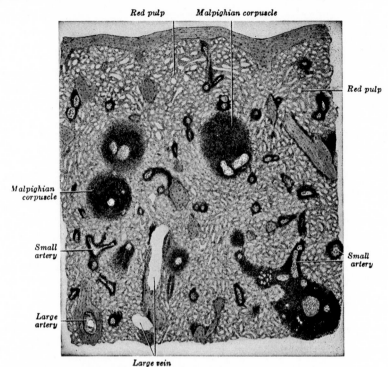

Figure 225. Human spleen. $\times$ 22. (Maximow and Bloom.)

FUNCTIONS OF THE SPLEEN.   Many different functions have been assigned to the spleen. Its histiocytes are able to ingest and destroy foreign particles, including bacteria; hence the organ has been called the "lymph node of the blood." It takes part in the destruction of red blood cells. The cells of the white pulp elaborate new lymphocytes. Other types of blood cells are not formed here normally, but they may be in certain diseases. The spleen is often classified with the ductless or endocrine glands, but a specific internal secretion has never been demonstrated in it.

Other organs which are composed of lymphoid tissue are the tonsils (p. 157), Peyer's patches (p. 165) and the thymus gland (Fig. 161). The last is large in young persons, but becomes small in the adult and normally disappears in the old.

THE BLOOD-FORMING AND BLOOD-DESTROYING ORGANS

The blood-forming organs are known collectively as the *hemopoietic*[19] *organs*. In the infant several structures take part in the process of blood formation, but in the adult their number is normally reduced to two, lymphoid tissue and red bone marrow.

---

[19] Hemopoietic: G., blood-forming.

Lymphoid tissue is the primary organ for the production of the nongranular leukocytes. These cells are formed in the lymph nodes, tonsils, malpighian corpuscles of the spleen, and wherever lymphoid tissue is found.

Red bone marrow is the organ for the production of granular leukocytes and erythrocytes. The regions of most active formation are the vertebrae, the ribs, the sternum, the diploë of the cranial bones, and the proximal ends of the humerus and femur.

The problem as to whether all the blood cells come from a single primitive cell type or from more than one type is much debated, but has not been definitely settled. The early developmental stages of the different blood cells are too complex to discuss here. We can only note that the cells from which the erythrocytes are developed have a nucleus, but that this nucleus is lost before the mature red cell circulates in the blood stream. Only in certain pathologic conditions are nucleated reds found in the blood.

The methods of destruction and elimination of blood cells are complex and are not altogether known. The erythrocytes live in the blood stream for a short period only—estimated to be from twenty-five to 100 days. They are then either destroyed in the spleen or are fragmented in the blood stream and removed by the histiocytes all over the body. It is interesting to calculate the rate at which new red cells must be produced.

The life span of the leukocytes in the blood is even shorter, probably less than three days. Many of the lymphocytes degenerate in the lymphoid tissues; others are lost by migration into the intestinal cavity. The method by which the granular leukocytes are destroyed is not clearly known.

PRACTICAL CONSIDERATIONS. In inflammatory conditions the total number of leukocytes circulating in the blood stream increases to a considerable degree, a condition known as leukocytosis. In the more acute and virulent infections the neutrophils are increased relatively more than the others, while in the more chronic disorders the lymphocytes predominate. In asthma and certain skin disorders the eosinophils are increased.

Anemia is a condition characterized by a reduction in the total number of erythrocytes. It may be either secondary to other recognized conditions, such as hemorrhage, exhausting illness, and the like, or it may be of the so-called primary or pernicious type. Pernicious anemia is of unknown origin and was, up until the introduction of liver feedings, almost invariably fatal. Leukemia is a disease characterized by an increase in the number of leukocytes. The increase may involve chiefly the lymphocytes, when it is known as lymphatic leukemia, or the granular leukocytes, when it is called myeloid leukemia.

THE RETICULO-ENDOTHELIAL SYSTEM

Scattered throughout the tissues of the body in different places are cells which have, among other functions, the capacity of engulfing and storing or destroying foreign particles. They are not all of the same form, and have accordingly been given different names in the various organs and tissues in which they are found. Collectively they have been called histiocytes, and also the cells of the reticulo-endothelial system. They have been described in loose connective tissue, in the lymph nodes, the spleen, the bone marrow, the liver, the hypophysis, and elsewhere. They play an important role in the defense against bacteria and in clearing the body of other foreign particles.

CHAPTER 13

THE NEURO-SENSORY SYSTEM

We HAVE now studied the organs and organ systems that carry on the activities of the living body, that enable it and its parts to move, that give it a degree of protection from its surroundings, that ingest, digest and absorb food to provide energy, that take in oxygen and give off carbon dioxide, that filter out and carry away non-volatile wastes, that carry materials from one part of the body to another, and that accomplish the production of new individuals. For convenience we have studied these systems of organs almost as though they existed independently of one another. Actually, of course, they are all parts of an organism that acts as a unit, an individual that cannot be separated into parts without destroying it. Now we may turn to the question, how are all these organs and systems of organs activated and coordinated? What starts them going, what speeds them up and slows them down and gets them to work together?

Such activation, control and coordination are accomplished by two means. One consists of a number of glands that release into the blood stream chemical substances that affect near or distant parts of the body. These glands are referred to collectively as the *endocrine system.* Anatomically they are not a system, being diverse in structure and embryonic origin and located at widely separated points. However, physiologically they do work together, and it will be convenient to describe them together in a later chapter.

The other means of activation, control and coordination is the *neuro-sensory system,* a system of communication between the parts of the body that is usually likened to a telephone system. A telephone system is an insufficient model, however, and it is more illuminating to compare the nervous system and sense organs to the automatic pilot in an airplane. This mechanism responds to a change in the direction of flight and initiates and controls appropriate activity.

Like this model, the neuro-sensory system must respond to significant changes or agents outside itself, convey a message to the proper place, and start something happening there. It must keep track of the activity while it is going on and control and modify it as needed. When the thing to be done is accomplished, it must change or stop the activity it started.

Let us take a simple example. The hand is lying quietly on a table. The person's attention is elsewhere. A hot object is brought into contact with the hand. Quickly the hand is jerked away. What has happened? A hot object brought into contact with the hand was a change in the environment, an external agent, that was significant because it would do harm to the body. The heat of the object is what a physiologist would call a *stimulus*. It was to this stimulus that there was response. From the point at which the stimulus was applied, some sort of message was transmitted to the appropriate muscles and that message activated them in such a way that the hand was withdrawn. All this was accomplished by the neuro-sensory system. The nervous system also carried messages to the brain that made the person aware of the pain and of the movements of his hand and arm. But the hand was pulled away before he had time to "decide" to withdraw it and send a message to the muscles to do so. Indeed, it can be shown in experimental animals that the brain is not involved in producing the action under these circumstances. Such an involuntary movement is called a *reflex action*.

If the person had been made aware of the approach of the hot object by messages from his eyes, he could have sent messages from the brain that would have withdrawn the hand before it was touched, or, on the other hand, he might have sent messages that would have inhibited the reflex and left the hand there to suffer the pain and damage.

Two other points should be noted. Whether the movement of the hand was reflex or voluntary, the messages were sent in patterns appropriate to produce the coordinated activity of a group of muscles. Second, if one sets out, say, to pick up a pencil, not only must the activity be initiated, but the nervous system must be kept informed by messages from the muscles, tendons and joints, and sometimes from the eyes, how much of the task has been accomplished, where the hand is, and in what direction it is moving in order that the actions of the muscles can be continually modified so as to carry the act to completion.

In addition to responding to external stimuli and information from muscles, tendons and joints, the neuro-sensory system responds to changes within the body so as to adjust the activities of the various organs to one another and to initiate appropriate activities of the body as a whole to meet changing internal needs.

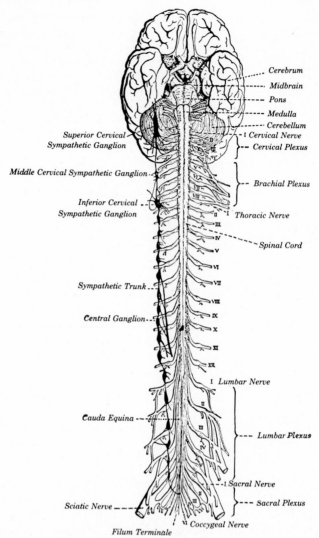

Cerebrum
Midbrain
Pons
Medulla
Cerebellum
Superior Cervical
Sympathetic Ganglion — I Cervical Nerve
— Cervical Plexus

Middle Cervical Sympathetic Ganglion — Brachial Plexus

Inferior Cervical
Sympathetic Ganglion — I Thoracic Nerve

— Spinal Cord

Sympathetic Trunk

Central Ganglion

I Lumbar Nerve

Cauda Equina

Lumbar Plexus

I Sacral Nerve

Sacral Plexus
Sciatic Nerve
VI Coccygeal Nerve
Filum Terminale

Figure 226. The human central nervous system and the proximal parts of the peripheral nerves. The autonomic system, shown on one side only, is drawn in black. Ventral aspect. (After Allen Thompson and Rauber.)

GENERAL PLAN

For convenience in description, the nervous system may be divided into brain, spinal cord and peripheral nerves (Fig. 226). The brain, which lies in the cranial cavity, and the spinal cord, which lies in the vertebral canal, are the two parts of a continuous structure, usually called the *central nervous system,* which, in the embryo, is a long tube closed at both ends (Figs. 323, 324). Thickenings, constrictions and outgrowths obscure this tubular structure in the adult, especially in the upper part which becomes the brain, but it is never obliterated. The student will do well to bear this in mind throughout his study of the central nervous system.

The peripheral nerves are often referred to as the *peripheral nervous system.* They arise from both the brain and the spinal cord. Those issuing from the brain are called cranial nerves; those issuing from the spinal cord are known as spinal nerves. The *cranial nerves* arise from the ventral aspect of the brain and supply chiefly the head and neck. The *spinal nerves* arise from the lateral aspects of the cord and supply the rest of the body.

The *autonomic nervous system* consists of those nerve trunks and ganglia which supply the internal viscera, blood vessels and glands.

NERVOUS TISSUE

The nervous system is composed of a special kind of tissue called nervous tissue. Nervous tissue contains two kinds of cells: (1) active conducting cells, called *neurons* or *nerve cells,* and (2) supporting elements called *neuroglia* or *glial cells.*

Nerve Cells. As was mentioned in the description of the cell in an earlier chapter, every cell responds to sudden changes in its environment, and the effect of stimulation at one point is transmitted to other parts of the cell. This property of responding to a stimulus is called *excitability.* Many agents can, under appropriate circumstances, act as stimuli: change in temperature, mechanical contact or damage, change in pressure, an electric current, radiation, and chemical substances.

A stimulus, if effective, results in a change in the structure and activity of the cell at the point stimulated. This change in structure and activity spreads to other parts of the cell. This is called *conduction.*

When a cell is stimulated and the excitation spreads, the result is a reaction characteristic of the cell. For example, a muscle cell when stimulated will contract, and, owing to conduction, the whole cell contracts, not just the part adjacent to the point stimulated. When a gland cell is stimulated, it releases its characteristic product; that is, it secretes.

The essential elements of the nervous system are specialized cells called *nerve cells* or *neurons.*[1] Their function is to be readily susceptible to stimulation under circumstances appropriate to their various situations, to conduct the state of excitation, here called

---

[1] Neuron: G., nerve.

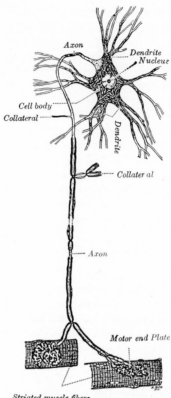

Figure 227. Diagram of a neuron. The type illustrated is a somatic motor neuron, and the terminal arborizations of the axon are motor end plates on striated muscle fibers. All but the proximal part of the axon is provided with myelin sheath and neurilemma. Compare with Figure 228. (After Barker, from Jordan: Textbook of Histology. D. Appleton-Century Company.)

the *nerve impulse,* rapidly and to stimulate, in turn, another neuron, a muscle cell or a gland cell as the case may be. As might be expected, nerve cells are primarily long fibers.

A typical *nerve cell* or *neuron* (Fig. 227) consists of a cell body and several processes. The cell body is varied in shape and may be round, pyramidal, stellate, and so on. It contains the usual central nucleus and surrounding cytoplasm. The nucleus is not essentially different from those found in cells elsewhere. The cytoplasm contains characteristic elements that need not detain us here.

The processes of the nerve cells, called *nerve fibers,* are thread-like extensions of the cytoplasm. They are of two types: axons and dendrites. There is only one *axon* to a cell. It is smooth and slender and is often of great length. Its branches, called *collaterals,* are few

Figure 228   *The Neuro-sensory System*   273

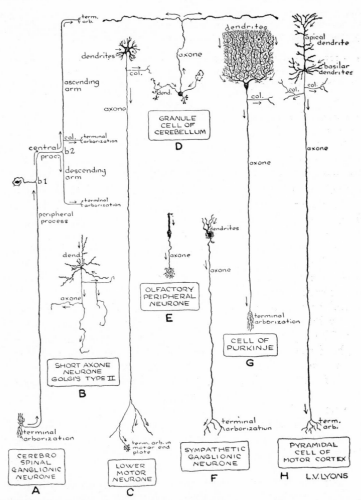

Figure 228. Some of the principal forms of neurons. The sheaths are not shown. The axons, except in B, are much shorter in proportion to the size of body and dendrites than they actually are. The direction of conduction is shown by the arrows. col., Collateral branch; proc., process; term. arb., terminal arborization. (Bailey's Textbook of Histology, published by The Williams & Wilkins Co.)

in number and pass off at a right angle to the main fiber. Both the axon and its collaterals terminate in a brush-like ending of small fibers known as the *terminal arborization*. The axon conducts impulses *away* from the cell body.

There are usually several or many *dendrites*[2] to a cell (Fig. 228).

_____

[2] Dendrite: from G. *dendron*, a tree.

Figure 229. Nonmyelinated nerve fibers with neurilemma. The nuclei shown belong to the cells of the neurilemma. The sheath itself is so thin that it cannot be distinguished here from the surface of the nerve fiber. (Maximow and Bloom, after Cajal.)

As a general rule they are thicker than the axon and break up into many tree-like branches close to the cell body. The dendrites conduct impulses *toward* the cell body.

The terms "axon" and "dendrite" are not applicable to one type of neuron (Fig. 228, A). In this type but one fiber issues from the cell body. It soon divides into two fibers. One, called the *peripheral process,* conducts impulses toward the cell body. The other, called the *central process,* conducts them away from the cell body. In this respect the second corresponds to an axon.

Axons and the central and peripheral processes are frequently surrounded by sheaths. One type of sheath is an extremely thin, continuous covering, the *neurilemma,* formed of cells (Fig. 229). The other is a non-cellular covering formed of fatty substances, the *myelin*[3] or *medullary sheath* (Fig. 230). When both are present, the myelin sheath lies between the neurilemma and the nerve fiber. The myelin sheath is not continuous throughout the whole length of the fiber, for it is broken at intervals into a number of separate segments, between which are connecting zones called *nodes of Ranvier* (Fig. 230). All fibers outside the spinal cord and brain have neurilemmal sheaths; some have myelin sheaths, and some do not. Within the spinal cord and brain, fibers do not have neurilemma—the glia cells (see below) serve the purpose. Fibers within the cord or brain may or may not have myelin sheaths. Because of the sheaths that surround it the nerve fiber proper is sometimes referred to as the *axis cylinder.*

Within the nervous system are countless neurons. In the brain and cord many run in parallel formation, forming tracts or columns of different lengths; others run singly or in small groups in various directions. They are further arranged in sequence so that they form longer or shorter chains. In these the terminal arborization of the axon of the first neuron comes in contact with the dendrites or cell body of the second, the terminal arborization of the second neuron touches the dendrites or cell body of the third, and so on. The places where these contacts are made are called *synapses.*[4]

Outside the brain and cord, the nerve fibers run in bundles

---

[3] Myelin: G., marrow.

[4] Synapse, synapsis: from G., conjugation, union.

Figure 230   **The Neuro-sensory System   275**

called *nerves.* When cell bodies occur in a nerve, they are usually congregated in one place where they produce an enlargement called a *ganglion.*[5]

THE NERVE IMPULSE AND THE SYNAPSE. A stimulus, to be effective—that is, to result in a nerve impulse—must produce certain changes in the surface layer of a nerve fiber or cell body. This local altered condition, this change at the spot where the stimulus impinged on the fiber or cell body, is the *nerve impulse.* It is attended by small, local electric currents. These currents flow into the adjacent undisturbed surface and are sufficient to produce the change there. Electric currents are, of course, set up in this newly stimulated area, and so the nerve impulse spreads over the surface of the cell body and propagates itself along a nerve fiber. The surface of the fiber or cell body is restored to its original condition within a few thousandths of a second after the disturbance has passed. This recovery permits a second impulse to follow the first after a short interval. Indeed, it is characteristic of nerve activity that impulses occur as longer or shorter bursts; a single impulse is probably rare except under experimental conditions. The *nerve impulse* is, then, a brief, self-propagating disturbance that travels over the surface of a nerve cell body and nerve fiber.

The rate at which a nerve impulse passes along a nerve fiber varies in proportion to the diameter of the fiber. The largest fibers, about 22 microns in diameter, conduct at a rate of about 120 meters per second (nearly 400 feet per second or about 270 miles per hour, something more than a third the speed of sound). The smallest, about 1 micron in diameter, conduct at a rate of about 6 meters per second (about 19½ feet per second or 13½ miles per hour).

There is but one kind of nerve impulse. The various sensations—pain, cold, touch, and so on—are not conveyed by different varieties of nerve impulse, but rather are the consequence of where the impulses arrive in the brain. This is further discussed on page 321. The impulse that causes a muscle to contract is the same as one that causes a gland to secrete, and neither differs from one that results in a sensation.

The intensity of a sensation is not related to the magnitude of the nerve impulse. The magnitude may vary under certain circumstances, but what determines the intensity of the sensation is the frequency with which the impulses follow one

[5] *Ganglion* (plural *ganglia*): G., a swelling.

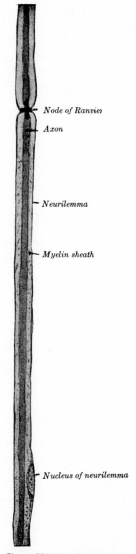

Node of Ranvier

Axon

Neurilemma

Myelin sheath

Nucleus of neurilemma

Figure 230. Myelinated nerve fiber. This fiber is from a peripheral nerve, and therefore it has, outside the myelin sheath, the neurilemma. (Cajal's Histology, published by the Williams & Wilkins Co.)

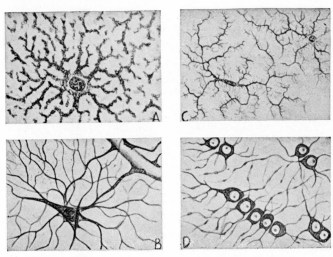

Figure 231. Glial cells. A, B, D, Various forms of macroglia; C, microglia. (Ranson, after del Rio Hortega.)

another. Consistent with this, the more intense a stimulus is, the greater the frequency of the resulting nerve impulses. Frequency also affects other results of nerve activity.

The tips of the terminal arborization of an axon are in contact with the dendrites or cell bodies of other neurons. (For axons that end in muscle or gland, see page 33.) Each tip terminates as a small enlargement or *end bulb.* The contact of an end bulb with the dendrite or cell body of another neuron is called a *synapse.* There seems to be no continuity between the two neurons at the synapse, only contact. Furthermore, the nerve impulse does not pass across the synapse from one neuron to another. Rather, when an impulse arrives at an end bulb, something happens there, that, after a slight delay, may stimulate the neuron on which it lies, or may make it more or less susceptible to stimulation by an adjacent end bulb of another neuron, or may have no apparent effect at all.

The propagation of a nerve impulse along a fiber is automatic. If the impulse is started, it goes to the end of the fiber. Nothing but damage to the neuron will stop it. At the synapse, on the contrary, a number of things may happen. The next neuron may be stimulated or it may not be, depending on circumstances of which we do not have adequate understanding. *In any event, from among the various possibilities, the final outcome of any nervous activity seems to be determined at the synapses.*

Glial Cells. The *glial cells* or *neuroglia*[6] (Fig. 231) are the supporting cells of the central nervous system and correspond to the connective tissue of other organs. They contain round or oval nuclei, a small amount of cytoplasm and a variable number of processes. They can be divided into two types: macroglia and microglia.

The *macroglia* form the chief supporting elements of the central

[6] Neuroglia: G., nerve glue.

Figure 232   *The Neuro-sensory System*   277

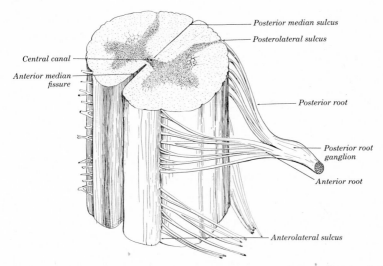

Figure 232.   Diagram of a section of the spinal cord and a spinal nerve. (Redrawn from M. W. Woerdeman: Atlas of Human Anatomy. Blakiston Co.)

nervous system. They replace the cells of the neurilemma of the peripheral nerves, and perhaps act as insulators for the conducting fibers.

The *microglia* are, as their name indicates, smaller than the macroglia. They are able to take up and destroy bacteria and other foreign bodies, and are perhaps related to the histiocytes and to the reticulo-endothelial system.

PRACTICAL CONSIDERATIONS.   Glial cells are clinically important because they sometimes give rise to tumors within the central nervous system. These tumors are called gliomas. They are divided into several groups which differ in their degree of malignancy. Some progress rapidly and lead to death within a few months; others take years to reach any appreciable size and are relatively benign. Some of them can be successfully removed surgically.

THE MAJOR STRUCTURAL FEATURES OF THE NERVOUS SYSTEM

The Spinal Cord.   The spinal cord is a long, slender cylinder lying within the vertebral canal. Superiorly it is continuous, as it passes through the foramen magnum, with the brain. Inferiorly, at the level of the first lumbar vertebra, it tapers off to a point and is continued, as a thin strand of non-nervous tissue, the *filum ter-minale*, to the lower end of the vertebral canal. From the sides of the spinal cord issue the *spinal nerves* (Fig. 232). The cord is enclosed in three layers of connective tissue which are described at the end of this chapter under Meninges.

The spinal cord is not uniform throughout its length in either

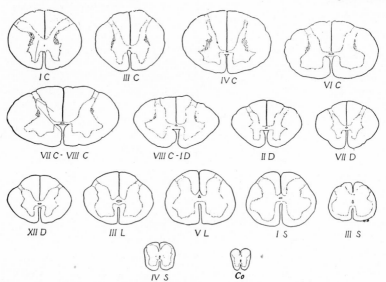

Figure 233. Outline drawings of sections through representative segments of the human spinal cord: C, cervical; D, dorsal or thoracic; L, lumbar; S, sacral; Co, coccygeal. (Ranson-Clark: Anatomy of the Nervous System. 9th edition.)

shape or diameter. It shows two swellings, the *cervical enlargement* in the lower cervical region and the *lumbar enlargement* somewhat above the lumbar region of the vertebral column. In cross section the spinal cord is oval in the regions of the enlargements, nearly round in the other parts (Fig. 233). Centrally it contains a small *central canal* which reminds us that the central nervous system, from an early stage in its development, was, and still is in the adult, a tubular structure. On the anterior surface of the cord is the deep *anterior median fissure,* cutting in almost to the central canal. On the posterior surface is the shallow *posterior median sulcus,*[7] beneath which the *posterior median septum* extends almost to the central canal. There is also an *anterolateral sulcus* and a *posterolateral sulcus* from which the roots of the spinal nerves emerge.

In cross section the cut surface shows distinct white and gray areas. The gray areas are roughly in the shape of a letter **H** (Fig. 232). The white areas surround this. The *white substance* of the spinal cord is composed almost entirely of nerve fibers, most of them with myelin sheaths which give the substance its white color. The *gray substance* is composed of fibers and nerve cell bodies

[7] *Sulcus:* L., groove or furrow.

and therefore contains less myelin. This same differentiation of white and gray substance is also present in the brain.

In most of our drawings of *sections* through spinal cord and brain the fibers are shown as dots. In these figures, therefore, the white matter is gray, and the gray matter more or less white. This reversal of shade is necessitated by the technique of drawing and must be borne in mind when studying these figures.

Returning to the gray substance of the spinal cord (Figs. 232, 249), the crossbar of the **H** is called the *gray commissure*. It passes on each side of the central canal. The lower limbs of the **H** are the *anterior columns*, "column" being an appropriate term when we consider the whole cord, not just the surface of a cross section. Similarly, the upper limbs of the **H** are called the *posterior columns*. Lateral to each posterior column is an area of mixed white and gray substance called the *recticular formation*.

In each lateral half of the cord the white substance is divided into three parts. The *anterior funiculus*[8] lies between the anterior median fissure, the anterior column of gray substance, and the anterolateral sulcus. The two anterior funiculi are connected by the *white commissure* anterior to the gray commissure. The *lateral funiculus* lies between the anterolateral sulcus and the posterior column of gray matter, partially surrounding the anterior column. The *posterior funiculus* lies between the posterior column and the posterior median septum.

Within each funiculus are numerous bundles of fibers having similar function or destination. These are called *tracts*. Ordinarily they can be distinguished only when by accidental or, in animals, experimental injury a group of nerve fibers has been cut. After a fiber has been cut it degenerates and can then be readily distinguished from the surrounding living fibers.

The Spinal Nerves. A *nerve* is a bundle of nerve fibers outside the spinal cord or brain. It may be likened to a telephone cable composed of many wires, each insulated from the rest and eventually leaving the cable and going to its own destination.

In a transverse section of a spinal nerve (Fig. 234) large numbers of closely packed fibers, some myelinated, some unmyelinated, can be seen. These fibers are grouped in small bundles called *fascicles*, each surrounded by a dense sheath of connective tissue, the *perineurium*. Surrounding the whole nerve and, to some extent, lying between the fascicles with their perineural sheaths is looser connective tissue, the *epineurium*. From the perineurium strands of connective tissue, called *endoneurium*, extend into the spaces between the individual nerve fibers.

The fibers in a nerve are functionally of two types: (1) *motor*

---

[8] Funiculus (plural *funiculi*): L., a little cord.

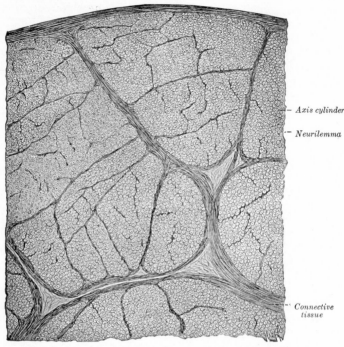

Axis cylinder

Neurilemma

Connective
tissue

Figure 234. Part of a cross section through a nerve trunk. The small circles represent the cross sections of medullated nerve fibers; the axis cylinders show as points in their centers. (Böhm, Davidoff and Huber.)

or *efferent*[9] *fibers*, which carry impulses from the central nervous system (brain or cord) to muscles or glands. These are the axons of nerve cells whose cell bodies lie in the cord or brain. (2) *Sensory* or *afferent*[10] *fibers*, which carry impulses from sense organs or sensory endings to the central nervous system. These fibers are the peripheral processes of neurons whose cell bodies lie in the dorsal root ganglia of spinal nerves or in the ganglia of cranial nerves.

The spinal nerves issue in pairs from the spinal cord. Each nerve has two roots, the *anterior root* and the *posterior root*. The former arises by a number of rootlets from the anterolateral sulcus, the latter in a similar manner from the posterolateral sulcus (Fig. 232).

On the posterior root is a swelling, the *posterior root ganglion*. In it are located the cell bodies of all the neurons whose fibers lie in the posterior root.

The anterior and posterior roots unite to form the main spinal nerve. This issues from the vertebral canal through the interverte-

---

[9] Efferent: from L. *ex*, out, plus *ferre*, to bear.
[10] Afferent: from L. *ad*, to, plus *ferre*, to bear.

Figure 235   **The Neuro-sensory System**   281

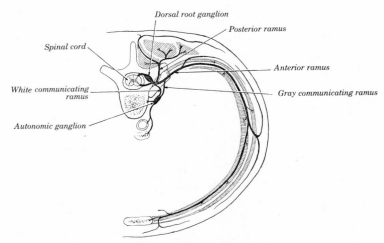

Dorsal root ganglion

Posterior ramus

Spinal cord

Anterior ramus

White communicating ramus

Gray communicating ramus

Autonomic ganglion

Figure 235. Diagram of distribution of spinal nerve in thoracic region. (Redrawn from M. W. Woerdeman: Atlas of Human Anatomy, Blakiston Co.)

bral foramen (Figs. 16, 21). Just outside the intervertebral foramen, the spinal nerve divides into a *posterior ramus* and an *anterior ramus* (Fig. 235). It also gives off two small branches anteriorly, the *white communicating ramus* and the *gray communicating ramus*. The gray ramus consists of unmyelinated fibers.

The spinal nerves issue from the cord in thirty-one pairs (Fig. 226), of which eight are cervical, twelve thoracic, five lumbar, five sacral and one coccygeal. The number of nerves corresponds to the number of vertebrae except in the cervical region, where eight nerves and seven vertebrae are present. The first cervical nerve issues between the skull and the first cervical vertebra. Each remaining cervical nerve issues above the vertebra of corresponding number. The eighth emerges between the seventh cervical and the first thoracic, and the remaining nerves issue below the vertebrae of corresponding number.

Within the vertebral canal the cervical and thoracic nerves pass out more or less horizontally to their places of exit. The remaining nerves pass downward before leaving the vertebral canal because the cord itself comes to an end opposite the first lumbar vertebra. The group of descending nerves below this level has been given the fanciful name of *cauda equina*.[11]

After leaving the vertebral canal the spinal nerves pass to be distributed to all parts of the body. The courses of the anterior and posterior rami and their main branches in the thoracic region are shown in Figure 235. The distribution in the abdominal region is

---

[11] Cauda equina: L., horse's tail.

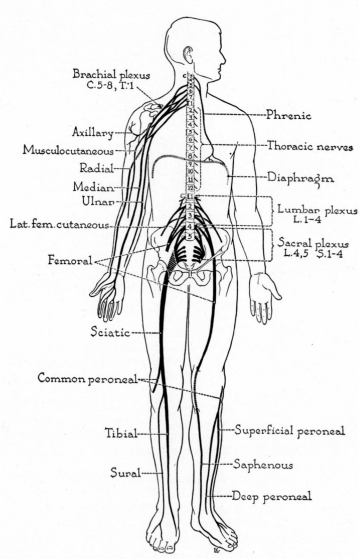

Brachial plexus
C.5-8, T.1

Axillary
Musculocutaneous
Radial
Median
Ulnar
Lat. fem. cutaneous

Femoral

Sciatic

Common peroneal

Tibial

Sural

Phrenic
Thoracic nerves
Diaphragm
Lumbar plexus
L. 1–4
Sacral plexus
L.4,5 S.1-4

Superficial peroneal
Saphenous
Deep peroneal

Figure 236. Distribution of the spinal nerves in the cervical and lumbar regions. (Millard and King: Human Anatomy and Physiology. 3rd edition.)

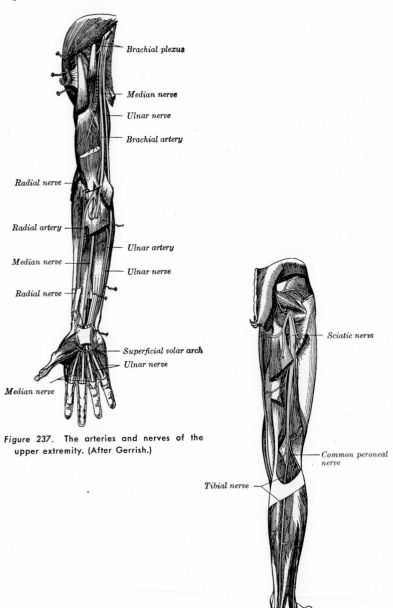

Brachial plexus

Median nerve

Ulnar nerve

Brachial artery

Radial nerve

Radial artery

Ulnar artery

Median nerve

Ulnar nerve

Radial nerve

Superficial volar arch

Ulnar nerve

Median nerve

Figure 237. The arteries and nerves of the
upper extremity. (After Gerrish.)

Sciatic nerve

Common peroneal
nerve

Tibial nerve

Figure 238.   Nerves of the right lower extremity, posterior view. (After Gerrish.)

similar. Those supplying the arm and leg are much larger than the others. They divide, recombine and divide again in complicated patterns to form two plexuses: the brachial plexus and the lumbosacral plexus.

The *brachial plexus* (Figs. 226, 236, 199, 211) is formed from the lower four cervical and the first thoracic nerves. The pattern of dividing and combining is too complicated to discuss here, and we shall note only that eventually three nerve cords, called the *cords of the brachial plexus,* are formed. From these cords the peripheral nerves to the arm are derived. Of these the most important are (1) the radial, (2) the ulnar, and (3) the median nerves.

1. The *radial nerve* (O.T., musculospiral) (Fig. 237) winds around the back of the humerus from the medial to the lateral side. Its terminal part passes down the radial side of the forearm. It carries motor fibers to the muscles of the back of the arm, i.e., to the triceps, extensor digitorum communis, and so on, and sensory fibers from parts of the back of the forearm and hand.

2. The *ulnar nerve* (Fig. 237) passes down the medial side of the upper arm and behind the medial epicondyle of the humerus. It then runs down the ulnar side of the forearm to the hand. It carries motor fibers to some of the muscles of the front of the forearm and hand, and sensory fibers from the ulnar aspect of the same region.

3. The *median nerve* (Fig. 237) passes down the middle of the anterior aspect of the forearm and enters the palm of the hand. It carries motor fibers to the muscles of the front of the forearm and hand not supplied by the ulnar nerve, and sensory fibers from the radial half of the palm.

The *lumbosacral plexus* (Figs. 226, 236, 206) is formed from the lumbar, sacral and coccygeal nerves. It gives rise to many peripheral branches, the most important of which are (1) the femoral and (2) the sciatic nerves.

1. The *femoral nerve* (Figs. 236, 206, 207, 79) passes across the iliac fossa and under the inguinal ligament to the front of the thigh. It gives off numerous motor and sensory branches to the muscles and skin on the anterior side of the thigh. One long sensory branch, the *saphenous nerve,* passes down the medial side of the lower leg to the foot.

2. The *sciatic*[12] *nerve* (Figs. 238, 79) is the longest nerve in the

---

[12] Sciatic: L. *sciaticus,* from G. *ischion,* hip.

~~Bone~~

17

Bones + Joints - _16 - 68_

Neuro-Sensory Sys. _268 -_
                   _341_

cartilagi

— BUY STRONGBARN —

body. It passes into the buttock and then runs down the back of the thigh, where it divides into two terminal branches, the tibial and the common peroneal nerves.

The *tibial nerve* (Fig. 238) passes down the back of the leg and enters the sole of the foot. The *common peroneal nerve* winds around the head of the fibula and supplies the peroneal region of the leg and the dorsum of the foot (Fig. 209). Both nerves contain motor and sensory fibers.

The spinal nerves not belonging to either the brachial or lumbosacral plexus are smaller than those just described and are divided into two groups. The first group, composed of the nerves above the brachial plexus, forms the *cervical plexus,* the branches of which are distributed chiefly to the skin and muscles of the neck and back of the head.

One important branch, the *phrenic*[13] *nerve* (Figs. 236, 162, 163, 199), passes downward to supply the diaphragm. It arises chiefly from the fourth cervical nerve, with contributions from the third and fifth. This curious origin so far from the muscle it innervates is explained by the course of embryonic development. In the early embryo the heart lies in the throat region. Just behind the heart arise the rudiments from which the diaphragm will develop. Later, as the lungs develop, the heart and the developing diaphragm move caudad to make room for them, and the nerve which has already established connection must follow. When we study the cranial nerves, we shall find that the vagus nerve has similarly followed the heart in its caudal migration.

The second group consists of the thoracic nerves, lying between the brachial and lumbosacral plexuses. Their distribution was described earlier.

PRACTICAL CONSIDERATIONS. The peripheral nerves are subject to injury, and if torn or seriously injured the part they supply is paralyzed and rendered insensitive. The brachial plexus is sometimes injured in babies during delivery, with the result that the child is born with a paralyzed arm. The radial nerve, clinging

---

[13] Phrenic: G. *phren*, (1) diaphragm and (2) brain. From this word, which dates back to the time when the heart was thought to be the seat of the emotions, two series of terms have been derived. From its first meaning, heart or diaphragm, we get the name of the phrenic nerve and such compound words as phrenospasm, phrenicotomy, *et cetera*. On the other hand, from its use signifying the brain, we get phrenology, several compound terms ending phrenia, such as schizophrenia, and the old term phrenitis, now transformed into frenzy. The heart continues to be thought of as the seat of the emotions only in amorous affairs, in which the mind plays little part.—From O. H. Perry Pepper: Medical Etymology.

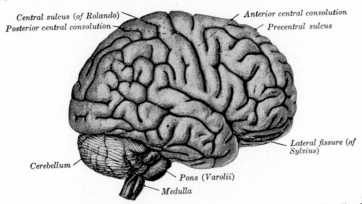

Central sulcus (of Rolando)
Posterior central convolution
Anterior central convolution
Precentral sulcus
Lateral fissure (of Sylvius)
Cerebellum
Pons (Varolii)
Medulla

Figure 239. The lateral surface of the human brain. (Reduced from Warren: Handbook of Anatomy, Harvard University Press.)

as it does so closely to the humerus, may be torn in fracture of this bone. The exposed position of the ulnar nerve behind the elbow makes it readily accessible to injury. The tingling in the fingers produced by a blow on the "funny bone" is due to injury to this nerve.

The peripheral nerves are sometimes diseased by toxic poisons such as alcohol and lead. Such poisons usually affect a number of nerves at the same time, so that the condition is known as multiple neuritis. A common effect is paralysis of the extensor muscles of the wrist, which produces the well known "wrist drop," and paralysis of the dorsiflexors of the ankle producing "foot drop."

The Lower Part of the Brain Stem. Within the foramen magnum the spinal cord becomes brain. The transition is not abrupt, and any exact dividing line between cord and brain is arbitrary. The axial part of the brain, the part which is obviously a continuation of the spinal cord, is called the brain stem. The lower part of the brain stem is subdivided into three parts, which, named from below upward, are the medulla[14] oblongata, the pons and the midbrain. The student would do well to read at this point the section on the development of the central nervous system on pages 371 and 393 to 395.

As we follow the brain stem up from the cord we find that it enlarges and that its surface features change. The anterior median fissure becomes shallower, and the areas between it and the anterolateral sulci become more prominent. These two enlarged areas are the *pyramids* (Fig. 241). They appear to end abruptly at a large transverse band of fibers that crosses the ventral surface of the brain stem. This band is called the *pons*. Actually the fibers that constitute the pyramids pass forward through the pons and appear above it in the *cerebral peduncles*. Where the fibers of the pyr-

---

[14] Medulla: L., marrow. The technical term for the spinal cord is medulla spinalis, though this is seldom used.

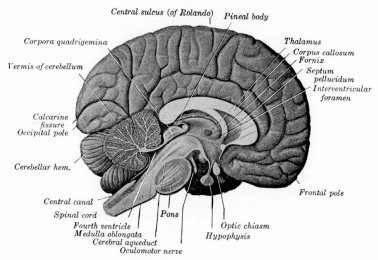

Central sulcus (of Rolando)   Pineal body

Corpora quadrigemina

Vermis of cerebellum

Thalamus
Corpus callosum
Fornix
Septum
pellucidum
Interventricular
foramen

Calcarine
fissure
Occipital pole

Cerebellar hem.

Frontal pole

Central canal
Spinal cord
Fourth ventricle
Medulla oblongata
Cerebral aqueduct
Oculomotor nerve

Pons

Optic chiasm
Hypophysis

Figure 240.   Median sagittal section of the human brain. (Sobotta and McMurrich.)

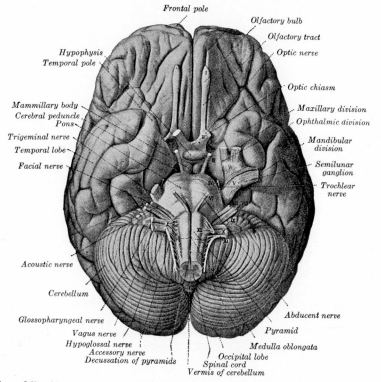

Frontal pole

Olfactory bulb

Olfactory tract

Optic nerve

Hypophysis
Temporal pole

Optic chiasm

Mammillary body
Cerebral peduncle
Pons

Trigeminal nerve
Temporal lobe

Facial nerve

Maxillary division
Ophthalmic division

Mandibular
division

Semilunar
ganglion

Trochlear
nerve

Acoustic nerve

Cerebellum

Glossopharyngeal nerve
Vagus nerve
Hypoglossal nerve
Accessory nerve
Decussation of pyramids

Abducent nerve

Pyramid

Medulla oblongata

Occipital lobe
Spinal cord
Vermis of cerebellum

Figure 241.   Ventral view of the human brain. (Sobotta and McMurrich.)

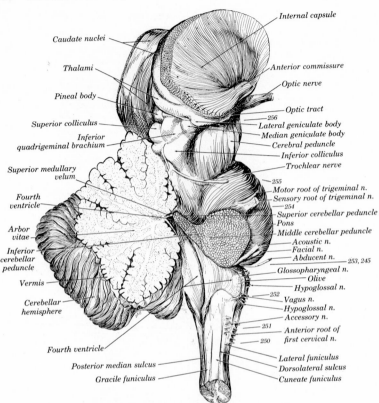

Figure 242. Dorsolateral view of the brain stem. Half of the cerebellum has been removed and all the posterior part of the roof of the fourth ventricle, including the choroid plexus. Most of both cerebral hemispheres has been removed, leaving little but the
internal capsules and the parts median to them and beneath the central parts of the
lateral ventricles. (Redrawn from M. W. Woerdeman: Atlas of Human Anatomy. Blakiston
Co.)

amids disappear into the pons there emerges a pair of cranial
nerves, the *abducent nerves.* In the anterior median fissure between the caudal parts of the pyramids can be seen small bands
of fibers crossing from one pyramid to the other. This is called the
decussation[15] *of the pyramids.* Several cranial nerves emerge from
the anterolateral sulci beside the pyramids. Posterior and lateral
to these nerves and to the superior part of the pyramid there is,
on each side, a prominent swelling, the *olive* (Fig. 242). This is
primarily due to an aggregation of nerve cell bodies beneath the
surface.

---

[15] Decussation: from L. *decussare,* to cross like an X, the Roman numeral 10.

An aggregation of nerve cell bodies within the brain is called a *nucleus*.[16] The term may be used for any column or layer of gray matter in the central nervous system, but usually these are referred to as *column* or *cortex*, and nucleus is reserved for more circumscribed areas.

The gray substance within the olive is the *inferior olivary nucleus* (Figs. 252, 253). (The *superior olivary nucleus* is a small body further craniad.)

Turning now to the dorsal side of the brain stem, we find a large folded mass of nerve tissue, the *cerebellum*[17] (Figs. 239, 242), which hides a large part of the brain stem. The cerebellum consists of two lobes, or *hemispheres*, united by a median part called the *vermis*.[18] The fibers of the pons, turning up on each side of the brain stem, run into the cerebellum and appear to support it. These anterolateral parts of the pons are, therefore, called the *cerebellar peduncles*.

If the cerebellar peduncles are cut, it will be found that each consists of three distinct bundles of fibers (Figs. 242, 244). The most lateral is the one from the pons. The second, lying medial to it, consists of fibers coming from inferior parts of the brain stem, and the third, lying medial to the second, consists of fibers coming from superior parts of the brain stem. These three bands of fibers are sometimes called the *superior, middle* and *inferior peduncles of the cerebellum*, the middle one being that from the pons. Frequently the superior cerebellar peduncle is called the *brachium conjunctivum;*[19] the middle cerebellar peduncle, the *brachium pontis;* and the inferior cerebellar peduncle, the *corpus restiforme* or *restiform*[20] *body*. Both sets of terms are used, and the student had best learn both.

Cutting the three peduncles on each side does not free the cerebellum, however. It is still attached superiorly to a thin sheet of nervous tissue, the *superior medullary velum,*[21] and inferiorly to a similar sheet, the *posterior medullary velum*. Cutting these permits the cerebellum to be lifted off.

Removing the cerebellum discloses a cavity called the *fourth ventricle* (Figs. 242, 243, 244), which extends up under the superior medullary velum and down under the inferior medullary velum. This cavity is part of the central canal of the whole nervous system and is continuous with the central canal of the spinal cord.

. [16] This must not be confused with the term "nucleus" as applied to a part of a cell.

[17] Cerebellum: L., the little brain.

[18] Vermis: L., a worm.

[19] Brachium conjunctivum: L., connecting arm.

[20] Restiform: L., rope-like.

[21] Velum: L., veil or covering.

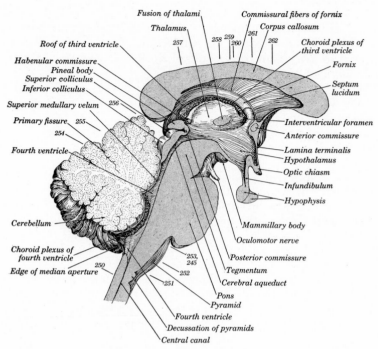

Figure 243. Sagittal section of the brain stem, cerebellum, and central parts of the cerebral hemisphere. The cerebral hemisphere peripheral to the corpus callosum has been removed. Compare with Figure 240. (Redrawn from Cunningham's Textbook of Anatomy. Oxford University Press.)

Caudal to the short inferior medullary velum, the roof of the fourth ventricle becomes very thin. It consists of an exceedingly delicate layer of tissue, the *ependyma*. The ependyma is the epithelium that lines the cavity of the brain and cord. It is formed from the embryonic neural tube, but contains no neurons. On the outside surface of the ependyma is a layer of connective tissue, parts of which are rich in blood vessels. This is part of the *pia* (see p. 339). These blood vessels push the ependyma into the cavity of the brain to form vascular tufts. This vascular roof is called the *choroid plexus of the fourth ventricle* (Fig. 243). At the caudal end of the thin roof of the fourth ventricle is a hole in the connective tissue and ependyma, the *median aperture of the fourth ventricle.* There are also small holes at the lateral corners of the roof. These are the only openings from the cavity of the original neural tube.

If the roof of the fourth ventricle is removed, the cavity is found to be diamond-shaped with a shallow lateral projection inferior to

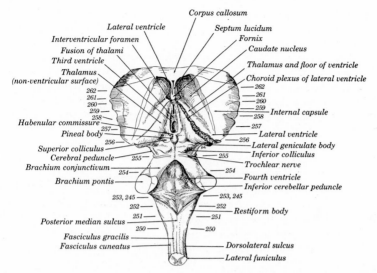

Figure 244. Brain stem and cerebrum, dorsal view. The cerebellum and all the roof of the fourth ventricle have been removed. A large part of each cerebral hemisphere has been dissected away, uncovering the anterior horn and central part of each lateral ventricle. The roof of the third ventricle has been removed. (Redrawn from figures in Strong and Elwyn: Human Neuroanatomy. Williams & Wilkins Company.)

each set of cerebral peduncles (Figs. 244, 242). It is bounded superiorly by the superior cerebellar peduncles, or brachia conjunctiva, and inferiorly by the inferior cerebellar peduncles, or restiform bodies, and the *gracile tubercles.* The central canal of the spinal cord opens into its inferior angle, and from the superior angle a narrow canal, the *cerebral aqueduct,* leads into the higher parts of the brain (Fig. 243).

The part of the brain stem from the spinal cord to the pons is called the *medulla oblongata.* We have already examined its ventral and lateral surfaces (pyramids and olives), its roof and its ventricle. It is the part of the brain most like the spinal cord, as comparison of a section through the decussation of the pyramids (Fig. 250) with a section through the cord (Fig. 249) will show. The central canal in both is small and central. In the medulla the anterior median fissure is partly obliterated by the fibers crossing from one pyramid to the other. The posterior funiculus consists, as in the cord, of two parts, the fasciculus cuneatus and the fasciculus gracilis, but on the medulla they are separated on the surface by a distinct sulcus. A short distance above this section both fascicles become larger and the gracilis ends in the *gracile tubercle.* In cross section (Fig. 251) we find gray matter in the lower parts of both fascicles. That in the fasciculus gracilis constitutes the *nucleus gracilis,* and that in the fasciculus cuneatus, the *nucleus cuneatus.* In this section the central canal is a little nearer the posterior surface.

Still further up, in a section through the caudal end of the fourth ventricle (Fig. 252), the appearance is quite different. Anteriorly are the two large bundles of fibers, the pyramids, with the deep anterior median fissure between them. Posterolateral to each is the olive. Internally, the nucleus, the gray matter, does not much resemble an olive. On the posterolateral surfaces are the most inferior parts of the inferior cerebellar peduncles. There is considerable gray matter in the floor of the ventricle.

A cross section just behind the cerebellar peduncles (Fig. 253) shows the pyramids and the superior part of the olive. The inferior cerebellar peduncle is now large; a little further forward it will turn posteriorly into the cerebellum. Bands of fibers, the *auditory striae,* arise from the median groove in the floor of the fourth ventricle and run transversely over the inferior peduncle and disappear anterior to it.

The pons,[22] in the limited use of the term, is the anterior transverse band of fibers earlier described. The term *pons,* however, is also applied to this section of the brain stem superior to the medulla oblongata. The cerebellum is part of this section of the brain, but it is more convenient not to include the cerebellum in the "pons" and restrict the term to the section of the brain stem proper.

Cross sections through the pons (Figs. 254, 255) cut across fibers of the pyramids (corticospinal tracts) that pass through the pons and continue up in the cerebral peduncles, and other fibers that have descended through the cerebral peduncles and will end in the pons (*corticopontile tracts*). The transverse fibers of the pons also show clearly. Between them is scattered gray substance, the *nuclei of the pons* (*nuclei pontis*). Laterally the transverse fibers become concentrated in the middle cerebellar peduncle. None of the transverse fibers pass from one cerebellar peduncle through the pons to the other peduncle; all take origin from cell bodies in the nuclei of the pons.

Dorsal to the pons, in the floor of the fourth ventricle are various nuclei and tracts of fibers, some of which will be mentioned later.

The Cerebellum. The cerebellum is an almost solid mass of nervous tissue, its tent-like cavity, a part of the fourth ventricle, extending only a little way into it. It is divided into two *cerebellar hemispheres* separated by a narrow median part, the *vermis.* It is also divided transversely into an *anterior lobe* and a *posterior lobe* by the inconspicuous *primary fissure* (Fig. 243). The surfaces of the hemispheres and of the vermis are divided into *folia* by deep,

---

[22] Pons: L., bridge.

Figure 245   *The Neuro-sensory System*   293

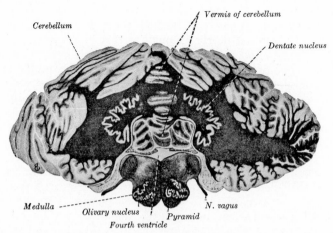

Cerebellum

Vermis of cerebellum

Dentate nucleus

Medulla

Olivary nucleus

Fourth ventricle

Pyramid

N. vagus

Figure 245. Cross section of the medulla oblongata (ventrally) and the cerebellum (dorsally). Nerve fibers stained dark; nuclei white. (Braus: Anatomie des Menschen.)

branching sulci. Gray substance forms a layer, the *cerebellar cortex*,[23] over the entire surface (Fig. 245). A conspicuous element of the microscopic structure of the cortex are the Purkinje[24] cells (Fig. 228, *G*), found only in this location. The interior consists of white substance except for some nuclei. In the vermis the white substance is thin, and, owing to the arrangement of the sulci and folia, it resembles, in sagittal section, a tree (Figs. 242, 243). This is called the *arbor vitae*.[25] In the hemispheres the white substance is thicker.

The fibers of the middle cerebellar peduncles sweep up into the white substance of the cerebellum and are distributed to the cortex of the hemispheres. The fibers of the inferior cerebellar peduncles enter the cerebellum medial to the middle peduncles and are distributed to the cortex of the vermis and hemispheres and to some small nuclei in the white substance.

In each cerebellar hemisphere, imbedded in the white substance, is a nucleus, the *dentate*[26] *nucleus* (Fig. 245), which resembles in appearance the olivary nucleus. Fibers from its cell bodies constitute the bulk of the superior peduncles. These peduncles run up each side of the anterior medullary velum (Fig. 254, *brachium conjunctivum*), turn anteriorly and cross in the anterior part of the next segment of the brain stem, the midbrain, described next.

[23] Cortex: L., outer layer or bark.
[24] From Johannes Evangelista von Purkinje (1789–1869), professor of physiology at Breslau and Prague.
[25] Arbor vitae: L., tree of life.
[26] Dentate: L., tooth-like.

The Midbrain. The next part of the brain stem is called the midbrain, or *mesencephalon*.[29] Its central canal is small (Figs. 243, 255, 256), though not nearly as small as that in the spinal cord. It is called the *cerebral aqueduct.*

On the roof of the midbrain are two pairs of rounded prominences, the *inferior* and *superior colliculi*,[27] or, collectively, the *corpora quadrigemina* (Figs. 242, 243, 244). From each inferior colliculus a tract of fibers, the *inferior quadrigeminal brachium,* can be seen on the surface passing obliquely upward. From each superior colliculus there is a similar *superior quadrigeminal brachium* almost transverse in position.

The ventrolateral parts of the midbrain are the *cerebral peduncles,* so called because from the inferior surface of the brain they appear to support the cerebral hemispheres (Fig. 242). The superficial part of each peduncle is the *basis pedunculi* (Fig. 256), consisting of fibers that enter the pons. Median and superior to the basis is the *substantia nigra,* a layer of gray matter containing numerous heavily pigmented nerve cells. The remainder of the peduncle is the *tegmentum.*[28] The two tegmenta are continuous with one another in the median plane. In sections lower down (Figs. 254, 255) are seen the fibers of the superior cerebellar peduncles (brachia conjunctiva). As these come into the tegmenta, they cross, forming the *decussation of the brachia conjunctiva.* After crossing, most of these fibers end in the large *red nuclei* (Fig. 256, *nucleus ruber*). The red nuclei are pink in the fresh condition. They lie in the tegmenta.

The Diencephalon. The next section of the brain stem, the *diencephalon*,[29] is largely hidden by the cerebral hemispheres. The diencephalon is that part of the brain between the midbrain and the *interventricular foramina* or *foramina of Munro* (Figs. 243, 247). The relations will be understood most readily by studying first the embryonic brain (Fig. 325). The part of the brain in front of the interventricular foramina, together with the cerebral hemispheres, is the *telencephalon.*

The cavity of the diencephalon is the *third ventricle,* which

---

[27] Colliculus: L., a little hill.

[28] Tegmentum: L., a cover.

[29] For purposes of description the brain of the embryo is divided into five regions: myelencephalon (G. *myelin,* marrow or medulla, plus *encephalon,* brain, from *en,* in, and *kephale,* head), metencephalon (G. *meta,* after), mesencephalon (G. *mesos,* middle), diencephalon (G. *dia,* through or, in this case, between), telencephalon (G. *telos,* end). The myelencephalon becomes the medulla oblongata; the metencephalon, the pons and cerebellum; the mesencephalon, the midbrain; the diencephalon and telencephalon remain to be described. These embryonic terms are sometimes convenient in describing the adult brain.

extends forward to the *lamina terminalis,* the most cranial part of the embryonic brain in the midsagittal plane. The third ventricle is also, therefore, in part, the cavity of the median part of the telencephalon. The cavities of the cerebral hemispheres are the *lateral ventricles.* Each communicates with the third ventricle by one of the interventricular foramina.

In the course of development the walls of the diencephalon become thick, and each, in the adult brain, is called the *thalamus.*[30] These become so thick, indeed, that in most brains they meet across the middle of the third ventricle and fuse so that when the brain is cut in the median sagittal plane, there is a little island of cut surface in the center of the ventricle. The thalamus consists largely of gray substance divided into several nuclei.

Most of the roof of the diencephalon is very thin, and there is a *choroid plexus of the third ventricle* (Fig. 243) resembling in structure that of the fourth ventricle. At the caudal end of the choroid plexus the roof turns forward to include the *habenular commissure,* a transverse band of fibers, then back to a small ovoid structure, the *pineal body.* A thickening in the roof of the diencephalon where it is continuous with the corpora quadrigemina is the *posterior commissure.*

The floor and ventro-lateral walls of the diencephalon constitute the *hypothalamus.* The floor of the third ventricle shows two pits. One, the *optic recess,* is just in front of the *optic chiasm.* The other is the *infundibulum,*[31] which extends down into the stalk of the *hypophysis,* an endocrine gland.

Inspecting now the inferior surface of the diencephalon (hypothalamus), we find between the cerebral peduncles and just behind the stalk of the hypophysis a pair of small hemispherical eminences, the *mammillary bodies* (Figs. 241, 243). Just in front of the stalk of the hypophysis the two large optic nerves from the eyes swing in to the optic chiasm. From the chiasm a bundle of fibers, the *optic tract* (Fig. 242), runs obliquely posterior and caudal on each side of the brain stem. In the chiasm, part of the fibers of each optic nerve cross to the optic tract of the opposite side; the rest turn back into the optic tract of the same side. Part of the fibers of the optic tract end in an inconspicuous body on the side of the diencephalon, the *lateral geniculate*[32] *body,* and part pass by this to become part of the superior quadrigeminal brachium. The cerebral hemisphere covers the lateral geniculate body, so that it cannot be seen in the intact brain except by pulling away the

---

[30] Thalamus: G., an inner chamber. The term is used in neurology to designate the side walls of the "inner chamber."

[31] Infundibulum: L., a funnel.

[32] Geniculate: L., like a little knee.

hemisphere. Just behind the lateral geniculate body is the *medial geniculate body.* The inferior quadrigeminal brachium enters it.

The cerebral peduncles diverge as they extend forward, and each passes median to (beneath) the optic tract (Fig. 242). Immediately in front of the optic tract the fibers constituting the basis pedunculi enter the median wall of the cerebral hemisphere, thus binding the thalamus to the median wall of the cerebral hemisphere. They are joined by fibers from the adjacent thalamus, and these two sets of fibers together form the *internal capsule* in the cerebral hemisphere. We shall return to this in a moment.

In the interpeduncular fossa, caudal to the mammillary bodies, are a number of holes which provide entrance for blood vessels. This area is called the *posterior perforated substance.* Anterolateral to the optic tracts are areas of similar appearance called the *anterior perforated substance.*

The Telencephalon. Turning now to that part of the third ventricle that lies in front of the interventricular foramina and is, therefore, a part of the *telencephalon,* we find the anterior wall to be a narrow, thin plate, the *lamina terminalis* (Fig. 243). This terminal plate extends from the optic recess below to the *anterior commissure* above. The latter is a bundle of fibers passing from one cerebral hemisphere to the other. From the anterior commissure the roof of the third ventricle swings up to the choroid plexus described earlier.

At this point the student should re-examine the figures of the embryonic brain (Figs. 324, 325), since in these a simple pattern is clear which becomes obscured in the adult brain, but is a key to understanding its structure. The *telencephalic vesicles,* as they are at first called, arise in the embryo as hollow outgrowths from the sides of the anterior end of the neural tube. They grow until they hide most of the rest of the brain. They become the cerebral hemispheres in the adult. The median surfaces of the cerebral hemispheres lie close together anterior to the lamina terminalis and above the diencephalon, midbrain and cerebellum.

The diencephalon and telencephalon together constitute the *cerebrum.*[33] Some writers include also the mesencephalon.

The Surfaces of the Cerebral Hemispheres. Each cerebral hemisphere has three surfaces: a dorsolateral surface (Fig. 239) lying in contact with the walls of the cranial vault; an inferior surface (Fig. 241) resting on the cranial floor; and a medial surface (Fig. 240) facing its fellow at the longitudinal fissure. In side view each hemisphere has three poles: a *frontal pole,* anteriorly and superiorly; a *temporal pole,* anteriorly and inferiorly; and an *occipital pole* posteriorly (Fig. 246).

---

[33] Cerebrum: L., the brain.

Figure 246   *The Neuro-sensory System*   297

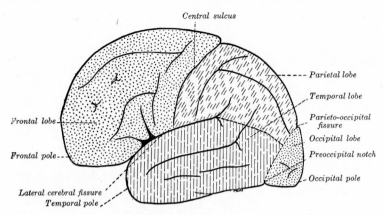

Figure 246. Diagram of the lobes on the lateral aspect of the human cerebral hemisphere. (Ranson.)

The surfaces of the hemispheres are thrown into a large number of folds called *convolutions* or *gyri,* with intervening grooves, called *fissures* or *sulci.* Many of the convolutions and fissures have been given special names. Here we can mention only a few.

The most prominent of the fissures is the large *lateral fissure* or the *fissure of Sylvius*[34] (Fig. 239). It begins in the notch between the frontal and temporal poles, and runs upward and backward on the lateral surface of the cerebrum. If the lips of the fissure are separated, a buried area of cortex, the *insula* (Fig. 259), will be found beneath. Part of the cortex of the under lip of the fissure is connected with the organ of hearing and is called the *auditory area* (Figs. 268, 269).

A second important fissure on the lateral surface of the hemisphere is the *central sulcus* or the *fissure of Rolando*[35] (Fig. 239). It arises from the top of the hemisphere from a point a little behind the middle, and runs downward and forward toward the lateral fissure. In front of it lies the *anterior central convolution* (*precentral gyrus*); behind it the *posterior central convolution* (*postcentral gyrus*). The anterior central convolution is an important part of the motor system and is called the *motor area* (Fig. 268). The posterior central convolution is an important sensory zone.

The *calcarine fissure* lies on the medial surface of the hemisphere (Fig. 240) and runs forward from the occipital pole. The cortex

---

[34] From François de la Boë, called Sylvius (1614–1672), professor of practical medicine in Leyden.

[35] From Luigi Rolando (1773–1831), physician to King Victor Emmanuel of Sardinia, and professor of anatomy at Turin.

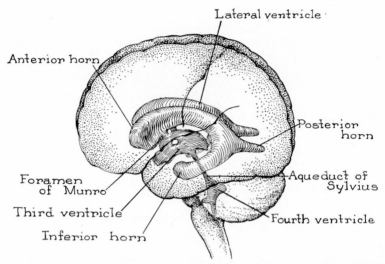

Lateral ventricle

Anterior horn

Posterior horn

Foramen of Munro

Aqueduct of Sylvius

Third ventricle

Inferior horn

Fourth ventricle

Figure 247. The ventricular system. (J. J. McDonald and J. G. Chusid: Correlative Neuroanatomy and Functional Neurology. 6th edition. Lange Medical Publications.)

in and around the fissure, the *calcarine cortex,* is concerned in vision and is called the *visual area* (Fig. 268).

The *hippocampal convolution* (Fig. 268, *olfactory area*) lies on the boundary of the inferior and medial aspects of the hemisphere. It is an end station for the sense of smell and probably also for taste.

Certain of the fissures are used to divide the hemisphere into subdivisions called *lobes* (Fig. 246). The most important of these lobes are the frontal, parietal, occipital and temporal lobes; they lie in general against the bones of the same name. They have little functional significance and are used chiefly as gross localizing zones in medicine and surgery.

Although most of the bulk of the cerebral hemispheres is due to the thickness of the walls, the *lateral ventricles* are of considerable size and somewhat complex in shape (Fig. 247). The *anterior horn* of each extends forward into the frontal lobe. The *posterior horn* extends into the occipital lobe. The *inferior horn* swings down and forward into the temporal lobe. The lateral ventricle lies near the median surface of the hemisphere. Along a line starting at the interventricular foramen, running back along the median inferior edge of the body of the ventricle and swinging down and forward on the median dorsal surface of the inferior horn, the wall of the ventricle is thin, and, as in the fourth and third ventricles, blood vessels push it in to form the *choroid plexus of the lateral ventricle* (Figs. 244, 257, 258, 259, 260). This choroid plexus is continuous at the interventricular foramen with the choroid plexus of the third ventricle (Fig. 260).

The Gray and White Substance of the Cerebral Hemispheres. The outer surface of each hemisphere consists of a layer of gray substance, the *cerebral cortex.* The cerebral cortex has an area of about 2½ square feet. Only about a third of this is visible on the surface, the other two thirds forming the walls and floors of the fissures and sulci. The average thickness of the cortex is about 2.5 mm., varying from 1.5 to 4.5 mm.

Besides the cortex, the chief masses of gray substance in the cerebral hemisphere are (1) the *corpus striatum*,[36] lying inferior and lateral to the body of the lateral ventricle and, therefore, lateral to the thalamus (see below); (2) the *hippocampus*, lying inferior to the inferior horn of the lateral ventricle (Figs. 257, 258).

The great bundles of fibers, the bases pedunculi, lie against the floor of the midbrain and pass forward and up beneath (medial to) the optic tracts. In front of the optic tracts each passes laterally into the adjacent wall of the cerebral hemisphere (Figs. 242, 257, 258) and there divides the *corpus striatum* into the *caudate nucleus* above, lying in the floor of the ventricle, and the *lenticular nucleus* (*putamen* and *pars pallidus*) below (Figs. 258, 259, 260, 261, 262). By passing from the wall of the diencephalon to the median wall of the cerebral hemisphere, these fibers unite the thalamus, that is, the wall of the diencephalon, to the median wall of the hemisphere. In the embryo these two parts were continuous only at the interventricular foramen; in the adult they are bound together as far back as the optic tract.

Where these fibers sweep up beside the thalamus and into the hemisphere between the caudate and lenticular nuclei, they are called the *internal capsule.* (The external capsule is a less important layer of fibers beneath the insula between the putamen and the claustrum in Figure 259.) The fibers of the internal capsule form a great fan-shaped sheet going to all parts of the cerebral cortex. After it emerges from the corpus striatum the internal capsule is joined by fibers running in many directions, and the resulting fibrous structure that fills much of the hemisphere is called the *corona radiata* (Figs. 259, 262).

Turning now to the median sagittal section of the brain (Figs. 240, 243), a thin sheet of tissue extends directly forward from the anterior commissure. This immediately thickens to become a heavy band of transverse fibers passing between the two cerebral hemispheres. It is the *corpus callosum.*[37] The corpus callosum runs

---

[36] Striatum: L., striped or banded. The corpus striatum is given a striate appearance by the numerous bands of fibers which cross it.

[37] Corpus callosum: L., hard body. Cf. callous.

forward a short distance and then turns superiorly and back above the diencephalon. At its caudal ends it thickens still more. The fibers that constitute this great commissure pass into each hemisphere, become part of the corona radiata, and go to all parts of the cortex.

Forming the floor of the ventral horn of the lateral ventricle is a column of gray substance, the *hippocampus*[38] (Figs. 257, 258). This is part of the cerebral cortex rolled into this position. The hippocampus becomes smaller as it is followed posteriorly and up, and it appears to end as it swings medially and up along the ventricle, but it can be traced as a delicate layer of gray matter, the *indusium griseum*, on the superior surface of the corpus callosum. It continues around the front of the corpus callosum and down to the olfactory area (Fig. 261).

From each mammillary body, which is largely made up of gray substance, a bundle of fibers passes forward and up in the thalamus, bends around in front of the interventricular foramen, and passes back in the median wall of the cerebral hemisphere. This pair of bundles constitute the *fornix*[39] (Figs. 240, 243, 257–261). Its parts are named in Figure 248. From the interventricular foramen back, each limb of the fornix lies just median to the choroid plexus of the lateral ventricle. As each crus swings down and forward along the inferior horn of the ventricle, it comes to lie along the median edge of the hippocampus. Here it is called the *fimbria*[40] *of the hippocampus* (Fig. 257), and here the fibers that constitute the fornix emerge from the hippocampus. The *hippocampal commissure* is a sheet-like layer of fibers passing from one limb of the fornix to the other. It lies between the corpus callosum above and the roof of the diencephalon below (Figs. 243, 248). Caudally it lies against the under surface of the corpus callosum, but forward of this it bends down and joins the roof of the third ventricle above the interventricular foramen.

Between each limb of the fornix and the corpus callosum, and extending forward into the bend of the corpus callosum, is a thin, vertical layer of non-nervous tissue. It forms the median wall of the lateral ventricle in this area. The two layers together are called the *septum lucidum* (Figs. 243, 244, 260, 261, 262). Sometimes they are more or less fused, but usually there is a cleft-like cavity between them. Each half of the septum may be considered a part

---

[38] Hippocampus: G. *hippos,* horse, and *kampos,* sea monster. The curved gyrus which bears this name was so called because its shape suggests that of the well known sea-horse. The gyrus was well described by Varolius (1543–1575).— From O. H. Perry Pepper: Medical Etymology.

[39] Fornix: L., an arch or vault.

[40] Fimbria: L., fringe.

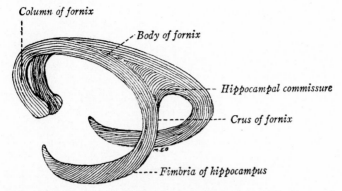

Column of fornix

Body of fornix

Hippocampal commissure

Crus of fornix

Fimbria of hippocampus

Figure 248.   Diagram of the fornix. (Ranson-Clark, The Anatomy of the Nervous System.)

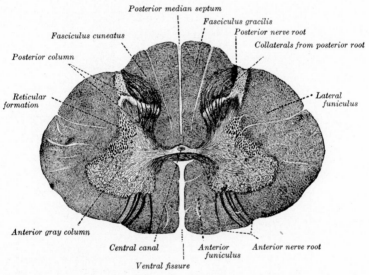

Posterior median septum

Fasciculus gracilis

Fasciculus cuneatus

Posterior nerve root

Collaterals from posterior root

Posterior column

Reticular formation

Lateral funiculus

Anterior gray column

Central canal

Anterior funiculus

Anterior nerve root

Ventral fissure

Figure 249.   Transverse section through the cervical portion of the spinal cord. (Looney, Anatomy of the Brain and Spinal Cord, F. A. Davis Co., Publisher.)

of the median wall of the cerebral hemisphere, though actually the corpus callosum, the hippocampal commissure, the septum lucidum and the anterior commissure all originate in the embryo in the lamina terminalis.

The main part of the *caudate*[41] *nucleus* lies lateral and inferior to the anterior horn of the lateral ventricle. It extends far forward, and in this region it is continuous, anterior to the internal capsule, with the lenticular nucleus (Fig. 262). Caudally, the caudate nu-

---

[41] Caudate: tailed, from L. *cauda*, tail.

Figure 250

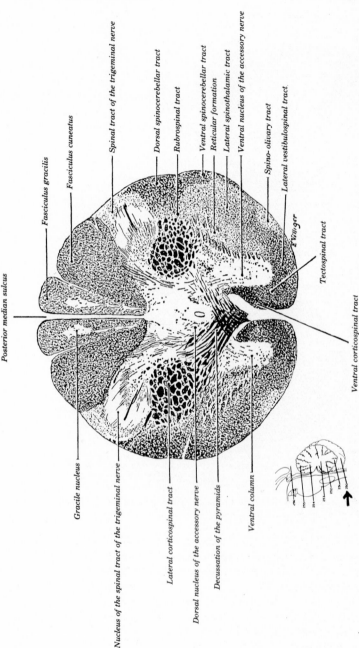

Posterior median sulcus

Fasciculus gracilis

Fasciculus cuneatus

Spinal tract of the trigeminal nerve

Dorsal spinocerebellar tract

Rubrospinal tract

Ventral spinocerebellar tract

Reticular formation

Lateral spinothalamic tract

Ventral nucleus of the accessory nerve

Spino-olivary tract

Lateral vestibulospinal tract.

Tectospinal tract

Ventral corticospinal tract

Gracile nucleus

Nucleus of the spinal tract of the trigeminal nerve

Lateral corticospinal tract

Dorsal nucleus of the accessory nerve

Decussation of the pyramids

Ventral column

Figure 250. Transverse section through the lower part of the medulla oblongata. The approximate location of the sections shown in Figures 250–262 are indicated on Figures 242, 243, 244, and the two sets of figures should be studied together. Modified from Rasmussen: Atlas of Cross Section Anatomy of the Brain—Guide to the Study of the Morphology and Fiber Tracts of the Human Brain. (Based on fifth section of Emil Villiger's Brain and Spinal Cord, 14th Edition, Blakiston Div. of McGraw-Hill Book Company, Inc.)

Figure 251   The Neuro-sensory System   303

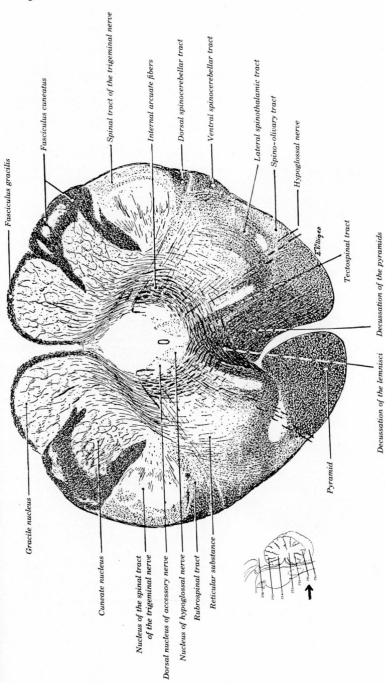

Figure 251. Transverse section through the medulla oblongata a short distance inferior to the olive. Modified from Rasmussen: Atlas of Cross Section Anatomy of the Brain—Guide to the Study of the Morphology and Fiber Tracts of the Human Brain. (Based on fifth section of Emil Villiger's Brain and Spinal Cord, 14th Edition, Blakiston Div. of McGraw-Hill Book Company, Inc.)

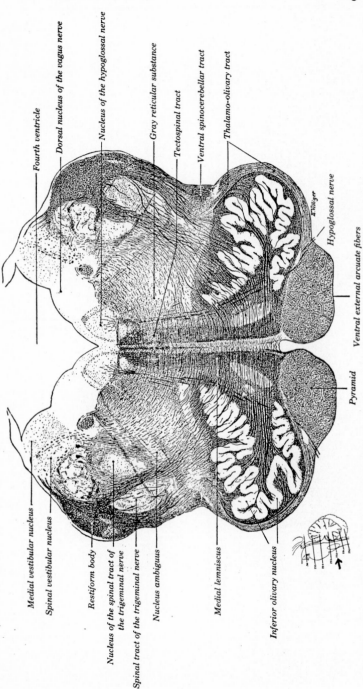

Fourth ventricle

Dorsal nucleus of the vagus nerve

Nucleus of the hypoglossal nerve

Gray reticular substance

Tectospinal tract

Ventral spinocerebellar tract

Thalamo-olivary tract

Hypoglossal nerve

Ventral external arcuate fibers

Pyramid

Medial vestibular nucleus

Spinal vestibular nucleus

Restiform body

Nucleus of the spinal tract of the trigeminal nerve

Spinal tract of the trigeminal nerve

Nucleus ambiguus

Medial lemniscus

Inferior olivary nucleus

Figure 252. Transverse section through the medulla oblongata in the region of the olive. Most of the roof of the fourth ventricle has been removed from this section. Modified from Rasmussen: Atlas of Cross Section Anatomy of the Brain—Guide to the Study of the Morphology and Fiber Tracts of the Human Brain. (Based on fifth section of Emil Villiger's Brain and Spinal Cord, 14th Edition, Blakiston Div. of McGraw-Hill Book Company, Inc.).

Figure 253   The Neuro-sensory System   305

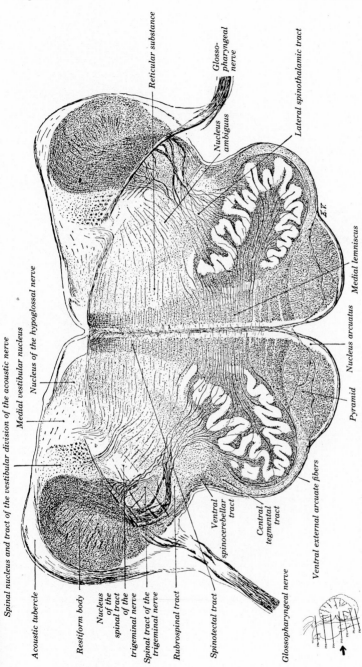

Acoustic tubercle

Spinal nucleus and tract of the vestibular division of the acoustic nerve

Medial vestibular nucleus

Nucleus of the hypoglossal nerve

Reticular substance

Glosso-pharyngeal nerve

Nucleus ambiguus

Lateral spinothalamic tract

Restiform body

Nucleus of the spinal tract of the trigeminal nerve

Spinal tract of the trigeminal nerve

Rubrospinal tract

Spinotectal tract

Ventral spinocerebellar tract

Central tegmental tract

Glossopharyngeal nerve

Ventral external arcuate fibers

Pyramid

Nucleus arcuatus

Medial lemniscus

Figure 253. Transverse section through the medulla oblongata just inferior to the pons. The thin roof and choroid plexus have been removed from this section so that the fourth ventricle is shown without a roof. The ventricle is very wide here. Compare with Figure 242. Modified from Rasmussen: Atlas of Cross Section Anatomy of the Brain—Guide to the Study of the Morphology and Fiber Tracts of the Human Brain. (Based on fifth section of Emil Villiger's Brain and Spinal Cord, 14th Edition, Blakiston Div. of McGraw-Hill Book Company, Inc.)

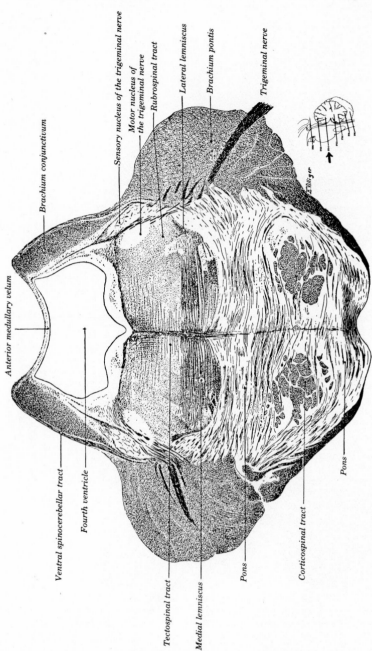

Figure 254. Transverse section through the pons superior to its connection with the cerebellum. Modified from Rasmussen: Atlas of Cross Section Anatomy of the Brain—Guide to the Study of the Morphology and Fiber Tracts of the Human Brain. (Based on fifth section of Emil Villiger's Brain and Spinal Cord, 14th Edition, Blakiston Div. of McGraw-Hill Book Company, Inc.)

Brachium conjunctivum

Sensory nucleus of the trigeminal nerve

Motor nucleus of the trigeminal nerve

Rubrospinal tract

Lateral lemniscus

Brachium pontis

Trigeminal nerve

Anterior medullary velum

Ventral spinocerebellar tract

Fourth ventricle

Tectospinal tract

Medial lemniscus

Pons

Corticospinal tract

Pons

Figure 255   **The Neuro-sensory System** 307

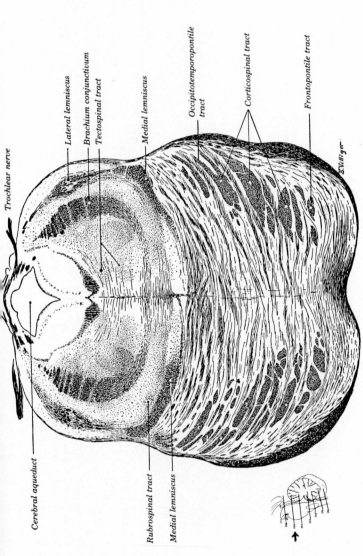

Figure 255. Transverse section passing through the pons below and the line between pons and midbrain above. The nucleus of the trochlear nerve lies in the gray matter just beneath the cerebral aqueduct and near the median plane in a section adjacent to the one shown. Its position is comparable with the position of the nucleus of the oculomotor nerve shown in Figure 256. Modified from Rasmussen: Atlas of Cross Section Anatomy of the Brain—Guide to the Study of the Morphology and Fiber Tracts of the Human Brain. (Based on the fifth section of Emil Villiger's Brain and Spinal Cord, 14th Edition, Blakiston Div. of McGraw-Hill Book Company, Inc.)

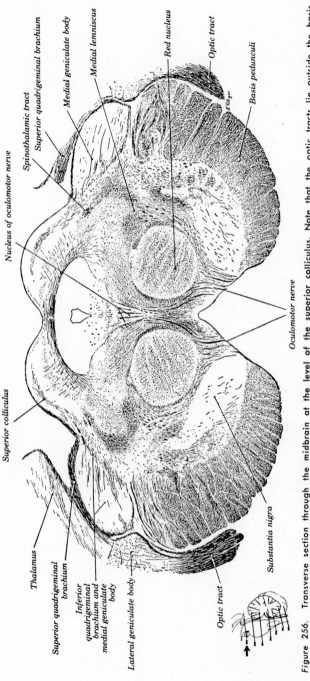

Figure 256. Transverse section through the midbrain at the level of the superior colliculus. Note that the optic tracts lie outside the basis pedunculi and that in the next section, Figure 257, the fibers of the basis pedunculi extend upward into the cerebral hemisphere median to the lateral geniculate body. Modified from Rasmussen: Atlas of Cross Section Anatomy of the Brain—Guide to the Study of the Morphology and Fiber Tracts of the Human Brain. (Based on fifth section of Emil Villiger's Brain and Spinal Cord, 14th Edition, Blakiston Div. of McGraw-Hill Book Company, Inc.)

Figure 257   **The Neuro-sensory System** 309

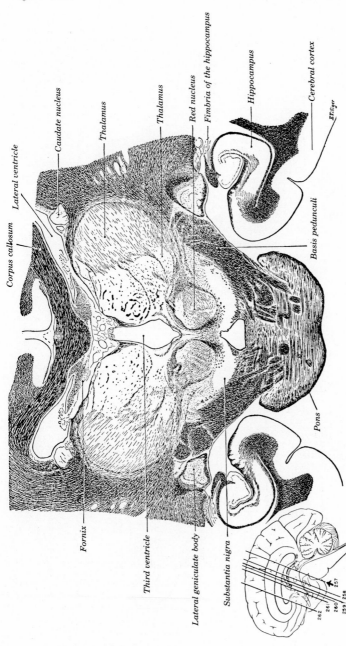

Corpus callosum

Lateral ventricle

Caudate nucleus

Thalamus

Thalamus

Red nucleus

Fimbria of the hippocampus

Hippocampus

Cerebral cortex

E.Villiger

Basis pedunculi

Pons

Fornix

Third ventricle

Lateral geniculate body

Substantia nigra

262
261
260
259/258
257

Figure 257. Oblique section through the pons, midbrain, diencephalon and adjacent parts of the cerebral hemispheres. The small cavity above the pons is outside the brain. It is the space between the two cerebral peduncles which extends back a short distance above the superior border of the pons. Modified from Rasmussen: Atlas of Cross Section Anatomy of the Brain—Guide to the Study of the Morphology and Fiber Tracts of the Human Brain. (Based on fifth section of Emil Villiger's Brain and Spinal Cord, 14th Edition, Blakiston Div. of McGraw-Hill Book Company, Inc.)

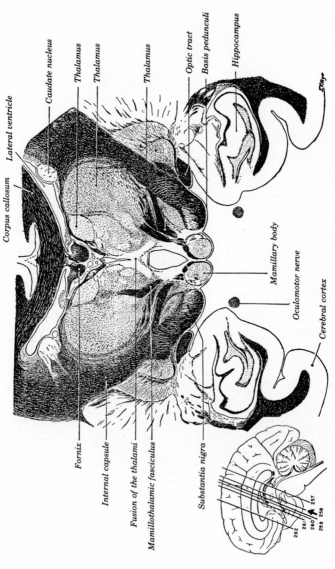

Figure 258. Oblique section through the diencephalon and adjacent parts of the cerebral hemispheres. The third ventricle is visible above and below the area in which the two thalami have fused. Modified from Rasmussen: Atlas of Cross Section Anatomy of the Brain—Guide to the Study of the Morphology and Fiber Tracts of the Human Brain. (Based on fifth section of Emil Villiger's Brain and Spinal Cord, 14th Edition, Blakiston Div. of McGraw-Hill Book Company, Inc.)

Corpus callosum

Lateral ventricle

Caudate nucleus

Thalamus

Thalamus

Thalamus

Optic tract

Basis pedunculi

Hippocampus

Fornix

Internal capsule

Fusion of the thalami

Mamillothalamic fasciculus

Substantia nigra

Mamillary body

Oculomotor nerve

Cerebral cortex

262
261
260
259 258
257

Figure 259   *The Neuro-sensory System*   311

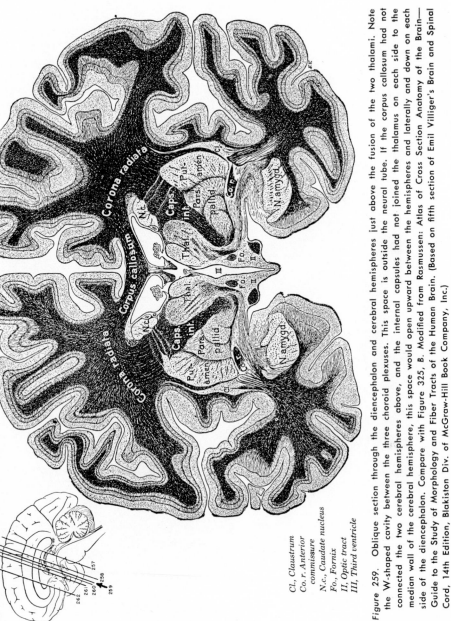

Cl., Claustrum
Co. r. Anterior commissure
N.c., Caudate nucleus
Fo., Fornix
II, Optic tract
III, Third ventricle

Figure 259. Oblique section through the diencephalon and cerebral hemispheres just above the fusion of the two thalami. Note the W-shaped cavity between the three choroid plexuses. This space is outside the neural tube. If the corpus callosum had not connected the two cerebral hemispheres above, and the internal capsules had not joined the thalamus on each side to the median wall of the cerebral hemisphere, this space would open upward between the hemispheres and laterally and down on each side of the diencephalon. Compare with Figure 325, B. Modified from Rasmussen: Atlas of Cross Section Anatomy of the Brain— Guide to the Study of Morphology and Fiber Tracts of the Human Brain. (Based on fifth section of Emil Villiger's Brain and Spinal Cord, 14th Edition, Blakiston Div. of McGraw-Hill Book Company, Inc.)

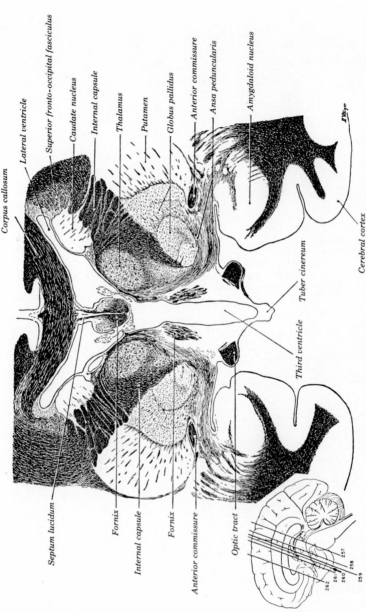

Corpus callosum

Lateral ventricle

Superior fronto-occipital fasciculus

Caudate nucleus

Internal capsule

Thalamus

Putamen

Globus pallidus

Anterior commissure

Ansa peduncularis

Amygdaloid nucleus

Cerebral cortex

Septum lucidum

Fornix

Internal capsule

Fornix

Anterior commissure

Optic tract

Tuber cinereum

Third ventricle

Figure 260. Oblique section through the diencephalon and adjacent parts of the cerebral hemispheres just behind the interventricular foramina. The choroid plexuses of the lateral ventricles are continuous here with the choroid plexus of the third ventricle. Modified from Rasmussen: Atlas of Cross Section Anatomy of the Brain—Guide to the Study of the Morphology and Fiber Tracts of the Human Brain. (Based on fifth section of Emil Villiger's Brain and Spinal Cord, 14th Edition, Blakiston Div. of McGraw-Hill Book Company, Inc.)

Figure 261   The Neuro-sensory System   313

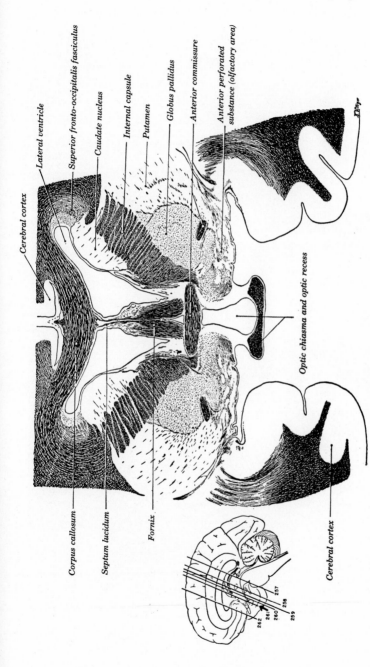

Cerebral cortex

Lateral ventricle

Superior fronto-occipitalis fasciculus

Caudate nucleus

Internal capsule

Putamen

Globus pallidus

Anterior commissure

Anterior perforated substance (olfactory area)

Corpus callosum

Septum lucidum

Fornix

Optic chiasma and optic recess

Cerebral cortex

Figure 261. Oblique section through the anterior end of the diencephalon, the fornix and the anterior commissure in front of the interventricular foramina. Modified from Rasmussen: Atlas of Cross Section Anatomy of the Brain—Guide to the Study of the Morphology and Fiber Tracts of the Human Brain. (Based on fifth section of Emil Villiger's Brain and Spinal Cord, 14th Edition, Blakiston Div. of McGraw-Hill Book Company, Inc.)

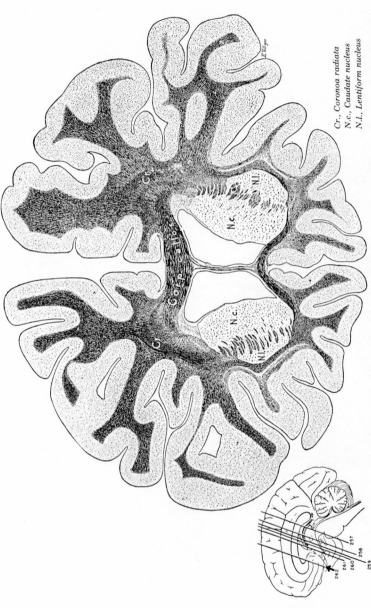

Cr., Coronoa radiata
N.c., Caudate nucleus
N.l., Lentiform nucleus

Figure 262. Section through the anterior parts of the cerebral hemispheres. This is through the anterior extremity of the internal capsule, only scattered strands of it showing between the caudate nucleus and the lentiform nucleus. The cavities are the anterior horns of the lateral ventricles. Modified from Rasmussen: Atlas of Cross Section Anatomy of the Brain—Guide to the Study of the Morphology and Fiber Tracts of the Human Brain. (Based on fifth section of Emil Villiger's Brain and Spinal Cord, 14th Edition, Blakiston Div. of McGraw-Hill Book Company, Inc.)

cleus becomes smaller as it swings around to lie in the roof of the inferior horn of the lateral ventricle. It ends in contact with the *amygdaloid nucleus,* which lies at the end of the inferior horn of the lateral ventricle and therefore in the anterior part of the temporal lobe (Figs. 258, 259). The amygdaloid nucleus is continuous with the cortex on the median side of the temporal lobe opposite the anterior perforated substance.

The Cranial Nerves. The cranial nerves (Fig. 241) issue from the cerebrum and brain stem. There are twelve pairs which are designated by name and number, the number being the order in which they are found, starting at the anterior end. They are as follows:

1. The olfactory nerve
2. The optic nerve
3. The oculomotor nerve
4. The trochlear nerve
5. The trigeminal nerve
6. The abducens nerve
7. The facial nerve
8. The acoustic nerve
9. The glossopharyngeal nerve
10. The vagus nerve
11. The accessory nerve
12. The hypoglossal nerve.

The first two cranial nerves, the olfactory and optic, are in no way comparable to the spinal nerves. The remainder are, in some respects, comparable. They fall into two series, an *anterior series* corresponding to the anterior roots of the spinal nerves, and a *posterior series* corresponding to the posterior roots of the spinal nerves, as follows:

1. The anterolateral sulcus of the spinal cord can be followed up onto the brain stem as far as the pons. From it, on the cord, arise the ventral roots of the spinal nerves. From it, on the brain stem, arise the roots of the hypoglossal nerve and the abducent nerve. In front of the pons the oculomotor nerve arises in a comparable position. The trochlear nerve, even though it arises from the roof of the midbrain, may, because of the position of its nucleus in the brain stem, at the same level as those of the hypoglossal and oculomotor, be considered to belong to this series.

2. The posterolateral sulcus of the spinal cord swings to a lateral position on the medulla oblongata. From it, on the cord, arise the dorsal roots of the spinal nerves. From it, on the medulla, arise the accessory, vagus, glossopharyngeal and, at the inferior border of the pons, the acoustic and the facial nerves. In line with these,

but emerging through the fibers of the pons, is the trigeminal nerve.

1. The *olfactory nerve*, the nerve of smell, consists of a number of small filaments which arise in the nasal cavity and pass upward through the cribriform plate of the ethmoid. They join the *olfactory bulb* of the brain, which in turn joins the *olfactory tract*, a nerve-like structure lying on the inferior aspect of the frontal lobe and often erroneously called the olfactory nerve (Fig. 241).

2. The *optic nerve* is the nerve of vision. It is, in reality, a tract of the brain, somewhat like the olfactory tract. The retina of the eye from which it leads is also a part of the brain embryologically. There is no true optic nerve, but the term is universally applied to this tract. The optic nerve passes backward through the optic foramen to the base of the brain, where it forms the *optic chiasm.* This lies in the optic groove in the skull (p. 36). Here a partial decussation of the fibers of the two sides takes place, and the re-formed tract, now called the *optic tract*, passes backward on the surface of the brain towards the thalamus and midbrain. The further course of these fibers will be described later (p. 332).

3. The *oculomotor nerve* supplies four of the six muscles that move the eyeball. It emerges from the ventral aspect of the midbrain (Fig. 243) and passes into the orbit through the superior orbital fissure.

PRACTICAL CONSIDERATIONS. Injury to this nerve, or to the fourth or sixth cranial nerve, causes a paralysis of certain of the muscles of the eye. The muscles which remain intact turn the eye away from the normal resting position, so that a strabismus, or squint, is produced.

4. The *trochlear*[42] *nerve* supplies one muscle of the eyeball (the superior oblique muscle). It issues from the dorsal aspect of the midbrain and then winds round it to pass into the orbit through the superior orbital fissure (Figs. 242, 255).

5. The *trigeminal*[43] *nerve* (Fig. 263) is sensory to the face and motor to the muscles of mastication. It emerges from the ventrolateral aspect of the pons and soon enlarges to form the *semilunar ganglion* (Fig. 241), a structure similar to the ganglia of the posterior roots of the spinal nerves. It then divides into three main divisions: (1) The *ophthalmic division* enters the orbit through the superior orbital fissure. Its main branches pass forward through the orbit to the face, where they innervate the skin of the nose, upper eyelid and forehead, and the upper part of the nasal passage. These are all sensory. (2) The *maxillary division*

---

[42] Trochlear: from L. *trochlea*, pulley. The muscle which it supplies passes through a pulley. When the muscle is contracted, it is supposed to give the face a pathetic appearance; hence the older term "pathetic nerve."

[43] Trigeminal: L., three born together.

Figure 263   **The Neuro-sensory System**   317

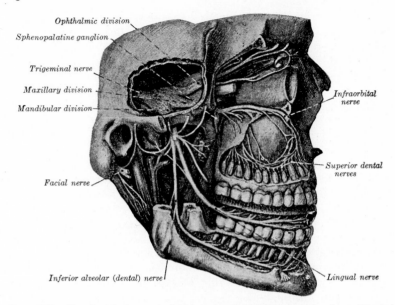

Figure 263.   The trigeminal nerve and its branches. Much of the bone has been dissected away to show the three divisions arising from the semilunar ganglion and the distribution of the terminal branches. (Reduced from Warren: Handbook of Anatomy. Harvard University Press.)

is also entirely sensory. It passes through the foramen rotundum and then gives off small branches that pass *through* the sphenopalatine ganglion (Fig. 263) to the palate and branches to the upper molar teeth. The sphenopalatine ganglion is a part of the craniosacral division of the autonomic system (Fig. 275). The nerve then passes into the orbit through the inferior orbital fissure. Within the orbit it gives off branches that run down to the remainder of the upper teeth. It emerges onto the face through the large foramen in the lower rim of the orbit (infraorbital foramen) (Fig. 24) and supplies the upper lip, the lower eyelid, the anterior part of the cheek and temporal region, and part of the lining of the nasal passage. (3) The *mandibular division* passes through the foramen ovale. It contains all the motor fibers of the trigeminal as well as a share of the sensory fibers. It sends a branch to the masseter, temporalis and pterygoid muscles (Figs. 56, 108) and to the inside of the cheek and the skin of the posterior part of the cheek and temporal region. A second branch, the *lingual* (Fig. 133), goes to the floor and sides of the mouth and to the tongue, which it provides with sensory fibers for touch, and so on, but not for taste. The third branch, the *inferior dental nerve,* gives off a small branch to the mylohyoid muscles and the anterior belly

of the digastric (Fig. 106) and then enters the mandibular foramen (Fig. 31). It is at this point that the nerve may be anes-
thetized to render all the lower teeth insensitive. Running inside
the mandible, it supplies all the lower teeth, and a branch emerges
through the mental foramen (Fig. 24) to supply the lower lip.

PRACTICAL CONSIDERATIONS. Trigeminal neuralgia or "tic douloureux" is a
painful affliction of the fifth nerve. It is characterized by severe shooting pains in
the region of one or more of the main divisions. To obtain a permanent cure,
alcohol may be injected into the nerve, or it may be necessary to open the cranial
cavity and to divide the nerve proximal to the semilunar ganglion.

6. The *abducens*[44] *nerve*, like the trochlear nerve, supplies one
muscle of the eyeball (the lateral rectus muscle). It issues from the
brain at the lower border of the pons and passes into the orbit
through the superior orbital fissure.

7. The *facial nerve* supplies the motor fibers to the muscles of
facial expression, and carries some of the sensory fibers for taste.
It issues from the brain at the lower border of the pons lateral to
the abducens nerve. It runs a complicated course through the
petrous temporal bone, entering at the internal acoustic meatus
and emerging through the stylomastoid foramen (Figs. 132, 263).
A small branch, the *chorda tympani*, carrying taste fibers, runs
through the middle ear, across the inner surface of the ear drum
and along the pharyngotympanic tube to the throat. It then joins
the lingual branch of the mandibular nerve and supplies the anterior two-thirds of the tongue.

PRACTICAL CONSIDERATIONS. If the facial nerve is injured, the muscles of
facial expression become paralyzed and the patient cannot, for example, close the
eye or show the teeth. The mouth is pulled over to the sound side by the opposing
muscles which remain intact. Because of its superficial position in front of the
ear these symptoms sometimes come on after exposure to cold, or the nerve may
be injured in babies during an instrumental delivery.

8. The *acoustic nerve* (O.T., auditory nerve) emerges from the
brain at the lower border of the pons lateral to the facial nerve and
enters the internal acoustic meatus to go to the internal ear in the
petromastoid part of the temporal bone. It consists of two functionally different portions, the cochlear nerve and the vestibular
nerve. The *cochlear nerve* is connected peripherally with the
cochlea and is the nerve of hearing. The *vestibular nerve* is connected with the nonauditory part of the internal ear, the semicircular canals, and so forth. It functions in balancing and in the
recognition of the position of the head in space.

PRACTICAL CONSIDERATIONS. Severe injury to the cochlear nerve results in
deafness; irritation of it causes noises in the ear, or tinnitus. Severe injury to the

---

[44] Abducens: derivative of the verb, to abduct. The muscle to which the nerve
runs rotates the eye laterally; i.e., it abducts it from the midline.

vestibular nerve may cause difficulty in the recognition of the position of the head without the aid of the eyes; irritation of it causes dizziness and vomiting as in sea-sickness. A peculiar kind of tumor (called acoustic neuroma) sometimes forms on the acoustic nerve. It can be removed by operation.

9. The *glossopharyngeal nerve* issues from the brain on the ventrolateral aspect of the medulla and passes out of the skull through the jugular foramen. It is a mixed nerve containing sensory and motor fibers. The sensory portion supplies the pharynx and back of the tongue. For the posterior third of the tongue it supplies both taste fibers and ordinary sensory fibers for touch, and so on. The motor portion supplies some of the muscles of swallowing.

10. The *vagus*[45] *nerve* arises from the ventrolateral aspect of the medulla, caudal to the glossopharyngeal nerve, and leaves the skull through the jugular foramen. It passes into the neck (Figs. 199, 211), thorax and abdomen and supplies the larynx, heart, lungs and some of the abdominal viscera with motor and sensory fibers. Most of the vagus belongs to the autonomic system and will be discussed there.

11. The *accessory nerve* (O.T., spinal accessory) arises from the ventrolateral aspect of the medulla, caudal to the vagus, and from the lateral aspect of the spinal cord as far down as the fifth or sixth cervical nerve. Its lower roots form a trunk which passes upward through the foramen magnum and joins the cranial roots. The nerve then emerges with the vagus and glossopharyngeal through the jugular foramen. It is a pure motor nerve. Some of its fibers join the vagus; others pass into the neck to supply the sternocleidomastoid and trapezius muscles.

12. The *hypoglossal nerve* arises from the ventral aspect of the medulla medial to the ninth and tenth cranial nerves and lateral to the pyramid. It sends motor fibers to the tongue (Fig. 199).

One pair of cranial nerves, the *terminal nerves,* were discovered and described long after the other twelve had been assigned their conventional numbers. These two nerves are extremely delicate. Each passes along the median side of one of the olfactory tracts and is distributed with fibers of the olfactory nerve to the nasal mucosa. The function of the terminal nerves has not been determined.

FUNCTIONAL ANATOMY OF THE NEURO-SENSORY SYSTEM

Now that we have described the major features of the nervous system and can, perhaps, find our way about in it, we can turn our attention to a few of the details of structure in terms of which the

---

[45] Vagus: L., wandering. In contrast to most of the other cranial nerves which have a restricted distribution, the vagus nerve "wanders" to a great many organs. Cf. vagabond.

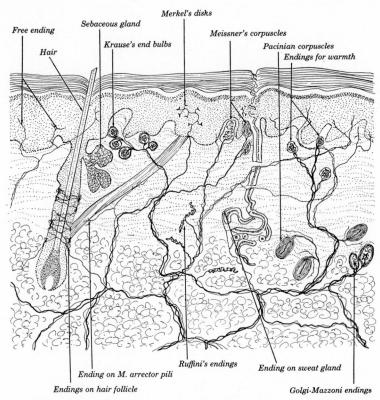

Figure 264. Schematic representation of nerve endings and sense organs in the skin. Note that there are efferent fibers to the muscle of the hair and to the sweat gland. The heavy lines are myelinated fibers, the light lines unmyelinated fibers. (Redrawn from Wollard et al.: J. Anat., Vol. 74.)

activities of the neuro-sensory system are carried on. We are concerned here primarily with the routes, or pathways, that messages may take as they course through the nervous system to bring about the activation, coordination and control that are its function. Only one or two of the many pathways that neurologists have been able to trace can be described here, but these may serve to give some idea of the working structure of the nervous system.

First we must turn our attention to the means by which nerve impulses are initiated. We shall describe at this point only the organs in the skin. Those deep within the body that respond to conditions there will be mentioned later. The organs of special sense—sight, hearing, taste and smell—will be discussed in a separate chapter.

Sensory Organs in the Skin. From the skin we experience

sensations of touch, pressure, cold, warmth and pain. Each of these sensations is served by a structurally different type of nerve ending. These are illustrated and named in Figure 264. Practically nothing is known about the mechanics of these endings, but each serves to lower the threshold of its fiber for a particular stimulus. For example, a slight drop in temperature will excite the fiber in a Krause's end bulb, but none of the others. A deformation of the skin, caused by a light touch, will deform slightly all the nerve endings in the area, but only Meissner's corpuscles and Merkel's disks will be stimulated. Almost any stimulus, if sufficiently intense, will stimulate the free nerve endings and result in a sensation of pain in addition to the sensation of touch, pressure, cold or warmth mediated by other endings.

PHYSIOLOGY OF SENSATION. The following physiologic facts have been established and must be borne in mind throughout the study of the nervous system. (1) There is only one kind of nerve impulse. The impulses that result in a sensation of warmth or cold, or cause a muscle to contract or a gland to secrete, are all the same. (2) Which agent will, under normal conditions, stimulate a certain sensory fiber depends on the structure of the ending of that fiber. However, under certain conditions almost any ending can be excited by almost any stimulus. (3) The sensation that results from excitation of a sensory ending is determined by where the pathway ends in the brain, not by the nature of the stimulus. If a nerve ending is experimentally stimulated by an agent other than that which normally excites it, the sensation will be the same as though it had been stimulated by its usual agent. If, for example, a Meissner's corpuscle is electrically stimulated, the resulting sensation will be one of touch. (4) The intensity of a sensation is a function of the frequency of the nerve impulses. A strong stimulus will result in a more rapid succession of the impulses and hence produce a more intense sensation than will a light stimulus.

Pathway from a Meissner's Corpuscle to Skeletal Muscle by Way of the Cerebral Cortex.

As stated earlier, a pathway through the nervous system consists of a sequence of neurons, joined by synaptic contacts between the axon (or central process) of one neuron and the dendrites or cell body of the next. In describing these pathways it is, therefore, convenient to number in order the successive neurons and to give for each the location of its cell body and the course of its axon or of its central and peripheral processes. Paths from receptors to centers of coordination within the central nervous system are called *afferent paths*. Routes from these centers to effectors (muscles or glands) are called *efferent paths*. The constituent neurons of these paths are called *afferent neurons* and *efferent neurons*, respectively.

We shall start with a Meissner's corpuscle in the skin of the trunk or of an extremity so that a spinal nerve rather than a cranial nerve will be involved.

AFFERENT NEURON I. The cell body of this neuron lies in the dorsal root ganglion of a spinal nerve (Fig. 265). Its peripheral

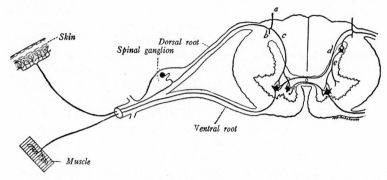

Figure 265. Diagrammatic section through the spinal cord and a spinal nerve to show the position of certain neurons. *a,* Ascending branch of afferent neuron. *c,* Branch forming part of a simple reflex arc. *e,* Association neuron. *f,* Commissural neuron. (Ranson-Clark: Anatomy of the Nervous System. 9th edition.)

process lies in the spinal nerve. The tip of the peripheral process is in a Meissner's corpuscle (Fig. 264). Its central process passes through the dorsal root into the posterior funiculus of the spinal cord and divides into an ascending and descending branch (Fig. 228, *A*). These ascending and descending fibers give off many branches called collaterals which enter the gray substance of the cord to make synaptic connections with other neurons (Fig. 270). The ascending fiber may travel a considerable distance before ending in the gray matter, or it may extend all the way up to the medulla oblongata, ending in the nucleus gracilis, nucleus cuneatus or lateral nucleus cuneatus.

As ascending fibers from each spinal nerve enter the posterior funiculus, they take up a position lateral to those already there. This results in those fibers coming from the lowest parts of the body lying nearest the posterior median septum, and each higher group, as they enter, lying lateral to those already there. The division of the posterior funiculus into medial *fasciculus gracilis* and lateral *fasciculus cuneatus* (Fig. 249) is not evident below the mid-thoracic region. Here the fasciculus cuneatus first appears and becomes larger at successively higher levels. An ascending fiber from a spinal nerve below the mid-thoracic region will, therefore, lie in the fasciculus gracilis, and one from a spinal nerve above the mid-thoracic region will lie in the fasciculus cuneatus.

AFFERENT NEURON II. The cell body of this neuron lies in the nucleus gracilis or nucleus cuneatus. Here the end of the central process of the first neuron makes synaptic connection with it or its dendrites. The axon of the second neuron runs anteriorly as one of the *internal arcuate fibers* (Fig. 251) and crosses in the

Figure 266   **The Neuro-sensory System**   323

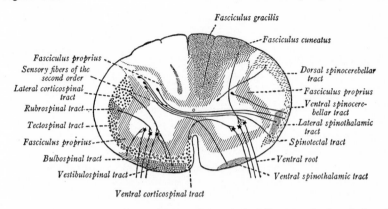

Figure 266. Diagram showing the location of the principal fiber tracts in the spinal cord of man. Ascending tracts on the right side, descending tracts on the left. (Ranson.)

decussation of the lemniscus[46] (Fig. 251) to the opposite side. Here it turns upward in the *medial lemniscus* (Figs. 252, 253, 254, 255, 256) to end in the thalamus.

AFFERENT NEURON II, ALTERNATE. The ascending branch of the central process of the first neuron, or one of its collaterals, may end in the posterior gray column of the spinal cord (branch *b* in Fig. 265). Here it will make contact with the cell body or dendrites of a neuron (afferent neuron II) whose axon will cross the median plane of the spinal cord (Fig. 266) and ascend in the *ventral spinothalamic tract*. In the medulla this tract joins the medial lemniscus, and the axon now runs with that of the other second afferent neuron to the thalamus. Note that in both cases the axon of the second afferent neuron crosses the midline, either in the medulla or in the spinal cord.

AFFERENT NEURON III. The nerve cell body of the third neuron lies in one of the nuclei that constitute the thalamus. Its axon joins the internal capsule and passes through the corona radiata to the *posterior central convolution* (Fig. 239) of the cerebral cortex on the same side. Note that we have arrived in the cerebral cortex on the side opposite to that on which the sense organ in the skin lies.

We shall for the present pass by the connections within the cerebral cortex and skip over to the *anterior central convolution* (Fig. 239).

EFFERENT NEURON I. In the part of the cerebral cortex that constitutes the anterior central gyrus lie the large cell bodies of the *pyramidal neurons* (Fig. 228, *H*), so called, not from the shape

---

[46] Lemniscus: G., a band or stripe.

of the cell bodies, but from the route the axons take. The axon of a pyramidal cell passes through the corona radiata and the internal capsule into the base of the cerebral peduncle. It continues through the pons in the *corticospinal tract* (Figs. 255, 254) and into the pyramid. At the decussation of the pyramids it may cross to the opposite side to enter the *lateral corticospinal tract* (Fig. 250). As this tract extends down the cord it constantly diminishes in size as fibers leave it one by one or in small groups to pass into the anterior gray substance of the anterior horn (Fig. 266).

Some of the fibers descending in the pyramids do not cross to the other side at the decussation, but instead continue down the same side, constituting the *ventral corticospinal tract* (Figs. 250, 266). Fibers leave this tract, a few at a time, much as they left the lateral corticospinal tract, and end in the anterior gray column *on the opposite side of the cord.* Thus all the corticospinal fibers eventually cross to the other side (some investigators believe there may be a few exceptions), the majority at the decussation of the pyramids, the remainder through the ventral commissure of the cord.

In most persons 75 to 90 per cent of the corticospinal fibers cross to the opposite side at the decussation of the pyramids, but the number is variable. In rare cases all the fibers cross and there is no ventral corticospinal tract. At the other extreme, also rarely found, none of the fibers cross at the decussation, the ventral corticospinal tracts are large, and the lateral tracts are absent. In the majority of cases the ventral tract does not extend below the upper thoracic region, its fibers supplying chiefly the neck and upper extremities.

EFFERENT NEURON II. The large cell bodies of *somatic motor neurons* (Fig. 228, *C*) are a conspicuous element in the anterior column of the spinal cord (Fig. 249). With one of these the axon of the pyramidal neuron may make synaptic contact, or it may contact an association neuron in the region which, in turn, contacts the somatic motor neuron. The axon of this last neuron passes out through the ventral root of a spinal nerve to end in skeletal muscle. (See The Somatic Motor Neuron, p. 330.)

The Cerebral Cortex. It has been estimated that the cerebral cortex contains the cell bodies of nearly 14,000,000,000 neurons. While it would, perhaps, be rash to say that every one of these is potentially connected, directly or indirectly, with every other one, the cortical mechanism must approach some such degree of complexity.

Figure 267 gives some idea of the organization of the cortex in terms of layers of cell bodies and of fibers. The different areas of the cortex are interconnected by neurons lying wholly within the

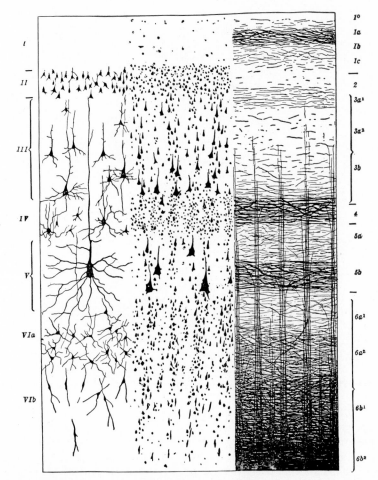

Figure 267. Diagram of the structure of the cerebral cortex. Cell organization shown on the left, fiber organization on the right. *I,* Molecular layer; *II,* layer of small pyramidal cells; *III,* layer of medium-sized and large pyramidal cells; *IV,* layer of small stellate cells; *V,* deep layer of large pyramidal cells; *VI,* layer of polymorphic cells. The large cells of the fifth layer are the giant cells of Betz. (Brodmann.)

cortex and by neurons whose fibers course through the underlying white substance. The latter connect distant areas with one another, sweeping through the corona radiata between parts of one hemisphere, or passing through the commissures, notably the corpus callosum, to connect areas of one hemisphere with those in the other.

The cerebral cortex probably functions pretty much as a whole. However, areas have been identified that seem to be more directly

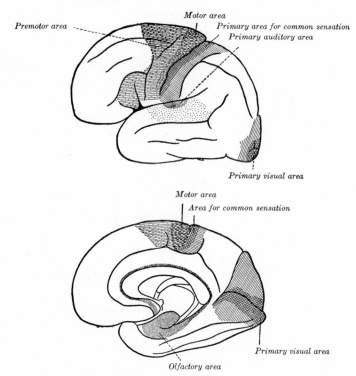

Figure 268.   The motor and sensory areas of the cerebral cortex. Primary sensory areas
deeply shaded; secondary sensory areas lightly shaded. (Ranson.)

concerned with certain functions than are other parts. Some of
these are shown in Figures 268 and 269. Artificial stimulation of
areas on the anterior central gyrus or convolution usually cause
movements of the parts named on Figure 269. The fibers of the
pyramidal tract, which transmit impulses for volitional movements
from the cortex to the motor neurons (see pathway described
above), arise principally from this area. Since all or most of the
fibers of the pyramidal tracts cross, stimulation causes movement
of the part on the opposite side. Figure 269 must not be taken to
represent an invariable one-to-one mechanism, however. The result of stimulating a point on the anterior central gyrus will vary
under different conditions, often unidentifiable, and, on the other
hand, movement of parts of the body can sometimes be elicited
by stimulation of other parts of the cortex.

The posterior central gyrus seems to be the part of the cortex
most directly concerned with general bodily sensations. Here fibers
from lower centers, notably the thalamus, end. Localization here

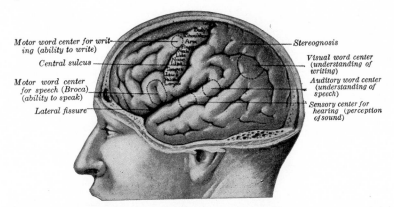

Figure 269. Localization of motor centers in the anterior central convolution, and the classical scheme of localization of speech centers. (Callander.)

closely parallels that on the anterior central gyrus. For example, sensations from the arm arrive at an area on the posterior central gyrus opposite the area on the anterior central gyrus whose stimulation is most apt to produce movement of the arm.

Recognition of the mere types of sensation—pain, temperature, touch, and so on—apparently enters consciousness at the level of the thalamus, since they can be perceived even when the posterior central gyrus has been destroyed. This part of the cortex is necessary, however, for identification of the point stimulated, for recognition of spatial relations, for sensing differences of intensity, and for appreciating similarities and differences of objects brought in contact with the skin.

Some other areas of the cortex will be mentioned in connection with special functions and pathways.

Reflex Arc. The involuntary movement of the hand in response to a stimulus, described as a reflex action at the beginning of this chapter, may involve a relatively short pathway through the central nervous system, not involving the brain at all. Starting with afferent neuron I of the pathway from Meissner's corpuscle described earlier, we find that the central process often sends a short branch (c in Fig. 265) into the anterior column at or near the level at which the fiber enters the cord. This fiber may make contact with a somatic motor neuron on the same side, or it may make contact with a commissural neuron (f in Fig. 265) that crosses to the other side and contacts a somatic motor neuron there. These are the simplest reflex arcs, and probably none this simple exist. Never would a single motor neuron be activated, but rather a vast number that would set in motion a pattern of muscles, often on

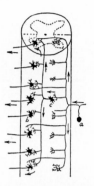

Figure 270. Diagram of the spinal cord, showing the elements concerned in a diffuse unilateral reflex: *a,* Spinal ganglion cell giving origin to a dorsal root fiber, one branch of which enters the cord and divides into an ascending and a descending branch; *b,* motor cell in anterior column; *c,* association neuron with axon in the lateral fasciculus propius. (Cajal.)

both sides of the body. Figure 270 is a diagram to suggest a possible arrangement, still on a simple scale.

The Proprioceptive System.   By no means all the sensory endings are located in the skin. Muscles, tendons and joints are provided with sensory endings, some simple, some complex, some encapsulated. These respond to pressure, tension and movement. They inform the nervous system of the position, activities and loads of the skeletal and muscular systems from moment to moment. Fibers carrying impulses originating in these sensory organs within the body are called *proprioceptive.*[47] The term *exteroceptive* is applied to fibers concerned with impulses arising from external stimuli.

The nerve cell bodies of these proprioceptive sensory neurons lie in the dorsal root ganglion of spinal nerves and in the nuclei of the dorsal series of cranial nerves. The central process of one of these sensory neurons in a spinal nerve may ascend in the posterior funiculus to the gracile or cuneate nucleus. From there a second neuron may send its axon to the thalamus, and a third, from the thalamus to the cerebral cortex. This is similar to the exteroceptive pathway described before. Alternately, a second neuron may run from the gracile or cuneate nucleus to the inferior cerebellar peduncle and with it into the cerebellum.

There are two other proprioceptive routes to the cerebellum. Collateral or terminal branches of the central process of a sensory neuron, instead of going to the cuneate or gracile nucleus, may

---

[47] Proprioceptive: from L. *proprio,* one's own, plus *recipere,* to receive. A corresponding term for somatic afferent is exteroceptive, and for visceral afferent, interoceptive.

Figure 271   *The Neuro-sensory System*   329

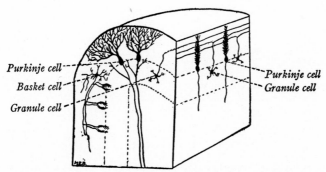

Purkinje cell
Basket cell
Granule cell

Purkinje cell
Granule cell

Figure 271. Diagrammatic representation of the structure of the cerebellar cortex as seen
in a section along the axis of a folium (on the right), and in a section at a right angle
to the axis of the folium (on the left). (Ranson-Clark: Anatomy of the Nervous System.
9th edition.)

end in the gray substance of the cord. Second neurons then send
axons from the gray substance through the *ventral spinocerebellar
tract* (Figs. 266, 250, 251, 253, 254) of the same or opposite side,
to bend around the middle cerebellar peduncle and enter the cerebellum with the superior peduncle or brachium conjunctivum (Fig.
254). Other second neurons in the gray substance of the cord send
axons in the *dorsal spinocerebellar tract* (Figs. 266, 250, 251)
which enter the inferior peduncle, or restiform body, and go with
it into the cerebellum.

Analogous routes are followed by proprioceptive fibers from the
cranial nerves.

The Cerebellum. The cerebellum is concerned chiefly with
synergy in the action of the voluntary muscles, that is, with the
numerous and complex adjustments that a large number of muscles
must make to permit even the simplest movement. It appears to
operate below the level of consciousness.

The cerebellum receives impulses from many sources, notably
from the proprioceptive endings in muscles, joints and tendons,
and from the vestibular part of the ear (see Chapter 14). It also
receives impulses from higher centers of the brain. Fibers from
the gray substance of the cord (*dorsal spinocerebellar tract*, Figs.
266, 250, 251), from the olivary nucleus and from other centers
enter through the inferior cerebellar peduncle and go to the cerebellar cortex. Fibers from the nuclei pontis enter by the middle
cerebellar peduncles and go to the cerebellar cortex. These fibers
receive impulses from fibers originating in the cerebral cortex, and
the arrangement is such that impulses from one cerebral hemisphere go to the opposite side of the cerebellum. The *ventral
spinocerebellar tract* (Figs. 266, 250, 251, 252, 254) swings up and

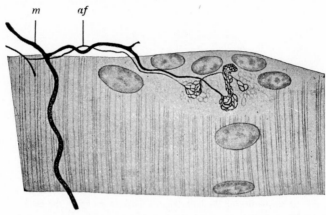

Figure 272. Motor end plate of striated muscle. *m,* Motor nerve fibers; *af,* accessory fiber of uncertain function. (Redrawn after Boeke. From Maximow and Bloom.)

back to enter the cerebellum alongside the superior peduncle. Nearly all fibers entering the cerebellum go directly to its cortex.

We shall mention only two of the several types of neuron in the cerebellar cortex. Many incoming fibers contact the *granule cells* (Figs. 271, 228, *D*) whose axons branch and run among the dendrites of the Purkinje cells (Figs. 271, 228, *G*), doubtless making contact with them. The axons of the Purkinje cells run to the dentate and other nuclei in the cerebellum, while the collaterals of their axons run among the dendrites of neighboring Purkinje cells.

A few fibers run from the cortex directly to the vestibular nuclei, but the great majority of the fibers leaving the cerebellum arise in the dentate or some of the smaller nuclei. They leave by the superior peduncles, which undergo complete decussation in the tegmentum of the midbrain beneath the inferior colliculi. The fibers then go to the *red nuclei* (Fig. 258) and to the thalami. One descending tract that may be mentioned here is the *rubrospinal tract* (Figs. 255, 254, 253, 252, 251, 250, 266), which originates in the red nucleus and goes to the lower motor neurons.

THE SOMATIC MOTOR NEURON. The somatic motor neuron, whose axon leads to a skeletal muscle, has been termed the "final common pathway" of motor activity. A great many nerve fibers converge upon it—collaterals of primary sensory neurons, association neurons, commissural neurons, pyramidal neurons, fibers from the red nuclei, fibers from the thalami, and others. It has been estimated that more than a thousand fibers terminate on the cell body and dendrites of a single motor neuron. From what was said about the synapse (p. 276), whether or not a motor neuron discharges and causes the muscle fibers of its motor unit to contract will be the resultant of all the impulses impinging upon it at any given moment.

This arrangement is the rule throughout the nervous system, and rarely, probably never, is the dendrite or cell body of a neuron anywhere reached by only one axon.

The Motor End Plate. As one of the terminal branches of the axon of a somatic motor neuron (Fig. 228, *C*) approaches a muscle fiber (muscle cell), it loses its myelin sheath. As it penetrates the sarcolemma, or just afterward, it loses its neurilemma. Where the fiber enters the muscle cell there is an area of sarcoplasm without muscle fibrils. Within this sarcoplasm the nerve fiber forms a small plexus. The sarcoplasm and the terminal plexus together constitute the *motor end plate* (Fig. 272). A nerve impulse arriving here stimulates the muscle fiber to contract.

THE MOTOR UNIT. When a muscle fiber is stimulated, normally at a motor end plate, if it reacts at all, it produces the full degree of tension of which it is at the moment capable. Physiologists refer to this type of reaction as "all-or-none." From this all-or-none reaction on the part of the muscle fiber it follows that the tension developed by a muscle at any given moment is a function of the number of fibers contracting at that moment. A few fibers, exerting all their force, produce but little pull; more fibers contracting produce a greater tension; all fibers activated at once result in the maximum pull of which the muscle is capable. (This last probably seldom or never happens under normal conditions.)

We find that there are many more muscle fibers in a muscle than there are motor fibers in the nerve that runs to it. Within the muscle, however, each nerve fiber divides into an extensive terminal arborization, giving rise to many more branches than are shown in Figure 228, *C*, sometimes as many as several hundred. Each terminal branch ends in a motor end plate in a muscle fiber. Impulses coming to a muscle on a single motor axon will, because of this arrangement, stimulate all the muscle fibers to which its terminal branches go. A single motor neuron together with the muscle fibers it innervates is, therefore, the functional unit of motor activity and is called a *motor unit*. The smallest tension that a muscle can produce is that produced by the fibers of one motor unit, and a muscle can show as many degrees of tension as it has motor units. A large muscle, such as one in the thigh, that does not need to make finely graded movements will have many muscle cells in each motor unit. On the other hand, a muscle such as one that moves a finger or one that moves the eyeball, where fine movements require nicely adjusted tensions, will have relatively few muscle cells in each motor unit. Stated in another way, in the former type of muscle the ratio of motor axons to muscle fibers will be small, one to several hundred; in the latter the ratio will be large, one to five or six.

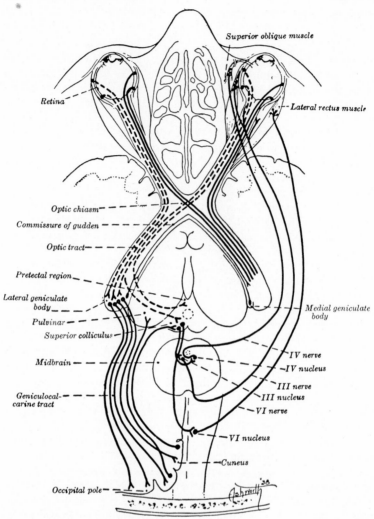

Superior oblique muscle

Retina

Lateral rectus muscle

Optic chiasm
Commissure of gudden
Optic tract
Pretectal region
Lateral geniculate body
Pulvinar
Superior colliculus
Midbrain
Geniculocalcarine tract
Occipital pole

Medial geniculate body
IV nerve
IV nucleus
III nerve
III nucleus
VI nerve
VI nucleus
Cuneus

Figure 273. Optic visual and reflex paths. (Larsell: Anatomy of the Nervous System. D. Appleton-Century Co.)

The Optic Pathways. Of the pathways from the organs of special sense, we shall describe only those from the organ of vision, the eye. The end organs for this sense lie in the retina and will be described later (p. 343). The axons leaving the retina pass backward in the *optic nerve* (Fig. 241) to the *optic chiasm,* where a partial decussation of fibers takes place (Fig. 273). Those from the left halves of both retinas come to lie in the left *optic tract;* those from the right halves of both retinas in the right optic tract. The neurons continue backward and terminate in the *lateral geniculate body*. From here a new order of neurons arises, the *geniculocalcarine tract* (Fig. 273), which sweep backward to the *primary visual cortex* (Fig. 268), lying in and around the calcarine fissure. The *secondary* or *psychovisual area* lies immediately adjacent to the primary visual area.

Fibers from the optic tract also go to the *superior colliculus* in the roof of the midbrain, as do fibers coming forward from the visual area of the cortex (Fig. 273). In nuclei located here connections are made with neurons going to the *nuclei of the oculomotor* (Fig. 256), *trochlear* and *abducens nerves* and to *motor nuclei* in the cervical region of the spinal cord. These connections mediate reflex movements of the eyes and head in response to visual stimuli.

PRACTICAL CONSIDERATIONS. Because of its long course through the brain, the optic system is frequently involved in intracranial disease. Lesions which interrupt the optic nerve produce blindness in the eye on the affected side. Lesions in the optic tract, optic radiations or optic cortex of, say, the left side render the left halves of both retinas insensitive.

The Olfactory System. The olfactory nerve is peculiar in that the cell bodies of its neurons (Fig. 228, *E*) lie in the nasal mucosa (p. 357). Their axons, which constitute the nerve, pass through the cribriform plate of the skull and end in the olfactory bulb (Fig. 241). Here they synapse with neurons whose axons constitute the olfactory tracts. These fibers end in the under side of the cerebral hemispheres in the region of the anterior perforated substance (Fig. 261). From this area the connections are too numerous and complicated to detail here. The mammillary bodies, the fornix and the hippocampi are main tracts and centers of the olfactory system. There are also numerous centers in the thalamus, cerebral hemispheres, midbrain and medulla.

The Speech Mechanism. The function of speech includes both sensory and motor elements. On the sensory side there is the ability to understand written and spoken language; on the motor side there is the capacity to speak and write. The neural mechanism for all these functions lies, in right-handed persons, in the left cerebral hemisphere (Fig. 269). Certain cortical regions near the secondary visual and auditory centers are necessary for the sensory aspects of speech. A small region called *Broca's area*,[48] which lies in the frontal cortex in front of the lower part of the anterior central convolution, is necessary for vocal speech. There may possibly be a specialized center in front of the arm area for writing. All these regions are intimately connected by association fibers.

---

[48] From Paul Broca (1824–1880), an anatomist, surgeon and anthropologist of Paris.

PRACTICAL CONSIDERATIONS. Aphasia is a general term for all the disorders of speech dependent upon lesions of the speech areas of the brain. There are many kinds of aphasia, the nature of which depends upon the particular cortical area involved. According to the classical conceptions, injuries in and around the visual speech area produce word-blindness, or the inability to understand written words; lesions in and around the auditory speech area produce word-deafness, or the inability to understand spoken language; and so on. According to the well-known English neurologist, Dr. Henry Head, word-blindness and word-deafness do not exist as separate entities. He recognizes four different primary aphasias. In the first (nominal aphasia) there is difficulty in the understanding and use of nouns or names. The second (verbal aphasia) is a disorder of the motor aspects of speech. The third (syntactical aphasia) is a disorder of grammatical structure, so that the patient talks jargon. The fourth (semantic aphasia) is a difficulty in comprehending whole paragraphs, or in understanding a plan as a whole, although the individual elements in it are properly perceived.

THE AUTONOMIC NERVOUS SYSTEM

The autonomic or vegetative nervous system includes those neurons concerned in the innervation and regulation of the viscera, i.e., the heart, lungs, gastro-intestinal tract, and so on. It is subdivided into two main divisions, one called the thoracolumbar division, the other the craniosacral[49] division. Both contain afferent and efferent fibers.

The Thoracolumbar Division. The efferent fibers of the thoracolumbar division leave the spinal cord through the twelve thoracic and the first two lumbar nerves. They then pass by way of small nerves called *white rami communicantes* (Fig. 235), into the *sympathetic trunk* (Figs. 226, 198), a band of nervous tissue extending from the neck to the pelvis and lying by the side of the vertebral column. Situated on the trunk at close intervals are several ganglia, the *central ganglia* or the *ganglia of the sympathetic trunk,* and from it axons are distributed in two directions. First, a group of fibers pass by way of small filaments, the *gray rami communicantes,*

---

[49] The variety of names given to this system as a whole and to its component parts is most confusing. The following six terminologies have been used by different writers:

For the System as a Whole	For the Thoracolumbar Division	For the Craniosacral Division
1. Autonomic	Thoracolumbar	Craniosacral
2. Autonomic	Sympathetic	Parasympathetic
3. Sympathetic	Thoracolumbar	Craniosacral
4. Vegetative	Sympathetic	Parasympathetic
5. Vegetative	Sympathetic	Autonomic
6. Involuntary	Sympathetic	Parasympathetic

In addition, the terms "sympathetic" and "parasympathetic" have been used in a functional sense, instead of referring to the specific regions of the central nervous system from which they arise (cf. p. 338). The terminology adopted here is number 1 above, though sometimes number 2 is used.

Figure 274 *The Neuro-sensory System* 335

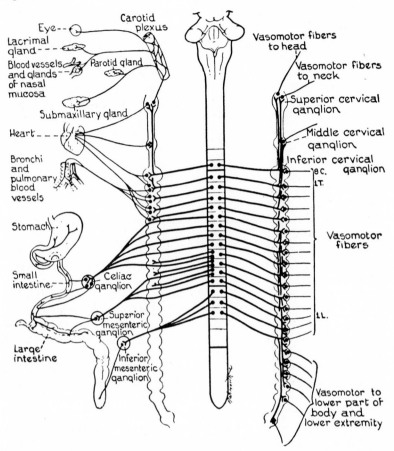

Figure 274. Schema of the thoracolumbar visceral efferent connections, showing those to internal viscera on the left side and those to the periphery on the right side. (Larsell: Anatomy of the Nervous System. D. Appleton-Century Co.)

into the spinal nerves (more or less parallel to the white rami communicantes), and are distributed with them to the blood vessels and sweat glands of the limbs and body wall (shown on the right side of Fig. 274). Second, a number of independent *peripheral autonomic nerves* pass to supply the internal viscera (shown on the left side of Fig. 274).

The best known of these peripheral autonomic nerves are the *cardiac nerves,* which supply the heart, and the *splanchnic nerves* (Fig. 198), which supply some of the abdominal viscera. In the lower part of their course the nerves of each group unite to form a complicated plexus from which the terminal branches are derived.

The plexus formed by the cardiac nerves is called the *cardiac plexus;* that formed by the splanchnic nerve, the *celiac* or *solar plexus.* Connected with each plexus are small ganglia, the *collateral ganglia.*

The thoracolumbar autonomic efferent pathways differ from the somatic motor pathways in that they consist of two orders of neurons: preganglionic neurons and postganglionic neurons (Fig. 274). The *preganglionic neurons* arise in the spinal cord and pass out to terminate in either the ganglia of the sympathetic trunk or in the collateral ganglia. The *postganglionic neurons* continue from these ganglia to the viscera.

The afferent or sensory sympathetic fibers pass uninterruptedly from the viscera to the spinal cord through the dorsal roots, where their nerve cell bodies will be found.

The Craniosacral Division.   The craniosacral division of the autonomic system (Fig. 275) consists, as its name implies, of two portions, a cranial portion and a sacral portion. The *cranial portion* consists of those visceral fibers which pass out of the brain through the cranial nerves. The largest number pass through the vagus. The *sacral portion* consists of those visceral fibers which leave the cord through the upper three or four sacral nerves. The fibers of the cranial division supply the head, thorax and the alimentary canal as far down as the proximal part of the colon. The fibers of the sacral division supply the remainder of the abdominal viscera and the pelvic organs.

The efferent paths of the craniosacral division, like those of the thoracolumbar, consist of two orders of neurons: preganglionic neurons and postganglionic neurons. They differ from the thoracolumbar group in that their ganglia are, as a rule, terminal and lie directly on or in the organs they supply. Thus the preganglionic craniosacral neurons run a long course from the central nervous system to the organs they supply, and the postganglionic craniosacral neurons both arise and terminate within the organ on which they act.

The afferent fibers pass through the ganglionated cranial nerves and the dorsal roots of the sacral nerves.

The Myenteric Reflex System.   In the gastro-intestinal tract certain local reflexes, called myenteric reflexes, have been observed after section of all the nerves which lead into it. These have been thought to be due to a peculiar autonomous reflex system resident within the walls of the viscera, called the myenteric reflex system, or the peripheral autonomic visceral nervous system. The nature and extent of this system have been much disputed. Some regard it as part of a widespread peripheral system more primitive than the rest of the nervous system. Others doubt that the myen-

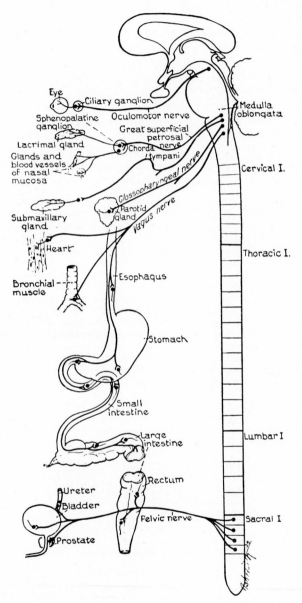

Figure 275. Schema of craniosacral visceral efferent connections. (Larsell: Anatomy of the Nervous System. D. Appleton-Century Co.)

teric system has any properties peculiar to itself, and regard it as simply the terminal portion of the autonomic system.

The Central Connections of the Autonomic System. The autonomic system in both its thoracolumbar and craniosacral divisions is under a certain regulation from centers within the central nervous system. In the *medulla,* for example, are centers for the regulation of the heart beat, respiration, and so on. The *hypothalamus,* the region of the brain in and around the walls of the third ventricle below the thalamus, is an important regulating center for many visceral and metabolic activities. There is some evidence to point to the possibility of visceral centers in the *cerebral cortex.* The course of the neurons from those higher centers down to the preganglionic fibers is inadequately known.

FUNCTIONS OF THE AUTONOMIC SYSTEM. It can readily be seen from the preceding discussion that the two main divisions of the autonomic system, although arising separately within the nervous system, overlap in their fields of distribution, so that many, perhaps all, of the viscera are innervated by both. The functions of the two groups are often antagonistic. Thus stimulation of the thoracolumbar division accelerates the heart: stimulation of the vagus, a cranial autonomic nerve, slows it. Stimulation of the thoracolumbar nerves to the intestine slows down peristalsis; stimulation of the vagus augments it. This antagonism, however, is not always demonstrable from the point of view of origin of the fibers from the central nervous system. A better statement of the case would probably be that there appear to be two functionally different systems within the autonomic system as a whole, the sympathetic and the parasympathetic systems. The sympathetic system arises in the main from the thoracolumbar division; the parasympathetic from the craniosacral division. These different sites of origin, however, are not necessarily absolute, for it may well be that certain parasympathetic fibers run in the thoracolumbar division.

The two systems show different chemical affinities. Stimulation of the sympathetic produces effects similar to those produced by the drug epinephrine; stimulation of the parasympathetic produces effects like those of acetylcholine. Indeed, epinephrine is produced in the adrenal gland by stimulation of the sympathetic; acetylcholine is produced in certain other regions by stimulation of the parasympathetic. The physiologic functions of the two systems are markedly different. The parasympathetic as a whole is protective and upbuilding. It promotes the flow of saliva and gastric juice for proper digestion, it slows down the heart for rest and recuperation, and so on. The sympathetic, on the other hand, mobilizes the body resources for use in emergencies, such as in the reactions of anger and fear. It liberates the sugar from the liver for use by the muscles; it increases the rate of the heart; and it increases the coagulability of the blood.

THE MENINGES

The meninges[50] are the membranes which cover the central nervous system. Named from without inward, they are the dura mater, the arachnoid and the pia mater.

The *dura mater,*[51] or simply the dura (Figs. 276, 277), is a rela-

---

[50] Meninges: G., membranes.

[51] Dura mater: L., hard mother, i.e., protector.

Figure 276   **The Neuro-sensory System**   339

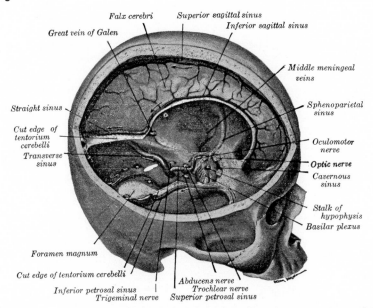

Figure 276.   Right lateral half of the cranial vault removed to show the dura and the dural sinuses. A segment is removed from the cerebellar tentorium to show the foramen magnum and the transverse sinus; arrows indicate the direction of venous flow. (Callander.)

tively thick fibrous sheet which forms the outermost covering of the nervous system and lies against the bony surroundings. From its internal surface two partitions, the falx cerebri and the tentorium cerebelli, pass inward between the different parts of the brain. The *falx*[52] *cerebri* intervenes in the longitudinal fissure between the right and left cerebral hemispheres. The *tentorium cerebelli* lies between the cerebrum and cerebellum. The large venous sinuses of the brain are found between folds in the dura.

The *arachnoid*[53] and the *pia mater*[54] (Fig. 277) are thin, almost transparent membranes. The pia lies next to the brain and dips down into the sulci; the arachnoid lies on top of the pia and bridges over the sulci. The space between the two membranes is called the *subarachnoid space*. In life it is filled with a liquid, called cerebrospinal fluid.

PRACTICAL CONSIDERATIONS.   Meningitis is primarily an inflammation of the arachnoid and the pia mater, although the superficial parts of the brain and cord

---

[52] Falx: L., sickle; so called because of its shape. Cf. falciform ligament, page 173.

[53] Arachnoid: G., like a spider's web.

[54] Pia mater: L., tender or fostering mother, protector.

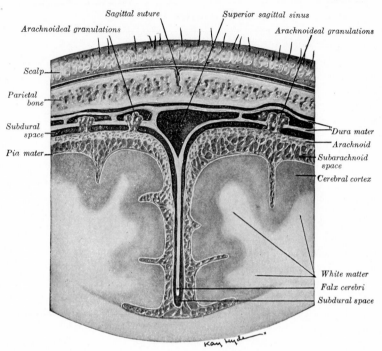

Figure 277. Frontal section through top of the cranium, showing the relations of the meninges. (Callander.)

are usually also involved to some extent as well. There are several types, infectious, epidemic and tuberculous, all serious conditions. Inflammation of the dura is relatively rare.

THE CEREBROSPINAL FLUID

The cerebrospinal fluid, or spinal fluid, is a pale watery fluid which surrounds the brain and spinal cord and fills up its central cavities. Outside the brain it lies in the subarachnoid space. It is produced chiefly in the choroid plexuses of the ventricles, and passes from the ventricular cavities to the subarachnoid space through small openings in the roof of the fourth ventricle (p. 290). It is drained away into the venous circulation through small bodies in the meninges called *arachnoideal granulations* (Fig. 277). It may be compared to the lymph in the rest of the body, though it is not identical.

PRACTICAL CONSIDERATIONS. If the drainage of cerebrospinal fluid from the ventricles is hindered by brain tumor, meningitis or other conditions, the pressure from the increasing amount of fluid often dilates the ventricles to an enormous extent. This pressure thins out the overlying brain substance, and, if the patient is an infant, the whole cranium may become enlarged. The condition is known as hydrocephalus.

Examination of the cerebrospinal fluid is often of value in diagnosing diseases of the central nervous system. It is obtained by a procedure known as lumbar puncture. A hollow needle is inserted in the midline of the back between two of the lumbar vertebrae, and is pushed forward until it enters the subarachnoid space. The desired amount of fluid may then be withdrawn. There is no danger of injuring the spinal cord, since it does not extend downward below the first lumbar vertebrae. The nerves of the cauda equina are rarely pierced, for they readily roll out of the way.

Cerebrospinal fluid may also be obtained by inserting a hollow needle into one of the lateral cerebral ventricles after making a hole in the cranial vault (ventricular puncture); or it may be procured from a puncture made between the under surface of the skull and the first cervical vertebra (cisternal puncture).

REGENERATION WITHIN THE NERVOUS SYSTEM. The capacity of the nervous system to regenerate after disease or injury is different in its peripheral and central portions. In the peripheral nervous system recovery is possible under certain conditions. Thus if a peripheral nerve is divided and the two cut surfaces are approximated, new fibers grow out from the central stump and pass down the track of the distal portion to form a new nerve. If the two portions are not approximated, this regeneration does not take place, for the growing fibers of the central stump appear to require the peripheral portion as a guide. After injury to the central nervous system only abortive attempts at recovery appear and no new fibers are formed. Lesions, therefore, which completely transect the nerve fibers of the brain and spinal cord are permanent. If these fibers, however, are not transected, but only pressed upon, recovery may take place.

CHAPTER 14

THE ORGANS OF SPECIAL SENSE

THE ORGANS of special sense are the peripheral receptors for vision, hearing, taste, smell, located in the eye, ear, mouth and nose respectively.

THE EYE

The organ of vision, the eye, is a spherical body which lies within the orbit. Its essential structure is similar to that of a camera, for it contains a lens which focuses the rays of light upon a sensitive plate, in this case the retina. Its walls are composed of three layers (Fig. 278): an outer fibrous coat, an intermediate vascular coat and an internal nervous coat. Its cavity contains three refracting media: the lens, the vitreous body and the aqueous humor.

The Coats of the Eyeball. The fibrous coat, the external layer of the eyeball, consists of two parts, the sclera and the cornea. The *sclera*[1] is a tough and fibrous covering which surrounds the eye posteriorly and at the sides; anteriorly it becomes transformed into the transparent *cornea*. Both surfaces of the cornea are covered by epithelium. The outer epithelium is stratified squamous; the inner, simple cuboidal.

The vascular coat consists of the choroid, the ciliary body and the outer layer of the iris. The *choroid* lies deep to the sclera and contains a rich plexus of blood vessels. Anteriorly it continues into the ciliary body. The *ciliary body* is a circular ridge projecting into the cavity of the eyeball beneath the sclerocorneal junction. It is formed largely of muscle, the *ciliary muscle*. The *iris* is a muscular diaphragm attached peripherally to the ciliary body, and containing centrally a circular opening called the *pupil*. It contains two muscles, the circular *sphincter pupillae* and the radial *dilator pupillae*. They alter the size of the pupil to adjust the eye to different intensities of light.

---

[1] Sclera: from G., hard.

Figure 278   ***The Organs of Special Sense*** 343

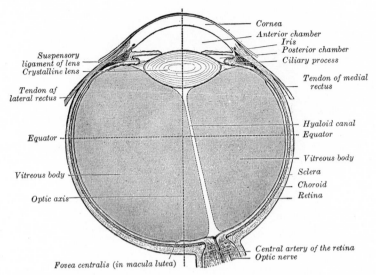

Figure 278. Diagram of a horizontal section through the left eyeball and the optic nerve. (Cunningham's Textbook of Anatomy.)

The nervous coat of the eyeball, the *retina*,[2] lies beneath the choroid. It can be divided into two parts: an optic portion, which participates in the visual mechanism, and a non-optic portion, which does not. The *optic portion* lines the posterior and lateral portions of the eyeball, and terminates anteriorly a short distance behind the ciliary body where the retina becomes abruptly thinner. The *non-optic portion* continues forward to line the ciliary body and the iris. The line of junction between the two parts of the retina is called the *ora serrata*.

The optic portion of the retina contains the end organs of vision, the *rods* and *cones,* and the beginnings of the fibers of the optic nerve. The optic nerve leaves the eye from a point a little to the nasal side of the posterior pole. The nerve head, called the *optic disc* (Fig. 279) appears in the interior of the eye as a white area, circular in shape and elevated slightly above the surrounding retina. From its center a number of arteries and veins spread out to course over the internal surface of the eye. There are no rods and cones in the nerve head, and it forms the "blind spot" of the eye. The *macula lutea*[3] is a yellowish area found in the posterior pole of the eyeball. It is the region of keenest vision.

MICROSCOPIC STRUCTURE OF THE RETINA. The optic portion of

---

[2] Retina: from L. *rete,* a net. The retina is not, however, net-like. The term was applied because of an error of some early anatomic works (Hyrtl).

[3] Macula (plural *maculae*): L., a spot or stain; macula lutea, yellow spot.

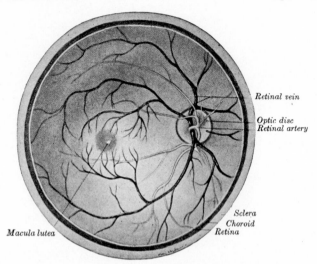

Retinal vein

Optic disc
Retinal artery

Sclera
Choroid
Retina

Macula lutea

Figure 279. The central part of the retina and its related structures (right eye). (Callander, after Testut and Jacob.)

the retina is a complicated structure, and in it, when stained by the usual procedures, ten different layers can be counted. A clearer insight into its essential structure can be gained by the use of special staining methods, and with these the number of fundamental layers can be reduced to four (Fig. 280). These are, named from without inward: (1) the layer of pigmented epithelium; (2) the layer of visual cells; (3) the layer of connecting or bipolar cells; and (4) the layer of the ganglionic cells of the optic nerve.

1. The *pigmented epithelium* consists of a single layer of cells. The cells contain pigment which alters its position, and thus appears to contract and expand, in varying conditions of light and shade.

2. The *layer of visual cells* contains two types of cells called *rod cells* and *cone cells*. Both types consist of a cell body with the nucleus and an external and internal process. The external processes are modified to form either the rod or cone-like structures which give the cells their names. The internal processes come in contact with the dendrites of the connecting cells. The rods and cones are the light-sensitive elements of the retina. The remainder of the rod cell or cone cell may be compared to a nerve cell, the fiber-like part of the external process between the rod or cone and the cell body corresponding to the dendrite, and the internal process to the axon.

3. The *layer of connecting* or *bipolar cells* consist of nerve cells with typical dendrites and axons. The dendrites pass externally to

Figure 280   **The Organs of Special Sense**   345

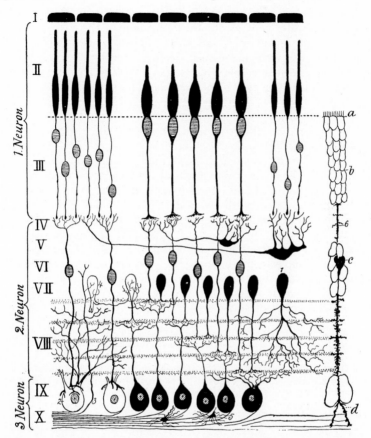

Figure 280.   Schema of the structure of the human retina. *I,* Layer of pigmented epithelium; *1.* Neuron, layer of visual cells; *2,* Neuron, layer of connecting or bipolar cells; *3,* Neuron, layer of ganglionic cells. Roman numerals indicate the ten layers as seen by the older staining methods. Nine rod and five cone cells are shown. At the extreme right is a supporting cell (of Müller). (Greeff.)

come in contact with the internal processes of the visual cells just described. The axons pass internally toward the layer of ganglionic cells.

4. The *layer of ganglionic cells* contains the large nerve cells whose axons form the optic nerve. These axons, lying at the inner surface of the retina, run to the optic disc, where they pass out of the eyeball. Their course from this point on has already been described (p. 322).

The early development of the eye shows that the retina is a part of the wall of the brain that has grown out to its present position and developed light-sensitive nerve cells. As in the wall of the brain proper, neuroglia cells are to be found among the neurons of the retina.

To reach the rods and cones, the light must penetrate most of the thickness of the retina, that is, the two layers of neurons with their glia elements and blood vessels. These are all transparent, however, and do not interfere greatly; nevertheless if one will look at the clear sky or similar illuminated surface, he can see the shadows of the red blood cells as they pass through the network of capillaries in the retina. Behind the rods and cones is the pigmented epithelium. It stops the light and prevents reflections within the eyeball. For some reason the rods and cones will not function unless they are in intimate contact with the pigmented epithelium.

The *macula lutea*, with its central portion, the *fovea centralis*, the region of sharpest vision, is thinner than the rest of the optic part of the retina, owing to the lengthening of the internal processes (axons) of the cones. (No rods are present here.) These fibers run obliquely to the periphery of the macula, putting the bipolar cells and the ganglion cells out of the way and leaving but little tissue through which the light must penetrate before it falls on the cones of this area.

FUNCTIONS OF THE OPTIC PART OF THE RETINA.   In spite of the fact that there has been a great deal of investigation on the mechanism of vision, much remains that is only imperfectly known. It is generally believed that there are two visual mechanisms, one operating in bright light and mediated by the cones, the other functioning in dim light and mediated by the rods. In the area of keenest vision, the macula, only cones are present, while peripherally in the retina both cones and rods are present, with rods predominating. The cones are regarded as the receptors of color. In the periphery of the retina, where there are no cones, objects can be seen indistinctly, but they have no color. In the macula, where there are no rods, it is sometimes impossible to see a dim object, such as a faint star, which will, however, become visible when one looks to one side of it, putting its image to one side of the macula. In very dim light the cones of the macula do not register color. The rods contain a substance called visual purple or rhodopsin, which bleaches when the eye is exposed to light and regains its color in the dark.

PRACTICAL CONSIDERATIONS.   The retina and the structures related to it, the optic disc, the macula lutea and the retinal vessels, can be inspected through the pupil by means of an instrument called the ophthalmoscope. Such an inspection is of value not only in diseases of the eye, but also in certain diseases of the nervous system. With brain tumors, for example, the optic disc becomes considerably altered and the retinal veins become engorged and tortuous.

The non-optic part of the retina consists of two layers of simple epithelium, one continuous with the pigmented epithelium and one continuous with the nervous layer. This double epithelium covers the ciliary body and forms the inner layer of the iris. In the iris both layers of cells are pigmented. The dilator muscle of the iris is derived from the outer layer of cells.

The Refracting Media of the Eyeball. The refracting media of the eyeball (Fig. 278) include the cornea, the lens, the vitreous body and the aqueous humor.

The cornea was described earlier. The *lens* is a transparent structure, convex on both its anterior and posterior surfaces. It is held in place behind the iris by the delicate fibers of the *suspensory ligament of the lens,* which passes peripherally to become attached to the retina that covers the ciliary body.

The *vitreous*[4] *body* fills the cavity of the eyeball posterior to the lens. It is of gelatinous consistency and is permeated throughout by a network of fibers. A canal, the *hyaloid canal,* runs through it from the back of the lens to the optic disc. In embryonic life this canal transmits an artery.

The *aqueous humor* is a watery fluid which fills the space between the cornea and the lens. Like the cerebrospinal fluid, it is constantly being formed and drained away. The cavity in which it lies is divided by the iris into two communicating portions called the *anterior* and *posterior chambers of the eye.*

FUNCTIONS OF THE REFRACTING MEDIA. The eye, as already stated, acts in much the same way as a camera; it has a lens which focuses the light upon a sensitive plate, the retina. Like a good camera, it has more than a simple lens. The most important refracting surface of its lens system is the outer curved surface of the cornea. Within is the lens with its two curved surfaces. The mechanism in the eye for adjustment to distance, that is, for focusing, differs from that in a camera. In the camera it is accomplished by altering the distance from the lens to the sensitive plate; in the eye it is obtained by varying the curvatures of the lens. The lens is elastic, and so is the choroid. The choroid, through the suspensory ligament, keeps the lens somewhat flattened and, if the eye is normal, focused for distant objects. The ciliary muscle, when it contracts, pulls counter to the choroid and lessens the tension on the suspensory ligament, allowing the lens to thicken and focus for near objects. With increasing age the lens gradually hardens and loses the power of accommodation.

For some reason the sphincter pupillae always contracts when the ciliary muscle does, the pupil becoming smaller when the eye accommodates for near vision.

The ciliary muscle and the sphincter pupillae are innervated by craniosacral autonomic fibers in the oculomotor nerve (Fig. 275). The dilator pupillae is innervated by thoracolumbar autonomic fibers that join a branch of the ophthalmic nerve to enter the orbit (Fig. 274).

PRACTICAL CONSIDERATIONS. Hyperopia, or far-sightedness, is a condition in which the anteroposterior diameter of the eyeball is relatively shortened. The rays of light come to a focus behind the retina, and vision, therefore, is blurred. In myopia, or short-sightedness, the reverse obtains. The eyeball is relatively too long, and the light rays come to a focus in front of the retina. The first is treated by convex lenses; the second by concave lenses.

In addition to hardening with advancing age, the lens may become opaque. This is known as cataract. The only remedy is surgical removal of the lens and the use of glasses to compensate for its absence from the refracting system of the eye.

---

[4] Vitreous: L., glassy.

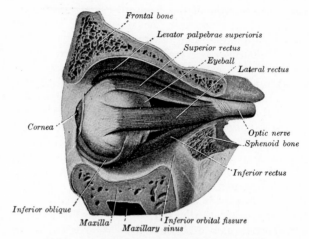

Frontal bone
Levator palpebrae superioris
Superior rectus
Eyeball
Lateral rectus
Cornea
Optic nerve
Sphenoid bone
Inferior rectus
Inferior oblique
Maxilla
Maxillary sinus
Inferior orbital fissure

Figure 281. Four of the muscles of the eye, lateral aspect. The medial rectus is similar to, and opposite, the lateral rectus. The superior oblique arises at the back of the orbit and runs forward on the median wall to a pulley. From there the tendon runs over the eyeball much as the inferior oblique runs below it. (Sobotta and McMurrich.)

Like the retina, the optic nerve is a part of the brain and not a true nerve, although it functions as one. The meninges of the brain continue upon it, and the dura fuses with the sclera.

The Muscles and Ligaments of the Eye.   The eyeball is held in position within the orbit by ligaments. It can be rotated in various directions by six muscles which pass to it from the orbital walls (Fig. 281). They are named the *superior rectus, inferior rectus, lateral rectus, medial rectus, superior oblique* and *inferior oblique muscles.* The first four pass directly forward from the back of the orbit; the last two pass obliquely across the eye in the positions named. The eye can be kept in any desired position by a proper balancing of the opposing, or antagonistic, muscles.

The Eyelids and the Lacrimal Apparatus.   The *eyelids* contain a central core of connective tissue and muscle, and a covering of skin and membrane. The connective tissue is largely condensed into the *tarsal plates* (Fig. 282), which give body to the lids. The eyelids are closed by the *orbicularis oculi muscle* (Fig. 107). A slip of the superior rectus muscle, the *levator palpebrae,* inserts on the upper lid and opens the eye, assisted by some smooth muscle fibers in each lid. When the eye is open, the levator palpebrae works with the muscles of the eye to keep the edge of the upper lid halfway between the upper edge of the pupil and the upper edge of the iris in all positions of the eyeball. The skin covers the superficial surfaces of the lids; the *conjunctiva,* a white glistening membrane, lines their deep surfaces and is reflected from them on to the

Figure 282 **The Organs of Special Sense** 349

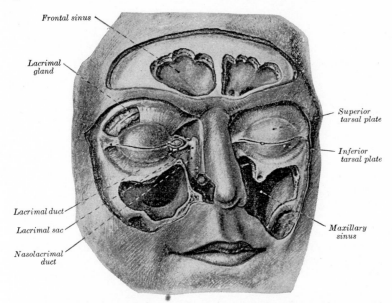

Frontal sinus

Lacrimal gland

Superior tarsal plate

Inferior tarsal plate

Lacrimal duct

Lacrimal sac

Maxillary sinus

Nasolacrimal duct

Figure 282. Partial dissection of the face, showing the lids, the lacrimal apparatus, the frontal sinuses and the maxillary sinuses. (Reduced from Warren: Handbook of Anatomy, Harvard University Press.)

anterior aspect of the eyeball. On the free margins of the lids the eyelashes and the openings of a number of glands may be found. The stratified epithelium on the outer surface of the cornea is continuous with that of the conjunctiva, and the latter is continuous with the epidermis.

PRACTICAL CONSIDERATIONS. Inflammation of the conjunctiva is called conjunctivitis. In its milder form it produces a diffuse redness and is often popularly known as "pink eye." Gonorrheal conjunctivitis is a serious condition, for it often leads to permanent blindness. It may be acquired by direct infection from the genital tract; hence it is the common practice to take preventive measures against its development in all newborn babies. A stye or hordeolum is an inflammation of a sebaceous follicle attached to an eyelash.

The *lacrimal apparatus* (Fig. 282) consists of the lacrimal gland and an associated system of ducts. The *lacrimal*[5] *gland* is situated in the orbit deep to the lateral portion of the upper eyelid. It pours its secretion, the tears, into the space between the eyelid and the eye. The system of ducts begins as two small channels which arise from the upper and lower margins of the lids near the nose. They open into a larger chamber, the *lacrimal sac,* which lies in a groove in the lacrimal bone. The *nasolacrimal duct* passes from this sac to

---

[5] Lacrimal (or lachrymal): from L. *lacrima,* a tear.

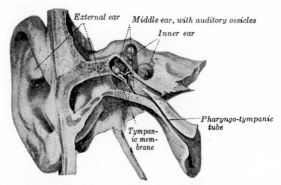

Figure 283. Section through the external and middle ears. The inner ear is shown as though the bone were transparent. (Braus: Anatomie des Menschen.)

open into the inferior meatus of the nose. The excess lacrimal fluid is drained through these channels into the nasal cavity. The exposed surface of the eyeball must be kept moist at all times.

THE EAR

The organ of hearing consists of a series of chambers through which the sound vibrations are transmitted to a sensitive receptor called the *organ of Corti.*[6] Associated with the auditory system is the *vestibular apparatus,* which is a sense organ concerned with the perception of position and movement of the head.

External Ear. On the outside of the head is the *auricle,* the part referred to in common speech as the "ear." From the auricle a passage about 25 mm. long leads to the ear drum or *tympanic*[7] *membrane.* This is a nearly circular sheet of fibrous tissue covered on each side by epithelium. The passage is the *external auditory meatus,* the bony part of which was identified in the temporal bone. The external third of the meatus, outside the bone, is supported by cartilage which is continuous with the cartilage that stiffens the auricle. The meatus is lined with skin, and the outer surface of the tympanic membrane is covered with epidermis. The ceruminous glands in the skin are modified sweat glands that produce ear wax or cerumen.

Middle Ear. Behind the tympanic membrane is an air-filled cavity, the *tympanic cavity,* which is in communication with the pharynx by the *pharyngo-tympanic* tube (O.T., auditory tube, eustachian tube). The tube emerges from the temporal bone between the foramen oval and the carotid canal (Fig. 27). It continues medially, with cartilaginous walls, to the nasopharynx,

---

[6] From Alfonso Corti, Italian histologist (1822–1876).

[7] Tympanic: L., from *tympanum,* a kettle drum.

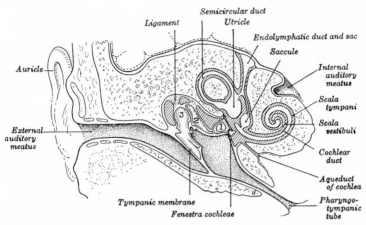

Figure 284.   Diagram of the ear. *1,* Stapes; *2,* incus; *3,* malleus. (Redrawn from Goodrich.)

opening about 10 mm. behind the inferior concha (Figs. 134, 154, 29). The pharyngo-tympanic tube is opened momentarily by swallowing or yawning, and the air pressure on the two sides of the tympanic membrane is thus equalized.

Stretching across the tympanic cavity is a chain of three small bones, the *auditory ossicles.* The first is the *malleus,*[8] which is attached to the ear drum. The second is the *incus,*[9] and the third is the *stapes.*[10] The two joints between the ossicles have synovial cavities. The foot-plate of the stirrup-shaped stapes lies in a small oval aperture, the *fenestra vestibulae,* in the bony median wall of the tympanic cavity leading to the vestibule of the inner ear. The annular ligament that holds the foot of the stapes in place forms a membrane that closes the fenestra vestibulae.

A small muscle is attached to the stapes and one to the malleus.

Below the fenestra vestibulae is a smaller hole, the *fenestra cochleae,* which is closed by the *secondary tympanic membrane.*

A thin epithelium continuous with that of the pharynx lines the pharyngo-tympanic tube and the tympanic cavity and covers the ossicles, their supporting ligaments and the surfaces of both tympanic membranes.

The upper portion of the middle ear, the *attic* (or epitympanic recess), opens posteriorly into a chamber in the mastoid portion of the temporal bone, the *tympanic antrum*[11] (O.T., mastoid antrum) (Fig. 285). The walls of the antrum are highly irregular

---

[8] Malleus: L., hammer.
[9] Incus: L., anvil.
[10] Stapes: L., stirrup.
[11] Antrum: L., a cavern or cavity.

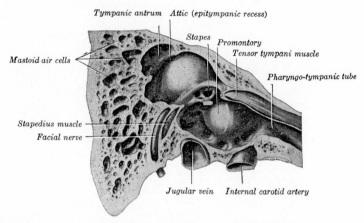

Tympanic antrum   Attic (epitympanic recess)

Stapes

Promontory

Tensor tympani muscle

Mastoid air cells

Pharyngo-tympanic tube

Stapedius muscle

Facial nerve

Jugular vein   Internal carotid artery

Figure 285. Medial wall of the right tympanic cavity and antrum. (Callander.)

and contain the openings of large numbers of *mastoid air cells.*
These air cells are small communicating chambers of variable number in different persons. In some they are relatively few; in others they literally honeycomb the whole mastoid.

Internal Ear.   Behind the fenestra vestibulae and fenestra cochleae, in the petrous part of the temporal bone, is a complicated system of tubes and chambers known as the *bony labyrinth.* The bone immediately around this labyrinth is harder than the surrounding bone and can be dissected out as in Figure 286. The central chamber of the bony labyrinth is the *vestibule.* Opening posteriorly from the vestibule are three *semicircular canals,* each with a swelling, or *ampulla,* at one end. These three semicircular canals are approximately at right angles to one another. Opening anteriorly from the vestibule is a spiral canal, the *cochlea.*[12] The apex of the cochlea lies under the promontory in the medial wall of the tympanic cavity (Fig. 285), and the base surrounds the bottom of the internal auditory meatus (Figs. 28, 29).

From the cochlea, near the vestibule, a small canal, the *aqueduct of the cochlea,* runs to the notch in the petrous bone at the edge of the jugular foramen (Fig. 28). From the vestibule the *aqueduct of the vestibule* runs to a small aperture a few millimeters lateral to the internal acoustic meatus.

Within the bony labyrinth lies a system of interconnected, delicate, membranous sacs and tubes, the *membranous labyrinth* (Fig. 287), lined with epithelium. In the vestibule lie two sacs, the *utricle*[13] and the *saccule,* connected by a fine duct. Opening from

---

[12] Cochlea: G., a snail.
[13] Utricle: L., diminutive of *uter,* a leather bottle or bag.

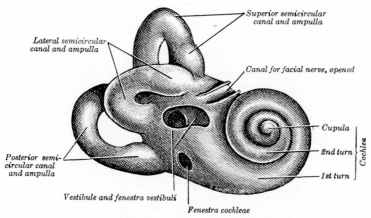

Figure 286. The bony labyrinth, lateral view, right side. (Redrawn from Grant.)

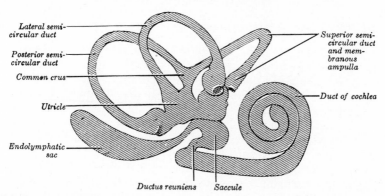

Figure 287. The membranous labyrinth, lateral view, right side. (Redrawn from Grant.)

the utricle are three *semicircular ducts,* one lying in each of the semicircular canals and each having an *ampulla.* The ducts are considerably smaller than the canals in which they lie (Fig. 288), and the space within the canal not occupied by the duct is called the *perilymphatic space.* There is also considerable perilymphatic space in the vestibule around the saccule and utricle. The perilymphatic space is not lined with epithelium.

From the utriculosaccular duct the *endolymphatic duct* leads through the vestibular aqueduct to end blindly beneath the dura on the surface of the petrous bone.

In the cochlea lies the *cochlear duct,* which leads from the saccule. The cochlear duct is triangular in cross section (*Dc,* Fig. 289). Its inner angle is supported by a thin shelf or lamina of bone that extends out from the axial wall of the cochlear canal. This

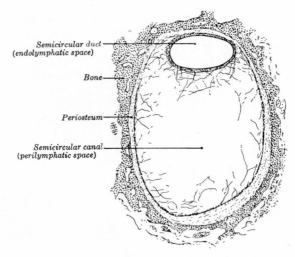

Semicircular *duct*
(*endolymphatic space*)

Bone

Periosteum

Semicircular *canal*
(*perilymphatic space*)

Figure 288.   Cross section of a semicircular canal and duct. (Maximow and Bloom.)

lamina and the cochlear duct divide the perilymphatic space in the cochlea into two parts, the *scala vestibulae* above (toward the apex) and the *scala tympani* below. The scala vestibulae is continuous with the perilymphatic space in the vestibule. The scala tympani ends behind the secondary tympanic membrane. The two scalae communicate by a small aperture at the apex of the cochlea, and the scala tympani communicates with the subarachnoid space through the cochlear aqueduct (Fig. 284).

The membranous labyrinth is filled with a clear fluid, the *endolymph*. The perilymphatic space is filled with a similar fluid, the *perilymph*. The perilymph is in communication with the cerebrospinal fluid through the cochlear aqueduct. The endolymphatic space, that is, the interior of the membranous labyrinth, is a closed system.

The receptor cells of the ear, the cells in which nerve impulses are produced by stimuli, are modified epithelial cells. Each is tall and somewhat goblet-shaped and bears a tuft of stiff, non-motile cilia. Any external force which will bend these cilia will thereby stimulate the cell. The ends of the sensory nerve fibers of the auditory nerve are in contact with the bases of the cells. These receptor cells are, unfortunately, called "hair cells."

FUNCTION OF THE VESTIBULAR APPARATUS.   There is a patch of hair cells, called a *crista*, in the ampulla of each semicircular duct. The cilia project into the endolymph. When the head is turned, the inertia of the fluid causes it to flow past the crista and bend the cilia to one side. (Compare with the water in a cup which does not move with the cup when the cup is rotated.) This bending of the cilia sets up nerve impulses which are transmitted to the brain by the nerve fibers.

CHAPTER 15

THE DUCTLESS GLANDS

THE DUCTLESS GLANDS are organs similar to ordinary glands in that they produce a secretion, but differ from them in that they do not possess any ducts for its discharge. Their products, called *internal secretions*, are absorbed into the blood stream and act frequently at regions far distant from the place of manufacture. The active principles of the secretions are called *hormones*.[1] The glands themselves are often called glands of internal secretion, or *endocrine glands*, in contrast to the glands of external secretion or *exocrine glands*.

Some of the ductless glands exist as independent structures, while others are embedded in other organs. Their exact number is not definitely known. The most important are the following:

1. The hypophysis   In the cranial cavity
2. The thyroid glands   ⎫
3. The parathyroid glands ⎬ In the neck
4. The adrenal glands   ⎫
5. The testes[2] and ovaries ⎪
6. The pancreas   ⎬ In the abdomen
7. The lining of the duodenum ⎭

In addition there is the pineal body in the cranial cavity and the thymus in the thorax, but the status of these as endocrine glands is uncertain.

FUNCTIONS OF THE ENDOCRINE SYSTEM. The endocrine glands, by means of their secretions, the hormones, play an important role in regulating certain processes in the body: (1) the growth of the body as a whole; (2) the development of ovaries and testes and secondary sex organs; (3) rhythmical or periodic activities, especially those concerned with reproduction; (4) the maintenance of the internal environment by regulating the concentration of salts, sugar, and the like, in the blood and body fluids and by regulating the rates of many metabolic processes such as the utilization of fats, sugars and proteins.

---

[1] Hormones: from a Greek verb, to incite. This has proved to be inappropriate, since the action of some of the secretions is inhibitory.

[2] The testes (after birth) are not in the abdominal cavity, but they belong to the gross region of the abdomen.

The endocrine glands cannot be wholly automatic. They respond in some cases directly to the conditions they regulate. This is a relatively simple "feedback" system of control. They are also controlled directly or indirectly by the nervous system, so that both internal and external agents affecting the nervous system may affect the activity of the endocrine system. Finally, the glands influence one another so that their regulatory activities are coordinated. For this reason they constitute a system functionally, even though they are scattered and of diverse embryonic origin.

Like other organs, the endocrine glands are susceptible to disorders of nutrition, to infection, to cancerous growths, and to other influences. Such disorders of units of this regulatory system will obviously have widespread and often complex and serious effects on the organism.

The Hypophysis. The hypophysis[3] (O.T., pituitary body[4]) (Figs. 293, 240) is a small organ, measuring no more than 1.5 cm. in its greatest axis, which lies in the floor of the cranial cavity. Inferiorly it lies in the sella turcica of the sphenoid bone; superiorly it is attached to the under surface of the diencephalon. Developmentally it consists of two different portions: (1) a *buccal* or *glandular portion* or *adenohypophysis,* derived from the roof of the mouth and lying anteriorly, and (2) a *nervous portion,* or *neurohypophysis,* derived from the brain and lying posteriorly. The glandular portion can be further subdivided into *anterior* and *intermediate divisions* (Fig. 294) and a small part, not shown in the figures, that extends up the infundibulum, the *pars tuberalis.* These two portions, buccal and nervous, are independent organs and have no known functional relation. They are both, however, controlled by the hyopthalamus. The buccal or glandular portion, or, more particularly, its anterior division, is usually known as the *anterior lobe.* The nervous portion is called the *posterior lobe.* The other parts of the buccal portion are the *pars intermedia* and the *pars tuberalis.*

Microscopically, the buccal portion of the hypophysis contains cells of the epithelial type arranged in various patterns. The nervous part consists of branching unmyelinated nerve fibers and branching cells (perhaps modified glia cells) called *pituicytes,* which are believed to be secretory.

The nerve fibers of the posterior lobe arise in the hypothalamus. Its blood supply enters posteriorly and presents no unusual features. The anterior lobe possesses few or no nerve endings. Its main blood supply is systemic, but a small supplementary supply flows first through a localized net of capillaries in the floor of the brain near the infundibulum, then through small vessels into capil-

---

[3] Hypophysis: G., a growth beneath.

[4] Pituitary: from L. *pituita,* phlegm. Phlegm was once thought to be an excretory product of the brain which was eliminated by the pituitary into the nasopharynx.

Figure 293   *The Ductless Glands*   361

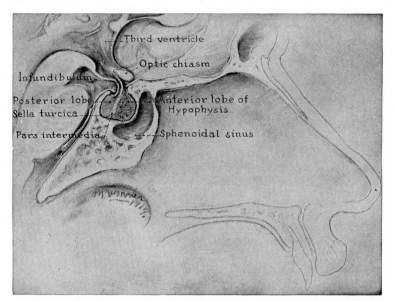

Figure 293. Midsagittal section of the hypophysis (pituitary gland) with its normal anatomic relations. (Adson.)

laries in the anterior lobe. The probable function of this supplementary supply is described in the section that follows.

FUNCTIONS OF THE ANTERIOR LOBE OF THE HYPOPHYSIS.   The anterior lobe
produces at least six hormones. There are three gonadotrophic[5] hormones. One,
the *follicle-stimulating hormone* (FSH), stimulates the development of follicles
in the ovary and causes ovulation, or, in males, the development of the seminiferous tubules and the maintenance of spermatogenesis. The second, the *lutein-
izing hormone* (LH), works with the follicle-stimulating hormone in the later
stages of follicular development and in ovulation, and stimulates the formation
of the corpus luteum. In the male it is necessary for the formation of interstitial
cells and the secretion of androgen. The third, the *lactogenic hormone,* stimulates
the production of milk after the mammary glands have been prepared by hormones from the ovaries, and maintains secretion by the corpus luteum. The
adrenocorticotrophic hormone (ACTH) controls the secretion by the adrenal
cortex of its hormones. The *thyrotrophic hormone* (TTH) governs both the production and the release of the hormone of the thyroid gland. The *growth hormone* is necessary for normal growth. Insufficiency results in one type of dwarf-
ism. Overproduction results in gigantism if the person is young, and an abnormal
type of growth, especially of the bones, called *acromegaly,* if it occurs in an adult.
    There is clear evidence that the nervous system plays an important part in
the control of the anterior lobe and that the hypothalamus is involved, even
though there are few or no nerve fibers to the gland. It appears that the control
is accomplished by means of some substance or substances produced in nuclei

---

    [5] Trophic: G. *trophe,* nourishment. Hormones regulate, but do not nourish,
organs or tissues.

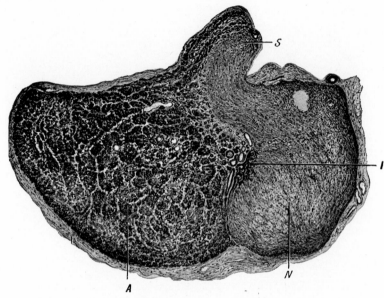

Figure 294. Median section of the hypophysis. *A,* Anterior part; *I,* intermediate part; *N,* nervous part; *S,* stalk. ✕ 16. (Schaffer.)

of the hypothalmus and transmitted to the anterior lobe in part, at least, by means of the small supplementary blood supply described above.

THE FUNCTIONS OF THE POSTERIOR LOBE OF THE HYPOPHYSIS.   The posterior lobe produces at least two types of hormones. The *oxytocic*[6] *hormone* accelerates the rhythmic contraction of smooth muscle, especially that of the uterus. It is useful, therefore, when artificially injected under certain conditions, in hastening parturition. The *vasopressor hormone* raises blood pressure by causing constriction of arterioles and capillaries, and it exercises some control over the kidneys, probably by stimulating the loop of Henle to resorb water from the urine.[7] In the absence of this hormone, large quantities of dilute urine are excreted. The urine does not contain sugar as in diabetes mellitus (see p. 367).

As is true of the anterior lobe, it is clear that the activities of the posterior lobe are in large part controlled by the nervous system through the hypothalamus. In this case the control appears to be directly by nerve fibers arising in the hypothalamus.

The Thyroid Gland.   The thyroid gland (Figs. 211, 161, 295) is a much larger organ than the two glands just described. It consists of two large lateral lobes and a connecting portion or isthmus. It lies in the anterior aspect of the neck below the larynx, with the isthmus running directly in front of the trachea. It is a highly vascular structure, and many relatively large arteries and veins are connected with it.

---

[6] Oxytocic: G. *oxys,* swift, plus *tokos,* birth.

[7] The effect on the kidney was until recently thought to be exercised by a separate secretion called the *antidiuretic hormone.*

Figure 295   *The Ductless Glands* 363

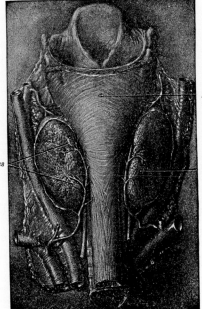

Pharynx

Parathyroid bodies

Thyroid gland

Figure 295.   The thyroid gland and parathyroid bodies. Posterior view. The isthmus, being anterior to the trachea, cannot be seen in this view (cf. Fig. 211). The parathyroid bodies vary in number and position; the condition shown here is frequent. (Halsted and Evans.)

Histologically (Fig. 296), the gland is made up of a large number of follicles lined with a single layer of cuboidal cells. The cavities of the follicles are filled with a homogeneous material called *colloid.*

FUNCTION.   The active principle of the thyroid hormone is called *thyroxin.* It is probably attached to protein molecules as it circulates in the blood. Its chief function is to control the rate of the metabolic processes in the body. In its absence these processes slow down to about 70 per cent of normal. The activity of the thyroid is usually measured clinically by measuring what is called the "basal metabolism," that is, the energy production of the body when no food is being absorbed and when the subject is awake but as quiet and inactive as possible. This is usually done by determining the rate at which oxygen is consumed. If the thyroid becomes overactive, it leads to the condition called Graves' disease or toxic goiter; underactivity leads to myxedema in adults, and to cretinism in children. In toxic goiter the metabolic rate is increased, the pulse rate is high, the patient loses weight, and there is muscular tremor. The eyes frequently become unduly prominent—a symptom which gives the name exophthalmic goiter to the disease. In myxedema many of the opposite symptoms appear. The metabolic rate is low, the patient puts on weight, and the mental processes become sluggish. In cretinism growth is stunted and mental development is seriously retarded. Enlargement of the thyroid gland is known as goiter. The enlargement may be associated with either excessive or diminished production

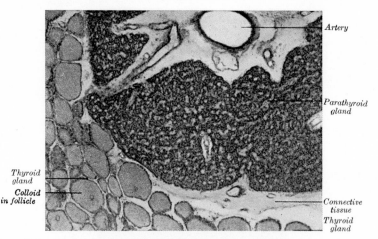

Figure 296. A section of the thyroid and parathyroid glands. (Maximow and Bloom.)

of hormone. In the former case it is known as toxic goiter, in the latter, simple goiter.

Both the production and the release of the thyroid hormone are controlled under normal conditions by the thyrotrophic hormone of the anterior lobe of the hypophysis.

The Parathyroid Glands. The parathyroid glands (Figs. 295, 296) are several, usually four, small bodies situated on the posterior aspect of the thyroid gland, two on each lateral lobe.

FUNCTION. The parathyroid glands function in the maintenance and regulation of the calcium and phosphorus metabolism of the body. If they are removed, the amount of calcium in the blood declines, the symptoms of tetany appear, and death eventually ensues. Tetany is a hypersensitive state of the nervous system, manifested clinically by muscular spasms.

The Adrenal Glands. The adrenal (suprarenal) glands (Fig. 203) are two small glands perched like cocked hats on the top of the kidneys. Histologically (Fig. 297), each consists of two parts, a superficial cortex and a deep-lying medulla. Developmentally, these portions arise from different sources, and in lower forms, like the fish, they remain separate organs. The medulla arises from the same region in the embryo which gives rise to the sympathetic nervous system; the cortex arises near the generative organs.

Small masses of tissue resembling the medulla are found in various places in the body, most commonly near the bifurcation of the common carotids (*carotid glands*). They contain a substance that is chemically related to the secretion of the medulla.

FUNCTIONS OF THE ADRENAL CORTEX. A large number of steroid (fat-like) compounds have been extracted and isolated from the adrenal cortex, and a

Figure 297   **The Ductless Glands** 365

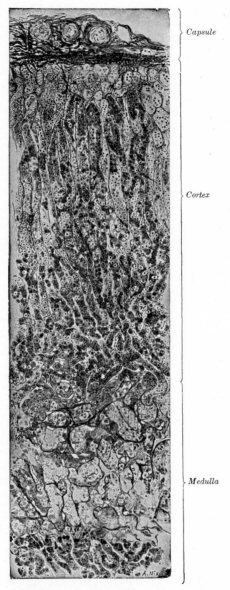

Figure 297. The adrenal gland in microscopic section. × 105. (Maximow and Bloom.)

number of them can maintain life in an animal whose adrenal cortex has been removed. Insufficiency of the hormones of the cortex upsets the salt and water balance and adversely affects the metabolism of carbohydrates, proteins and fats. The organism loses its ability to meet conditions of stress, e.g., cold and shock, and its resistance to infection is greatly diminished. Recently preparations of one of these hormones, called cortisone, and related compounds have given spectacular relief in certain types of arthritis, though the relief has been accompanied by undesirable side affects and has not proved to be a cure. It is interesting that small quantities of the male and female hormones are found in the adrenal cortex of both sexes. Tumors in the cortex in women often result in the appearance of masculine characteristics.

The activity of the adrenal cortex is controlled by the adrenocorticotrophic hormone of the anterior lobe of the hypophysis.

FUNCTION OF THE ADRENAL MEDULLA. The adrenal medulla produces two hormones, *epinephrine* (or *adrenalin*) and *norepinephrine*. These substances, when injected artificially, produce many of the symptoms of stimulation of the thoracolumbar division of the autonomic nervous system, such as vasoconstriction, a rise in blood pressure, acceleration of the heart, and so on. They are used by physicians to stimulate the heart and to raise the blood pressure in certain emergencies. Epinephrine also raises the level of sugar in the blood by increasing its rate of release from the liver. Norepinephrine does not have this effect.

The adrenal medulla is innervated by preganglionic fibers of the thoracolumbar division of the autonomic nervous system, and it secretes only in response to stimulation by these nerve fibers. The secretory cells are, in fact, modified autonomic ganglion cells, and the gland is a sort of extension of the thoracolumbar system.

The Ovary. The portions of the ovary of chief endocrine importance are the follicles and the corpus luteum. The microscopic appearance of these structures has already been described (p. 220).

FUNCTIONS. The ovarian hormones are important factors in the development and functioning of the female sexual apparatus. Removal of the ovaries in a young person leads to a regression or involution of the organs and the onset of the phenomena of the menopause.

The principal ovarian hormone, called *estrogen,* is produced chiefly in the follicles. In the adult it is an important factor in the development of the new mucosa of the uterus after menstruation, and it promotes many of the other phenomena of the menstrual cycle, notably enlargement of the mammary glands. In animals it has been used experimentally to develop the uterine mucosa after it has regressed from removal of the ovaries. In primates, when the administration of the hormone is stopped, hemorrhage appears similar to that of normal menstruation.

The hormone of the corpus luteum, called *progesterone,* is active in pregnancy. It inhibits menstruation and ovulation during pregnancy, and promotes those changes in the uterine mucosa necessary for the retention of the fertilized ovum. It is active until the function is taken over by secretions of the placenta.

Events in the ovary are controlled by the gonadotrophic hormones of the anterior lobe of the hypophysis.

The Testis. The testis, in addition to being an organ for the production of spermatozoa, is a gland of internal secretion. Its hormone, known as *testosterone,* is produced by the interstitial cells.

FUNCTION. The hormone of the testis is responsible for the maintenance of the other male genital organs as well as for the development of many peculiarly masculine bodily characters, such as beard, voice, and so on. The endocrine activity of the interstitial cells is controlled by the gonadotrophic hormones of the anterior lobe of the hypophysis.

The Pancreas. The islands of Langerhans are the main endocrine elements of the pancreas. Their histologic characters have been described earlier (p. 177).

FUNCTION. The hormone of the pancreas, insulin, plays an important role in the metabolism of carbohydrates. When insulin is present in insufficient amounts, sugar cannot be adequately assimilated by the tissues and accumulates in excess in the blood. As a result, the kidneys secrete large quantities of urine containing sugar, a condition known medically as diabetes mellitus.[8]

Failure to utilize carbohydrates at normal rates results in the abnormal use of fats and proteins as sources of energy. The result eventually resembles, in certain respects, starvation.

In the normal organism the rate of secretion of insulin seems to be controlled directly by the concentration of sugar in the blood. This is one of the mechanisms for keeping the blood sugar always within the narrow limits necessary for normal metabolism.

The Duodenum. The lining cells of the duodenum produce, in addition to intestinal juices, a hormone called *secretin.*

FUNCTION. The production of secretin is started when the acid contents of the stomach pass through the pyloric sphincter and enter the duodenum. The hormone is absorbed by the blood and circulates to the pancreas, where it leads to the production of pancreatic juice. Secretin was the first hormone to be identified and studied, and the term "hormone" was first coined in connection with it.

Organs of Uncertain Endocrine Function. The *pineal body* (p. 295) has in the past been assigned many functions, including the assertion that it is the seat of the soul. Investigation still goes on, but the results are inconclusive.

The *thymus* (p. 265) has been thought to be a gland of internal secretion, but no one has succeeded in isolating a hormone from it or in assigning to it an indisputable function.

---

[8] Mellitus: L., sweetened with honey.

CHAPTER 16

DEVELOPMENTAL ANATOMY

THE DEVELOPMENT of a new individual results from the fusion of two cells, the male cell or *spermatozoon,* and the female cell or *ovum.* The process of union of these two cells is called *fertilization;* the combined organism is called the *zygote,*[1] *oosperm*[2] or *fertilized ovum.*[3] From the zygote the *embryo*[4] is developed. At the end of the second month, when the embryo begins to assume definitely human characters, it is called the *fetus.*[5]

Determination of Sex. The sex of the new individual is determined at the time of fertilization, and is dependent chiefly upon the chromosomal content of the male cell, the spermatozoon. The spermatozoon and ovum each have twenty-four chromosomes, one of which is known as the *sex chromosome.* In the ova the sex chromosomes are more or less similar and are called X chromosomes. In the spermatozoa there are two types, designated as X and Y chromosomes. If a spermatozoon carrying an X chromosome unites with the ovum (which carries an X chromosome), the resulting organism will be a female; if a Y-carrying spermatozoon unites with the ovum, a male is produced. Other factors besides this may possibly be involved, but if so their mode of action is not yet clear.

Fertilization. The discharge of the ovum from the ovary and its entrance and course down the uterine tube have already been described. The spermatozoa are deposited in the vagina, and some few make their way into the uterus and uterine tube. They are transported partly by their own movement and partly by the action of the surrounding muscles. The role of the cilia in the uterine tube is not clear.

---

[1] Zygote: G., yoked, joined. Cf. zygomatic process, azygos vein.

[2] Oosperm: a combination of ovum plus sperm.

[3] Ovum: the term is used loosely for the female sex cells, the fertilized ovum and even the very young embryo.

[4] Embryo: G., within, plus to be full of.

[5] Fetus (or foetus): L., offspring.

Figure 298 **Developmental Anatomy** 369

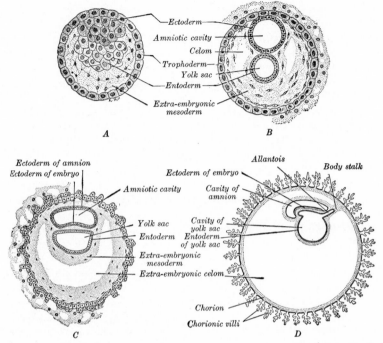

Figure 298. Diagram of the early development of human embryos. (Arey, from Prentiss.)

The sperm cell usually meets the ovum in the uterine tube, and here fertilization takes place. The spermatozoon enters the cytoplasm of the ovum, after which the tail shrivels up and disappears. The dense nucleus which constitutes most of the head of the spermatozoon then enlarges to a more normal form and unites with the nucleus of the ovum.

The zygote begins to develop and at the same time passes downward to the uterus, where it becomes implanted. The early developmental process will be described first, the implantation process later.

Early Stages of Development. Shortly after it is formed, the zygote divides by mitosis, and two daughter cells are formed. These in turn divide, and four cells are formed, then eight, sixteen, thirty-two, and so on. At first the cells are arranged as a solid sphere, and the mass is called a *morula*.[6]

The next stage is the differentiation of the cells of the morula into four groups (Fig. 298, *A*, *B*), one of which lies externally, the others internally. The external group of cells forms the trophecto-

---

[6] Morula: L., a small mulberry.

derm or *trophoderm*[7]; the internal cell groups form the *ectoderm,*[8] the *entoderm*[9] and the *extra-embryonic mesoderm.*[10] The ectoderm and entoderm become formed into hollow spheres so placed that the ectoderm lies in contact with the trophoderm, and the entoderm in contact with ectoderm. The extra-embryonic mesoderm surrounds both. Clefts appear in it which fuse to form a large cavity, the *extra-embryonic celom.*[11]

The important structures for us here are the ectoderm and the entoderm, and particularly the region of attachment of the two, for here the future embryo will develop (Fig. 298, C, D). The cavity of the ectoderm becomes the *amniotic cavity;* its side walls form the *amniotic*[12] *membrane,* one of the coverings of the embryo. The cavity of the entoderm becomes the *yolk sac.* The attachment of the ectoderm and entoderm to the trophoblast forms the *body stalk.*

The area of union of ectoderm and entoderm is in the form of a flat disk and is shaped more or less like a leaf. It is called the *primitive disk* or the *embryonic disk* (Fig. 299), for here the embryo will arise. In its long axis a streak appears called the *primitive streak.* From it a new layer, the embryonic *mesoderm,* spreads out between the ectoderm and entoderm. The disk now contains three primary layers which, named from above, that is, from the amniotic cavity, downward, are the ectoderm, the mesoderm, and the entoderm.

The forward end of the primitive streak ends in a swelling or node. From it a rod of mesoderm, the *head process,* continues forward between ectoderm and entoderm. This forms the notochord, around which the vertebral column will subsequently develop. It grows rapidly in length, while the primitive streak becomes relatively shorter.

The next great change is the transformation of the flat embryonic disk into the more or less cylindrical form of the embryo. The portion of the disk near the head process grows more rapidly than the parts farther away, and accordingly becomes thrown up in a fold (Fig. 303). The ectoderm, being on top, forms the outer wall of the fold; the entoderm forms the lining. The cavity inside becomes the primitive gastro-intestinal cavity, or cavity of the gut, and opens at this stage directly into the yolk sac. This opening between gut and yolk sac is at first large, almost as large as the embryo

[7] Trophoderm: G., nourishing skin.

[8] Ectoderm: G., outside skin.

[9] Entoderm: G., inside skin.

[10] Mesoderm: G., middle skin. Extra-embryonic outside the embryo.

[11] Celom (or coelom): G., hollow, the same root as found in celiac.

[12] Amniotic: from amnion, a membrane around the fetus. It is derived from the Greek word meaning sheep, in which it must have been first observed.

Figure 299   **Developmental Anatomy**   371

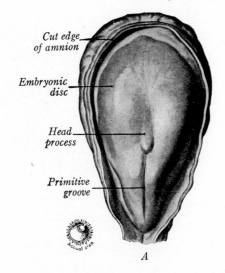

Cut edge
of amnion

Embryonic
disc

Head
process

Primitive
groove

Actual size

A

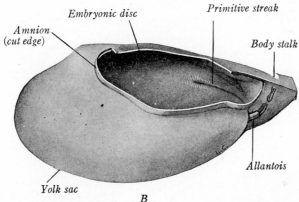

Embryonic disc   Primitive streak

Amnion
(cut edge)

Body stalk

Allantois

Yolk sac
B

Figure 299.   Embryonic disks of early human embryos. A, Embryo of 18 days, viewed from
above. The amnion has been removed. × 45. B, Embryo of 16 days, viewed from the
left and above. The amnion has been cut away, leaving only the embryonic disk and
the yolk sac. × 50. (Arey: Developmental Anatomy, 6th edition.)

itself, but as the embryo grows in length it becomes relatively
smaller and smaller. The mechanism of the development of a cylindrical body from a flat disk can be best understood by the analogy
of blowing a larger and larger soap bubble from a flat soap film
on the end of a pipe.

Simultaneously with the gross developmental changes described,
local alterations have been taking place within the three primitive layers. In the ectoderm a shallow groove (the neural groove,

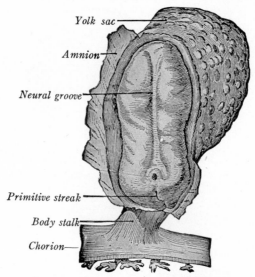

Yolk sac

Amnion

Neural groove

Primitive streak

Body stalk

Chorion

Figure 300. Human embryo of about nineteen days, viewed from above. × 23. (Spee.)

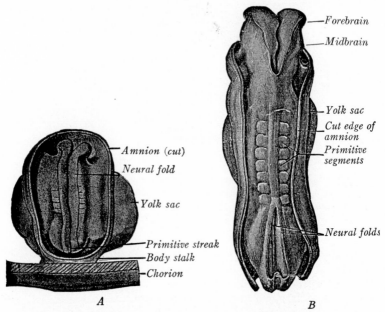

Forebrain

Midbrain

Yolk sac

Cut edge of amnion

Primitive segments

Amnion (cut)

Neural fold

Yolk sac

Primitive streak

Body stalk

Chorion

Neural folds

A

B

Figure 301. Origin of the neural tube in human embryos. A, Six-somite embryo with open neural groove, viewed from above. × 20. (After Keibel and Elze.) B, Nine-somite embryo with partially closed neural groove, viewed from above. × 35. (Eternod.)

Figure 302 **Developmental Anatomy** 373

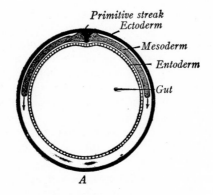

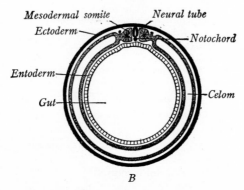

Figure 302. Diagrammatic transverse sections of embryos, showing changes in the mesoderm. A, The stage of development corresponding to that shown in Figure 299, A and B.
B, The formation of the somites and the splitting of the mesoderm laterally, corresponding approximately to Figure 301, B.

Fig. 300) develops along the long axis of the embryo, which soon
becomes a deep canal through the uprising of its sides in folds.
The folds, called *neural folds* (Fig. 301), close over and fuse, so
that a long cylindrical tube is formed which runs the length of
the body. It later separates from the overlying ectoderm (Fig. 323)
and becomes eventually the central nervous system.

During this time the mesoderm has increased in amount. In that
portion of it lying by the side of the neural folds, transverse clefts
appear which divide it into segments. These segments (Fig. 301)
are the *mesodermal somites,* from which part of the bony and muscular systems will arise. Laterally the mesoderm does not segment,
but splits into inner and outer layers (Fig. 302). The inner layer
remains attached to the entoderm and helps to form the walls of
the gut, while the outer layer, together with the ectoderm, forms the
main body wall. The space between the two layers of mesoderm

becomes the three serous cavities of the body, the peritoneal, pleural and pericardial cavities.

Implantation. When the fertilized ovum reaches the uterus, it is usually in the morula stage. It becomes nested in some part of the uterine mucosa. The uterine epithelium is then eroded away, and the ovum sinks into the connective tissue. The epithelium then heals over, and the embryo develops within the tissues of the wall of the uterus and not within the cavity of the uterus as it does in most lower animals. The connective tissue in which it rests is called the *decidua*[13] *basalis;* the mucosa covering it, the *decidua capsularis* (Fig. 304).

PRACTICAL CONSIDERATIONS. Although the fertilized ovum normally descends to the uterus, it occasionally becomes implanted in the uterine tube. This condition, called ectopic pregnancy, is a serious one, for the slender tube cannot stand the strain of the enlarging embryo, and unless the embryo is removed before it attains any great size, the tube will rupture. Such a rupture produces severe bleeding and may prove rapidly fatal unless the abdomen is quickly opened and the blood vessels ligated.

An abnormally low implantation in the uterus is also a serious problem, for the placenta or "after-birth" lies over the cervical opening and must be torn through before the child can be born. Such a tearing leads to severe hemorrhage.

The Fetal Membranes and the Placenta. In the preceding sections the formation of three cavities within the developing ovum, viz., the amniotic cavity, the cavity of the yolk sac and the extra-embryonic celom, was described. The extra-embryonic celom increases in size (Fig. 298), and soon the ovum, or early embryo, consists essentially of one large sphere, the trophoblast, containing two smaller ones, the amniotic cavity and the yolk sac. In later development the three spheres progress differently (Fig. 303). The external sphere becomes the external fetal membrane, the *chorion.*[14] The amniotic cavity progressively increases in size at the expense of the yolk sac and practically fills the entire larger cavity. Its covering, the *amniotic membrane,* then lies next to the chorion and becomes the internal fetal membrane. The yolk sac becomes reduced to extremely small proportions, and becomes enclosed, along with the body stalk, within the *umbilical cord.*

The chorion becomes firmly anchored to the surrounding decidua by means of numerous finger-like processes, called *chorionic villi* (Figs. 303, 304), which grow out from its external surface. As the embryo grows larger the chorion expands until eventually the whole uterus is filled. The decidua capsularis now comes in contact with the opposite uterine wall, so that the original uterine cavity is obliterated. At a later stage the decidua capsularis

---

[13] Decidua: from L. verb, to fall off. The decidua goes into the formation of the fetal membranes, which are cast off at parturition. Cf. deciduous teeth.

[14] Chorion: G., skin; the external fetal membrane.

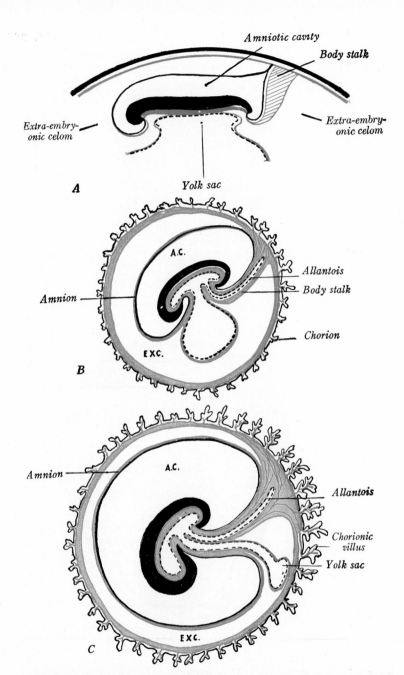

Figure 303. Diagrams of the early development of body form and the formation of the umbilical cord. The figures represent a continuation of the process shown in Figure 298, A corresponding to the state reached in Figure 298, D. The sections are cut in the same plane. A.C., Amniotic cavity; EXC., extra-embryonic celom; solid black, ectoderm; red, mesoderm; dotted black, entoderm. (DeLee.)

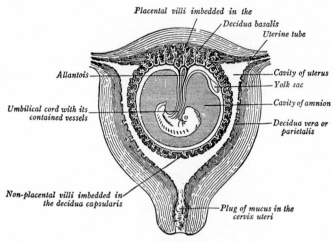

Placental villi imbedded in the
Decidua basalis
Uterine tube

Allantois

Cavity of uterus
Yolk sac
Cavity of amnion

Umbilical cord with its
contained vessels

Decidua vera or
parietalis

Non-placental villi imbedded in
the decidua capsularis

Plug of mucus in the
cervix uteri

Figure 304.   Sectional plan of the pregnant uterus at three months. (Arey, after Wagner.)

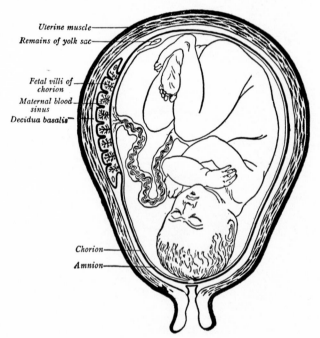

Uterine muscle
Remains of yolk sac

Fetal villi of
chorion
Maternal blood
sinus
Decidua basalis

Chorion
Amnion

Figure 305.   Diagrammatic section of the uterus, illustrating the relation of an advanced
fetus to the placenta and other membranes. (Ahlfeld.)

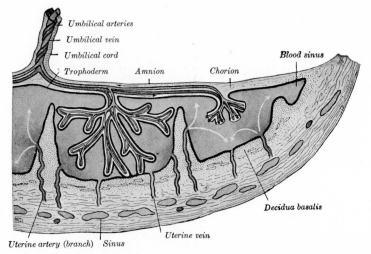

Figure 306. Scheme of circulation in the human placenta, as shown in a vertical section. The half of the placenta represented bears one chorionic villus and the stump of another extending into the large maternal blood sinuses. (Arey.)

atrophies; the chorion attached to it loses most of its villi and becomes simply a membrane. The decidua basilaris, on the other hand, does not atrophy. It forms, along with its attached chorion, the placenta (Fig. 305).

The *placenta*,[15] therefore, consists of two portions (Figs. 304, 305, 306). One is derived from the uterus of the mother and is called the *deciduous portion;* the other comes from the embryo and is called the *chorionic portion.* Each contains its own vascular system. The deciduous portion contains large sinuses which are connected with the blood vessels of the mother. The chorionic villi, which project into these sinuses, are connected with the blood vessels of the embryo. These two systems are not directly connected, and there is no actual interchange of blood between the two circulations. Nutritive substances, however, diffuse from the sinuses of the uterus through the walls of the chorionic villi into the capillaries of the embryo, and products for excretion pass in the reverse direction.

Formation of the Face. In a previous section we left the study of the embryo itself after the discussion of the development of its cylindrical body. The next striking feature from the point of view of external form is the appearance, in the region of the future neck and face, of a series of cartilaginous arches which correspond to

---

[15] Placenta: G., a flat cake.

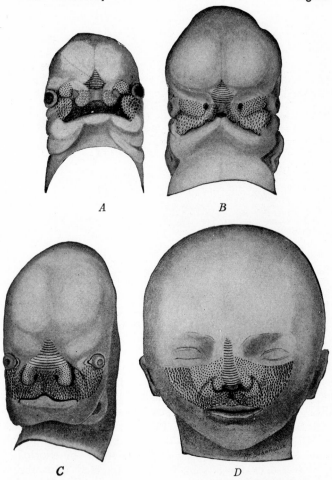

A   *B*

C   *D*

Figure 307.   Stages in the development of the human face. A, At five weeks; B, at six weeks; C, at eight weeks; D, at sixteen weeks. In all, the nasal part of the frontonasal process is indicated by horizontal lines, the median nasal processes by circles, the lateral nasal processes by dots, and the maxillary processes by crosses. (Arey, adapted from His, Rabl, Retzius and Scammon.)

the gill arches of the fish and like them are called *branchial*[16] *arches* (Fig. 326). Capping them in the region of the forehead is the *frontonasal process*. The eyes lie on the side of the head, in the interval between the lateral part of the frontonasal process and the first branchial arch. The future nasal orifices are wide apart, and the nose has not yet arisen from the face (Fig. 327).

---

[16] Branchial: G., pertaining to the gills.

At a later stage various changes take place (Fig. 307). The frontonasal process narrows and elongates, with the result that the eyes are brought forward and the nose is lengthened, narrowed, and raised above the face. The first branchial arch develops on its lateral aspect a process, the *maxillary process*, which grows forward and becomes the maxilla. The medial portion of the same arch forms the lower jaw. The remaining arches form various structures in the head and neck.

PRACTICAL CONSIDERATIONS. Sometimes normal fusion of the various components of the face fails to take place. If the maxillary process fails to fuse with the more medial parts, there is a cleft from the mouth to the eye. More commonly, the median nasal and the maxillary processes fail to fuse, usually on one side only, resulting in a cleft from the lip to one nostril. This is known as "harelip," a misnomer, because the cleft in the lip of the hare or rabbit is median. A median cleft is rare in man. The harelip cleft may involve only the lip or may affect the maxilla and even the palate (cleft palate).

Formation of the Limbs.   The first sign of limbs in the embryo is seen about the fifth week, when small rounded elevations, called *limb buds* (Fig. 326), appear on both sides of the body. By the sixth week the buds for the arm have grown considerably, the distal parts have become flattened or paddle-like, and a constriction marks the location of the wrist (Fig. 327). A little later a second constriction appears which marks the site of the elbow. Longitudinal furrows appear on the paddle-like extremity, and these eventually deepen into fissures and separate the fingers. The sequence of events in the development of the leg is similar to that in the arm, except that it lags somewhat behind in the time of its development.

PRACTICAL CONSIDERATIONS. Occasionally the longitudinal furrows in the hand or foot do not deepen enough to separate the fingers or toes, so that a "web-hand" or a "web-foot" is formed.

The Bones and Joints.   The bones and joints develop from the embryonic mesoderm. In the limb buds, for example, the process of differentiation begins as early as the sixth week, starting at the proximal end of the limb and spreading distally. The bones begin as a condensation of the mesoderm along the main axis of the limb; later, lines of separation appear which mark the position of the joints. From this point development may progress in either of two ways, known as development in membrane and development in cartilage.

Development in membrane occurs chiefly in the bones of the skull. The cells of the embryonic connective tissue become differentiated into bone-forming cells or osteoblasts. They produce the ground substance, which becomes calcified and forms the solid

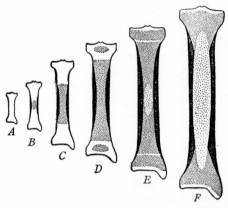

Figure 308. Stages in the development of a long bone. *A,* Formation of cartilage; *B, C,* ossification beginning in the shaft; *D,* ossification centers present in the epiphyses; *E,* note the narrow epiphysial cartilages; *F,* resorption of the central portion of the shaft to form the medullary cavity. The epiphyses have fused to the shaft. The black represents dense bone laid down under the perichondrium. (Arey.)

mass of the bone; some of the osteoblasts become enclosed in the mass and form the bone cells. The bone formation does not begin all over the bone at once, but starts in localized areas called *centers of ossification.*

Development in cartilage is a more complicated process. It is also a more common one, for most of the bones of the body are formed by this method. The structure to be built of bone is first formed of cartilage, and the cartilage is subsequently replaced by bone. In a typical long bone (Fig. 308) this replacement begins in three centers of ossification, one in the shaft, the *diaphysis,* and one in each end, the *epiphysis.* The bony deposit spreads out from these centers until only two thin strips of cartilage between the shaft and epiphyses remain. Growth in length occurs in these strips, called *epiphysial cartilages,* for many years; it ceases when the cartilage is completely replaced by bone. Growth in diameter occurs by deposit of bone beneath the periosteum. In both membranous and cartilaginous bone the primary deposit of bone is not permanent. Much that is first laid down is later resorbed, and a new formation replaces the old. Thus the bone grows and is sculptured to its final shape. The extent of ossification at different ages is shown in Figure 309.

In the bones which form the cranial vault the ossification process begins in the center and spreads in concentric rings. The process is not complete at birth, so that the suture lines are not united and there are large unossified areas at the corners of the bones. There

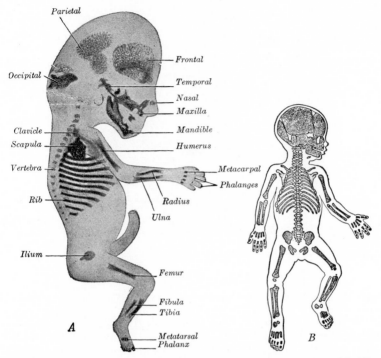

Figure 309.   Extent of ossification in human fetuses. A, At eleven weeks. ×1.5. (After Broman.) B, At birth. × ⅛. (Scammon, after Hess.)

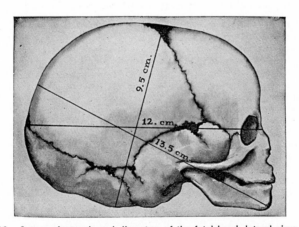

Figure 310.   Sutures, fontanels and diameters of the fetal head, lateral view. (Bickham.)

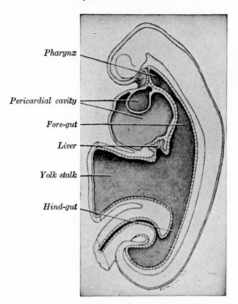

Pharynx

Pericardial cavity

Fore-gut

Liver

Yolk stalk

Hind-gut

Figure 311. Sagittal section of a 2.15-mm. human embryo. ✕ 25. (Prentiss, after His.)

are thus left a number of "soft spots" called fontanels[17] (Fig. 310), the most important of which is the large *anterior fontanel* at the junction of the two parietals with the frontal bone, and the smaller *posterior fontanel* at the junction of the parietals with the occipital. These spaces close after birth, the posterior one at approximately two months, and the anterior at about one and one-half years.

PRACTICAL CONSIDERATIONS.   The unossified epiphysial lines of the limb bones of children are regions of relative weakness, so that separation of an epiphysis sometimes occurs under circumstances which would lead to fracture in an adult. Also the relative softness of children's bones permits of bending and partial breakage (greenstick fracture), a rare occurrence in older people. The lack of complete ossification of the fetal skull at childbirth makes possible the molding of the head in a difficult delivery.

Regeneration of bone after injury is largely the result of activity of the inner cells of the periosteum, and the process of regeneration is essentially similar to the process of development already described. It can thus be seen that when it is necessary to remove a part of a bone, and new bone is desired in its place, the periosteum must be left intact.

The Digestive System.   In an earlier section we described the development of the gastro-intestinal tract up to the point where it

---

[17] Fontanel (or fontanelle): L., a little fountain. Originally a fontanel was an artificial ulcer produced on the skull by a hot iron, through which injurious humors were supposed to escape, as from a fountain. The ulcers were made at the junction of the sagittal and coronal sutures, and the name was subsequently applied to the pulsating spot at this and other areas of the skull in children.

Figure 312   **Developmental Anatomy** 383

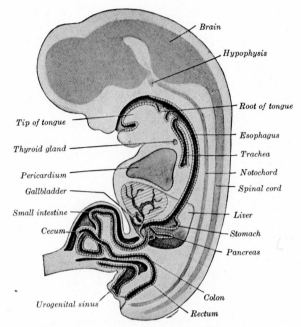

Figure 312. Sagittal section of a 17-mm. human embryo. (Prentiss, after Mall.)

occupied practically the whole of the cylindrical body of the embryo (Fig. 303). At this stage the true body cavity or celom is just beginning to develop. As the embryo grows older, the celom becomes gradually larger, and the cavity of the gut becomes relatively smaller (Figs. 311, 312). At first the gut is a straight tube; later it increases in length faster than does the cavity in which it lies, and it becomes thrown into loops and coils. The part which is to form the large intestine does not increase as rapidly as the rest, and undergoes a rotation from its original position in the midline. The cecum then comes to lie on the right side of the body, and the colon takes the adult position.

In early embryonic life the opening into the yolk sac is the only opening of the digestive system. This opening gradually closes off, and the mouth and anal orifices appear. At the mouth a rather deep pouch of ectoderm develops (Fig. 311). The membrane of ectoderm and endoderm then breaks through. The anterior two-thirds of the mouth, including the part in which the teeth develop, is therefore lined with epithelium derived from ectoderm. The anus develops in much the same manner.

The liver and pancreas begin as outpouchings from the walls of the duodenum; their final form depends on many factors, including

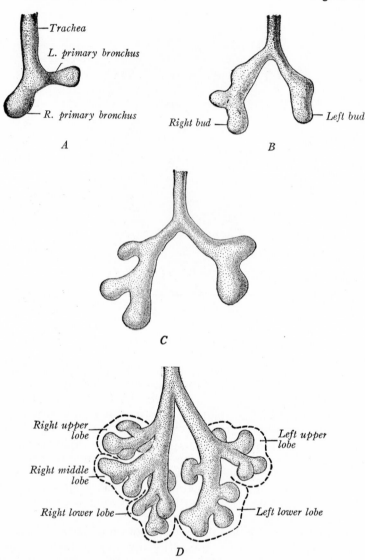

Figure 313. Development of the lobes and chief bronchi in the human lung. A, At 5 mm.; B, at 7 mm.; C, at 8.5 mm.; D, at 13.5 mm. (Arey.)

pressure from the surrounding organs. Thus the left lobe of the liver undergoes a change of form and a certain atrophy from pressure by the stomach.

The Lungs and Pleural Cavities.   The pulmonary system arises as an outgrowth from the digestive tract. It begins as a small hol-

Figure 314   **Developmental Anatomy   385**

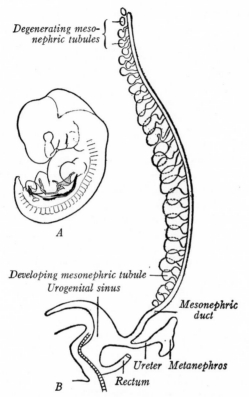

Degenerating meso- {
    nephric tubules {

A

Developing mesonephric tubule
Urogenital sinus

Mesonephric
duct

Ureter   Metanephros
B   *Rectum*

Figure 314.   Diagram of the human mesonephros. A, Position and extent of the left mesonephros at 8 mm. × 4.5. (After Shikinami.) B, Composition of the mesonephros at 9.5
mm., as viewed from the left side. × 35. (Prentiss, after Felix.)

low pouch or bud which grows out from the ventral part of the
pharynx (Fig. 312). This pouch increases in length and then
divides into right and left branches; the main stem forms the
trachea, the branches become the primary bronchi (Fig. 313).
The ends of the primary bronchi continue to grow and divide until
eventually the complex bronchial tree with the terminal alveoli is
formed.

The pleural cavity is at first in direct communication with the
abdominal cavity, the two together forming the celom. Later they
become separated by the diaphragm.

PRACTICAL CONSIDERATIONS.   Occasionally the formation of the diaphragm is
incomplete, and a permanent opening is left which connects the pleural and abdominal cavities. The contents of the abdomen are then often forced into the
pleural space, where they press on the heart and lungs.

The Urinary System. In the human embryo three different pairs of kidneys are developed in sequence. The first, called the *pronephros* or forekidney, consists of a long tube which develops along the posterior body wall close to the midline, and to which are attached a variable number of small tubules that develop far forward, in the region of the heart. The tubules never function, and soon disappear. The second kidney is called the *mesonephros,* or midkidney. In it the pronephric tube, now called the *mesonephric* or *wolffian*[18] duct (Fig. 314), is used and a new set of more complicated tubules, developed in the middle region of the body, becomes attached to it. The latter are derived from a ridge on the posterior abdominal wall called the *urogenital fold.* The mesonephros functions for a time and is then replaced by the third and final kidney, the *metanephros.* The metanephros, like the mesonephros, is derived from two separate sources. The ureter, the renal pelvis and the collecting ducts develop from an outpouching of the lower part of the mesonephric duct (Fig. 314); the rest of the organ develops from the caudal part of the urogenital fold. The main part of the mesonephric or wolffian duct does not enter into the formation of the final kidney. It degenerates in the female, but in the male it becomes transformed into the ductus deferens (Fig. 315).

The Reproductive System. The testis of the male is derived from the medial portion of the urogenital fold. In the early stages it lies inside the abdominal cavity, but in later embryonic life it descends through the inguinal canal into the scrotum, as has already been described on page 208. The mesonephric duct (red in Fig. 315, *A, C*), described with the urinary system, becomes the ductus deferens and obtains attachment to the testis. A second pair of ducts, called *müllerian*[19] *ducts* (blue in figure), develop for a time and lie alongside the mesonephric ducts. They soon atrophy, however, and leave only a trace of their presence in the prostatic utricle and in some vestigial structures attached to the testes.

In the female the ovary, like the testis of the male, develops from the urogenital fold. The mesonephric and müllerian ducts, however, progress differently (Fig. 315, *A, B*). Here the mesonephric ducts (red in figure) develop for a time and then degenerate, leaving only a trace in some vestigial structures near the ovary. The müllerian ducts (blue in figure), on the contrary, persist. Their upper ends come to lie close to the ovaries and form

[18] From Kaspar Friedrich Wolff of Berlin (1733–1794), one of the founders of modern embryology.

[19] After Johannes Peter Müller (1801–1858), the greatest German physiologist of his time; professor of anatomy and physiology at the University of Berlin.

Figure 315

Developmental Anatomy   387

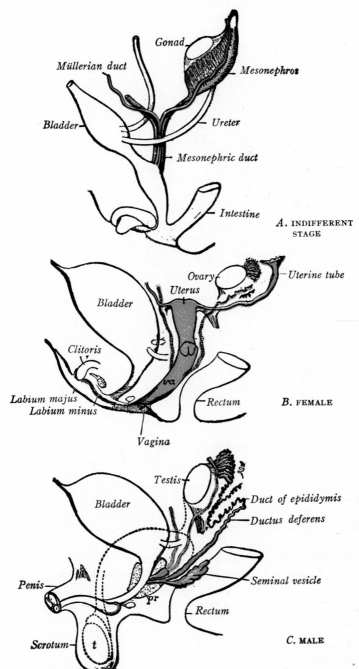

Figure 315. Diagrams illustrating the transformation of an indifferent primitive genital system into the definitive male and female types. (Thompson.)

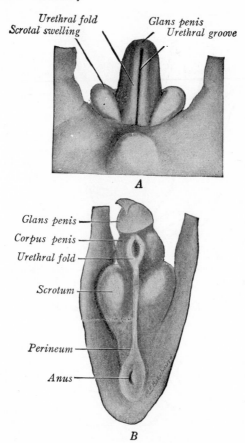

Figure 316. Stages in the development of the external genitalia of the human male. A, At nearly eight weeks (× 12); B, at twelve weeks (× 8). (Arey, after Spaulding.)

the uterine tubes; their lower ends fuse into a single channel which later becomes differentiated into the uterus and vagina.

The external generative organs of both sexes in the early stages are so similar that male and female can hardly be differentiated (Figs. 316, 317). The penis and clitoris are homologous organs.

The Circulatory System. The earliest evidence of a vascular system in the ovum is the appearance on the yolk sac of solid masses of mesodermal cells called *blood islands.* These masses hollow out and form both the primitive blood vessels and the blood cells. The vessels coalesce and increase in number, and a primitive vascular system is produced.

Eventually two large arteries and a number of veins are formed. Connecting these arteries and veins are two *heart tubes* lying side

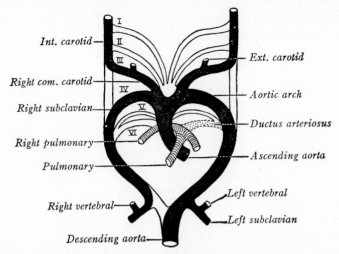

Figure 321. Scheme, in ventral view, to show the transformation of the human aortic arches into definite vessels. The dorsal vessels are represented as spread laterally to the same plane as the ventral ones. (Arey.)

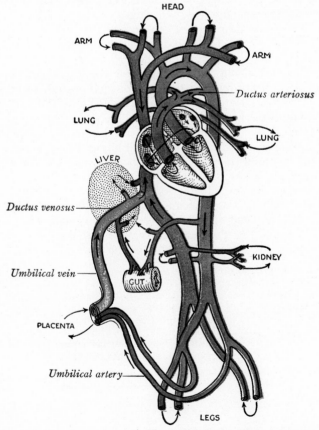

Figure 322. Diagram of the human circulation before birth. Colors show the quality of the blood and arrows indicate its direction of flow. (Arey, adapted from Dodds.)

are the primitive right and left aortic vessels (Fig. 318). With the fusion of the heart tubes these meet at their origin; later a union of their abdominal portions occurs. In this way two large primary aortic arches are formed, one on each side of the body. A number of communicating branches cross between the ascending and descending portions of the primary arches, and in all, six pairs of arches can be counted (Fig. 321). In later embryonic life most of these crossing vessels disappear; a few remain and take on new names. Thus the fourth left arch becomes the aortic arch of the adult; the fourth right arch becomes the right subclavian artery; the third pair of arches becomes the two common carotid arteries.

In the fetus, since the oxygenation of the blood takes place in the placenta and not in the lungs, the pattern of the circulatory system is different from that of the adult. It will be briefly reviewed (Fig. 322). The blood leaving the placenta, and therefore carrying oxygen and food, passes through the *umbilical vein* to the inferior vena cava, and then enters the right atrium of the heart. From here it may continue in either of two ways: (1) it may pass through the foramen ovale into the left atrium and thus enter the left ventricle and the aorta; or (2) it may enter the right ventricle and then the pulmonary artery. From the pulmonary artery two routes may be taken: (1) the blood may enter the lungs and then pass through the left atrium, and the left ventricle to the aorta; or (2) it may enter the aorta directly through a communicating vessel, the *ductus arteriosus*. From the aorta the blood is distributed to all parts of the body; some of it returns to the placenta through the *umbilical arteries* carrying carbon dioxide and other waste.

At birth the lungs become the respiratory organ and the placenta is removed. As a result three fundamental changes take place in the circulatory system: (1) the foramen ovale of the heart becomes closed at once; (2) the ductus arteriosus atrophies in a short time and becomes reduced to a fibrous cord, the *ligamentum arteriosum* (Fig. 191); and (3) the umbilical vessels atrophy. The umbilical vein becomes the *ligamentum teres* of the liver (Fig. 144).

PRACTICAL CONSIDERATIONS. The foramen ovale of the heart occasionally fails to close and thus leaves an orifice through which the blood from the right atrium can pass directly to the left side of the heart. Similarly, the ductus arteriosus may remain open, in which case part of the blood from the right side of the heart is sent directly to the aorta without passing through the lungs. In either case, if the opening is small, this need not be particularly serious; if it is large, the blood as a whole is never sufficiently aerated. These defects are two of the causes of "blue baby." Recent developments in surgery have made possible their correction in many cases.

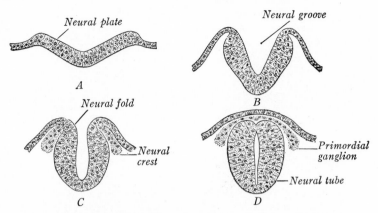

Figure 323. Origin of the neural tube and neural crest, as illustrated by transverse sections from early human embryos. $\times$ 125. (Arey.)

The Nervous System. In an earlier section (p. 371) we described the formation of the neural grove and the primitive neural tube (Figs. 300, 301, 323). The changes that take place later are highly complicated and can be only briefly described.

In the cranial part of the neural tube the most complex changes take place (Fig. 324). Three swellings develop, which, named from before backward, are the forebrain, the midbrain and the hindbrain. The *forebrain* forms the larger part of the adult cerebrum. From its sides a pair of outpouchings develop (optic vesicle in Fig. 324, *A*) which pass forward in the head to form the retina of the eyes and the optic nerves. Later another pair of outpouchings appear (cerebral hemisphere in Fig. 324, *C*). These increase in size and eventually become so enormous that they almost completely envelop the central portion. They form the cerebral hemispheres. The original cavity of the forebrain becomes the third ventricle; the cavities in the ballooned-out hemispheres become the lateral ventricles.

The *midbrain* alters relatively little from its original form, although its walls become thicker and its cavity smaller. The *hindbrain* becomes differentiated into pons and medulla. Its cavity widens out to form the fourth ventricle; in its roof a solid swelling appears which eventually forms the cerebellum. The remainder of the neural tube becomes the spinal cord.

At the junction of the primitive neural tube with the overlying

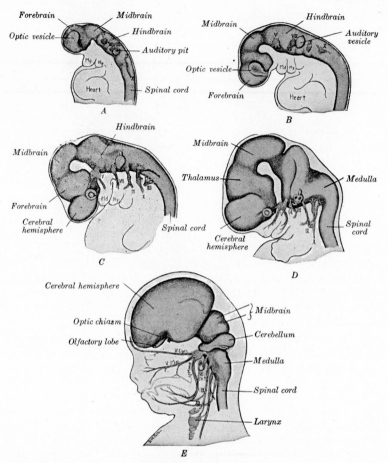

Figure 324. Stages in the development of the human brain. A, At 3 mm.; B, at 4 mm.; C, at 8 mm.; D, at seven weeks; E, at three months. (Patten.)

ectoderm, a group of cells is separated from the others to form the *neural crest* (Fig. 323). From it the spinal ganglia develop. Its cells develop peripherally and centrally directed processes. The peripheral processes pass laterally and form the spinal nerves; the central processes pass medially to enter the cord and to form the posterior roots. The anterior roots and the motor nerves are developed as outgrowths of axons from cells lying in the ventral part of the spinal cord.

PRACTICAL CONSIDERATIONS.   Developmental deficiencies of many types occur within the nervous system, some of which are compatible with life, while others are not. The more severe developmental anomalies are often associated

Figure 325   **Developmental Anatomy**   395

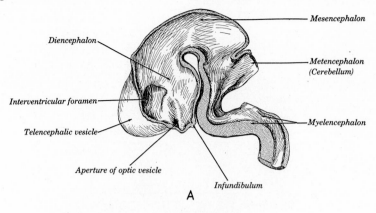

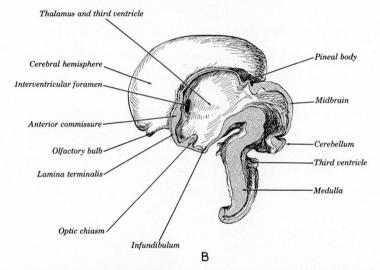

Figure 325. Sagittal sections of brains of embryos. *A,* At six weeks, 13.8 mm. *B,* At nine and one-half weeks, 46.5 mm. The specimen in *A* is between *C* and *D* in Figure 324, and the specimen in *B* is a little younger than *E.* (Redrawn from M. W. Woerdeman: Atlas of Human Anatomy. Blakiston Co.)

with imperfect development of the surrounding bones. Thus acrania is a condition in which there is an absence of the cranial vault and gross deficiencies in the structure of the brain. In spina bifida the vertebral column is incomplete in its lower part, and the spinal cord is often defective as well. In porencephaly large cavities are formed within the brain which communicate with the subarachnoid space. Failure of complete development of the cerebral cortex leads to certain forms of mental defect.

The Development of External Form in Relation to Age.   Finally we may briefly summarize the size and appearance of the embryo

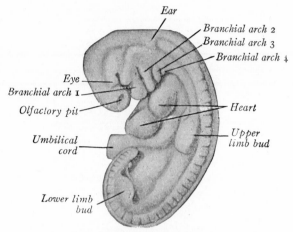

Figure 326.   Human embryo of 8 mm., viewed from the left side. (After His.)

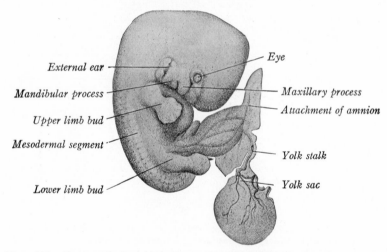

Figure 327.   Human embryo of 12 mm., viewed from the right side. (Prentiss.)

at the different stages of its development. The approximate size after the first month is given in crown-rump measurements, or the length from the top of the crown to the bottom of the rump. This measurement is given because the coiled-up manner in which the embryo develops makes the actual total length difficult to obtain.

In the first two weeks the embryo is small, and few specimens have been collected. It develops through the stages shown in Figure 298.

In the third week the length is about 2.5 mm. The stage of de-

Figure 328   **Developmental Anatomy** 397

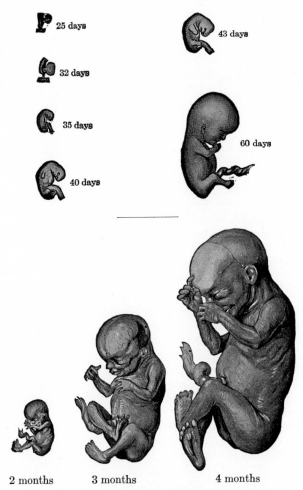

25 days

32 days

35 days

40 days

43 days

60 days

2 months   3 months   4 months

Figure 328.   Human embryos and fetuses of ages from twenty-five days to four months.
Upper six figures, natural size. (His.) Lower three figures, three-fifths natural size. (DeLee.)

velopment is that of the embryonic disk with a prominent primitive
streak and a beginning neural groove (Figs. 299, 300).

In the fourth week the embryo has reached approximately 5.0
mm. (Fig. 301). The body arises from the disk and partly con-
stricts from the yolk sac. The neural groove becomes the neural
tube, and the somites begin to appear. The branchial arches are
beginning to be evident.

By the fifth week the length has increased to 8.0 mm. (Fig. 326).
The embryo has risen completely from the disk and the body stalk

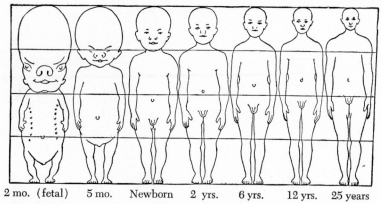

2 mo. (fetal)   5 mo.   Newborn   2 yrs.   6 yrs.   12 yrs.   25 years

Figure 329. Diagrams to illustrate the changing proportions of the human body during prenatal and postnatal growth. (Scammon, after Stratz.)

is reduced to slender proportions. The branchial arches are completed, and all the somites are present. The heart, in the form of a bent tube, is prominent. The limb buds are beginning to form.

By the sixth week the length is around 12 mm. (Fig. 327). The body is markedly flexed and possesses a prominent tail. The eyes are present, and the limb buds are definite. The heart has receded somewhat, and the liver becomes the prominent ventral organ.

By eight weeks or two months the crown-rump length has reached about 25 mm. or approximately 1 inch, and distinctly human characteristics are beginning to be apparent. The branchial arches are lost, and the tail is receding. The face, however, is rather pig-like, the nose is flat, and the eyes are wide apart. The digits are well formed. The sex can hardly be determined.

By the end of the third month the fetus is around 68 mm. or slightly under 3 inches in length. The features are better formed, and the sex is clearly apparent. From this time on progress in development is in the nature of finer differentiation, and the external form is only slightly affected (Fig. 328).

At birth the organs are all present, but have not attained either their adult proportions or their complete internal development. To mention only the most obvious of examples, the head is enormously large in proportion to the rest of the body (Fig. 329); the liver is relatively large and occupies the larger part of the abdominal cavity; and the urinary bladder is essentially an abdominal and not a pelvic organ. An example of incomplete internal development can be easily found in the central nervous system, where at birth only few of the fibers have acquired their myelin sheaths. The remainder are gradually acquired during the first two years of life.